Mechanisms of Colour Vision

Selected papers of W. S. Stiles, F.R.S., with a new introductory essay

Mechanisms of Colour Vision

Selected papers of W. S. Stiles, F.R.S., with a new introductory essay

W. S. Stiles

1978

ACADEMIC PRESS

London · New York · San Francisco

A Subsidiary of Harcourt Brace Jovanovich, Publishers

ACADEMIC PRESS INC. (LONDON) LTD
24–28 Oval Road
London NW1

United States Edition published by
ACADEMIC PRESS INC.
111 Fifth Avenue
New York, New York 10003

Library of Congress Catalog Card Number: 77-74371
ISBN: 0-12-671350-2

PRINTED IN GREAT BRITAIN BY
T. AND A. CONSTABLE LTD
EDINBURGH

Preface

The excitability of the eye depends upon the adequacy of the exciting light and upon the state of adaptation of the retina upon which the light falls. For 50 years Dr W. S. Stiles, F.R.S., in a series of measurements exemplary in their care and scope had addressed himself to the part played by these two factors.

It might have been hoped—and indeed at first there was some ground to believe—that all adaptation to white light was the result of a single variable, the "bleaching" in the Hecht–Wald photochemical theory or the "equivalent equilibrium background" in the Stiles–Crawford transform. Stiles' work showed that even with white adaptation more than one parameter was involved, and with coloured adaptation and coloured test flashes on the fovea, a rather complex situation was found.

Stiles was able to analyse this approximately in a way nicely reconcilable with Young's trichromacy of colour vision. In the parafovea at luminances below cone threshold, i.e. where rods alone were excited, lights of whatever wavelength, whether adapting or stimulating, were equivalent and might be replaced one by another if expressed in scotopic units, i.e. their relative absorption by rhodopsin. To a first approximation on the fovea we might suppose three classes of cone containing not rhodopsin but three different visual pigments. Supposing each cone with its excitable mechanism behaves like rods with the rhodopsin mechanism, and is uninfluenced by any other kind of cone, then these three independent cone mechanisms will respond predictably to flashes and backgrounds of any kind.

What Stiles measured was chiefly the threshold for detecting an increment of light on a steady background and he found that this accorded in general with the assumption that each mechanism acted independently of the others and that in any situation the most excitable mechanism defined the threshold. And conversely the observed threshold defined the action spectrum of the mechanism.

There are many well-known observations of contrast, brightness, etc., which show that, well above threshold, the various cone mechanisms certainly interact, and Stiles was able to show that the foregoing generalisation was too simple to explain all his observations even at threshold. Thus some of the chief interest of his work lies in his very extensive observations into the domain where cone interactions take place.

It has now become accepted that Stiles' conclusions are authoritative and deep and most of those working in this field wish to consult them. Unfortunately Stiles has not published his important series of papers in sequence in one journal but seems to have given his latest paper to whatever conference asked him for it when it was ready, and then he felt it redundant to say the same again in a more accessible publication. It therefore is very welcome that Academic Press at the suggestion of

John Mollon has agreed to reprint the present series of papers that readers might find great difficulty in obtaining otherwise. It is particularly valuable to have the first chapter, hitherto unpublished, which gives Stiles' own account of the history of his ideas as they developed under his hands, and also his present mature views in relation to the extension of the subject by the many investigators that his work has inspired.

W. A. H. Rushton
October 1977

Contents

Acknowledgements

I am much indebted to Dr John Mollon for help in preparing the material for this book, and to my old collaborator, Dr Brian Crawford, for permission to include a joint paper. For genial associations over the years with many fellow-workers on vision, and particularly with Dr Crawford, Professors David Wright and William Rushton and Dr Günter Wyszecki, I take the occasion to express my appreciation and thanks.

W. S. Stiles
October 1977

Increment Thresholds in the Analysis of Colour-sensitive Mechanisms of Vision: Historical Retrospect and Comment on Recent Developments

Two experimental techniques have dominated the psychophysics of colour vision, resting respectively on the matching and on the discrimination of visual stimuli. The experimental data of the present collection of papers were mostly obtained by discrimination measurements of the type known as increment thresholds. While many early visual threshold measurements—for example, in studies of absolute light sensitivity and of dark adaptation—might now be described as of this type, it was only in the nineteen thirties that the usefulness of the broadly defined increment threshold was recognised. It belongs to a group of measurements of visual response in which the stimuli used can be regarded as comprising (i) a conditioning stimulus and (ii) a test stimulus. The former is supposed specified completely at each part of the subject's visual field. It may be steady and exposed for a sufficient time for the retina and visual system generally to have become fully adapted to it by the time the test stimulus is applied. This is the equilibrium case. Alternatively, it may undergo a prescribed sequence of changes so that when, at a specified time in the sequence, the application of the test stimulus commences, the adaptation of the visual system will also in general be in the process of changing. This is the dynamic or non-equilibrium case. The characteristic of the test stimulus is that at a given moment it is superimposed on the conditioning stimulus and has a limited duration. Otherwise, it represents a stimulus distribution in the field—which may even vary in some defined way during the time of its exposure—the specification of which in all its aspects may be chosen at will in different measurements with no necessary limitation imposed by the particular conditioning stimulus to which it is applied. A psycho-physical measurement is obtained if (i) the subject makes a visual observation, associated with the application of the test stimulus, that can be expressed as an assertion or denial by the subject of some statement put to him about what he sees and, (ii) if a particular parameter in the specification of the test stimulus is chosen as test variable and by repeated performances of the whole test using different values of this variable, the frequency of the subject's "yes" and "no" answers to the observational proposition is determined as a function of the value used. In practice the result of the measurement is commonly condensed to reporting one or two critical features of the frequency distribution, such as the value of the test variable for 50 per cent "yes" answers and the gradient of the distribution curve at this value. In practice, too, short-cut methods of finding the critical features are often used that do not involve determining a complete frequency distribution curve, but are believed to lead to closely similar results.

The original motive in considering psychophysical measurements of this very general type sprang from attempts to clarify the concept of visual adaptation, the underlying intention being (i) to control the adaptive condition of the visual response system by using various conditioning stimuli and, (ii) to modify in various ways the test stimulus and the observational proposition put to the subject, so that the results obtained are predominantly determined in different measurements by the properties of different parts of the response system. "Different parts" may mean associated with different local retinal areas or with different mechanisms operating in the same area. The interpretation of results will be facilitated if any disturbance by the test stimulus of the adaptation produced by the conditioning stimulus is slight and, it may be expected, that this requirement will best be met in measurements where the subject has merely to detect—or fail to detect—the application of the test stimulus. Such measurements are designated "increment thresholds"; as a rule, the test variable they use is a factor by which all the intensities involved in specifying the test stimulus are raised or lowered without altering the test stimulus pattern in any other way. Commonly the test stimulus is reduced to a briefly exposed, small, uniform light patch imaged within the local retinal area under study, while its size, exposure time and, especially, its relative spectral composition are the main parameters by variations in which it is aimed to obtain results determined predominantly, in turn, by such different component mechanisms as may be functional in the area. An additional parameter that has proved valuable is the effective entrance pupil of the eye for the test stimulus, as it is on this that the angular incidence conditions of the stimulus on the retina—now known to play a role—depend.

Increment thresholds of the foregoing elementary type were used to test whether, if the conditioning stimuli are restricted to those employing only white light, the adaptation in a localised retinal area might be specifiable by a single variable. This work (Paper II) led to the formulation of two equivalence principles: the equivalent surround principle and the equivalent background principle. The former aims to specify the condition of the response systems belonging to a localised retinal area under any white light conditioning stimulus which is such that in a period embracing the time and duration of the test stimulus, the area in question is not directly illuminated by the conditioning stimulus, i.e. it receives no light from the latter's regular retinal image, although it may be receiving light scattered in the eye from rays proceeding to other parts of the retina. If, at a particular epoch in the time sequence of a conditioning stimulus conforming to the above limitations, the increment threshold for a particular test stimulus has the same value as in the equilibrium case for a uniform white field of brightness (strictly, luminance) α surrounding but not covering the localised area and if the same value α is always obtained when test stimuli of any other characteristics are used, then α defines the equivalent surround brightness, which by convention can be taken as the single variable specifying the adaptation in the area. Alternatively, the limitation on admissible conditioning stimuli may be relaxed to the extent that the localised area during and prior to the test period may be covered by a featureless and approximately uniform field. If it can be assumed that any modification of a measured increment threshold by this uniform coverage can be attributed solely to its contribution in determining the adaptation of the local area and if this adaptation is specifiable by a single variable, then an equivalent background β can be defined similarly to the equivalent surround and β can be adopted, by convention, to specify the adaptation of the area. Explicitly, β is the uniform white background, covering also the test area, that gives in the equilibrium case the same increment threshold for any test stimulus, as is obtained at the specified epoch of any particular white conditioning stimulus admissible under the wider conditions.

While the tests of these two principles, described in Paper II, were on the whole favourable in both the equilibrium and dynamic cases examined, they were certainly insufficient for firm conclusions. Later studies by Crawford (1937a, 1947) on the outstanding dynamic case—the changing adaptation during recovery in the dark after the exposure of the retina to a high intensity uniform white field—provided more evidence for the equivalent background principle and, in probably the most carefully controlled test, Blakemore and Rushton (1965) working with a rod mono-chromat as the subject found close agreement with the principle in the same dynamic case. A novel aspect of equivalent background emerged from the work of Barlow and Sparrock (1964) who matched in subjective brightness the positive after-image of a uniform white field with an external stimulus, the retinal image of which was stabilised against all eye motions. They concluded that during dark-adaptation the equivalent brightness may be identified with the positive after-image of the original intense adapting field. Although this after-image has a low subjective brightness—like the actual image of the comparison stimulus which being held absolutely stationary on the retina is subject to fading—it seems nevertheless still capable of determining the increment threshold as though it were the unstabilised image of an external stimulus equal in brightness to the equivalent background.

Despite the measure of success of the equivalent background, the idea of a specification of adaptation by a single variable, even when only white light conditioning stimuli are admitted, has been questioned from another standpoint (Paper XII, pp. 154 and 162). The objection derives from the plausible hypothesis that, after the extinction of a large uniform conditioning field and when the whole retina is recovering in the dark, the changes in state from any given moment onwards will be determined by the condition obtaining at that moment. The notion of a single adaptation variable would then suggest that threshold recovery curves—all determined with the same test stimulus—following white conditioning stimuli of different exposure periods and intensities, would all be parts of a single common recovery curve but displaced to different positions along the time axis. Experimentally, however, this is not borne out. To this dilemma two escapes suggest themselves. Firstly, the argument as given above (and in Paper XII) is tacitly assuming that we can treat the whole retina as a unity in its recovery process and, even if the conditioning is confined to large uniform fields centered on the test area, such an assumption is difficult to support. The areas surrounding the test area—all of which will be changing state during recovery—may be modifying the state of the test area and as they have somewhat different properties the effect they produce may well be different for the various conditioning stimuli used. The second explanation is that the adaptation in a localised area may in fact require more than one variable for its specification under white conditioning, but the characteristics of the various test stimuli used in testing the equivalent background principle have not been sufficiently diverse to separate these variables in their effects on increment thresholds. For example, suppose two adaptation variables ξ_1 and ξ_2 are required, say for specifying respectively receptor-pigment and neural conditions. While both may contribute to determining the result of any visual test under a specified white conditioning, for tests belonging to some special group—possibly all increment thresholds—they may do so only by modifying a condition in the response system that, together with the test parameters, determines the result of any test in the group and which is specifiable by a single variable, $\Psi(\xi_1, \xi_2)$. In recovery from a particular high brightness conditioning, ξ_1, ξ_2 and Ψ would be functions of time, $\xi_1 = \xi_1'(t)$, $\xi_2 = \xi_2'(t)$, $\Psi = \Psi\{\xi_1'(t), \xi_2'(t)\}$ respectively, but in measurements with different tests of the group the equivalent background principle would be confirmed. However, in recovery from a different high brightness conditioning, $\xi_1 = \xi_1''(t)$, $\xi_2 = \xi_2''(t)$ and $\Psi = \Psi\{\xi_1''(t), \xi_2''(t)\}$ could be different functions of time and, while again the equivalence principle would be confirmed, the recovery curves in the two cases, plotted as curves of equivalent background against time could not in general be regarded as parts of a common curve displaced along the time axis. Possibly, tests incorporating more radical variations than those available with the elementary increment thresholds so far used might separate the adaptation variables.

The colour of the test stimulus was among the parameters varied in testing the equivalence principles and, before dropping the limitation to white conditioning stimuli, it is of interest to recall the remarkable differences in shape of the curve of log (reciprocal increment threshold), i.e. log (threshold sensitivity), against test wavelength obtained with low and high white conditioning stimuli (Stiles and Crawford, 1933). When the threshold intensity of the monochromatic test stimulus is expressed in energy units, the log (sensitivity) curve for a dark field, typifying low conditioning levels, has the familiar single peak form with a maximum in the green at about 500 nm if the test area lies in the extrafoveal retina; with a foveal test area the comparable curve for most subjects has its single maximum displaced towards a longer wavelength—greater than 550 nm but also much more variable from subject to subject. On the other hand, for intense white conditioning stimuli (equilibrium case)—whether produced by a surround, a background or an isolated extremely bright spot (glare source)—the log (sensitivity) curve shows two peaks at about 440 nm and 540 nm respectively and a hump or rudimentary peak in the neighbourhood of 600 nm. Figure 1 gives an example of the kind of curves obtained for a white surround (colour temperature about 2800°K) around a 1·28° diam. central dark

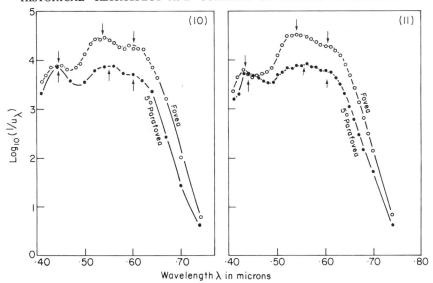

FIG. 1. Log (threshold sensitivity in reciprocal energy units) plotted against test stimulus wavelength: log $(1/U_\lambda)$ v. λ. Conditioning stimulus: white light surround of luminance 300 candles/sq. ft. Mean data for foveal and 5°-parafoveal vision. Curves for W.S.S. and B.H.C. respectively on the left and right. (Stiles and Crawford, 1933.)

patch within which the rectangular test stimulus (0·7°, 0·16°) was exposed in 1 sec flashes (5° extrafoveal test area) or continuously (foveal test area). These results suggested that for a given white conditioning stimulus, the foveal log (sensitivity) curve for a test stimulus of fixed characteristics (other than wavelength) might be the resultant of three single peak component curves of fixed shape, whose different heights in the diagram varied as the intensity of the conditioning stimulus was increased from zero upwards. It seemed (i) that in all probability these component curves would correspond to the spectral threshold sensitivities of the three colour systems postulated in trichromatic theory on the basis of the data provided by the completely different methods of colour-matching, (ii) that the heights of the component curves might be regarded as three adaptation variables—η_1, η_2, η_3, say— which would assume different sets of values for various conditioning stimuli, but which, provided only white conditioning was used, would all be determined by a single parameter identifiable with the equivalent background β and, (iii) that when the limitation to white conditioning was dropped, the log (sensitivity) curve might be similarly represented except that the use of various coloured conditionings would enable the three adaptation variables to be changed independently. Supporting evidence for the prediction in (iii) was obtained in preliminary measurements with coloured surrounds and backgrounds, and this provided the starting point for the later two-colour threshold analysis (Papers III, VI and VII).

Two positions adopted in the 1933 paper just quoted were wrong or misleading. The proposal to represent the resultant foveal spectral sensitivity as a linear combina- tion of fixed component sensitivities was soon realised to be inconsistent with any acceptable shapes of these component curves, and was replaced in the later analysis by the assumption that the threshold of the most sensitive component mechanism at each wavelength would determine the resultant sensitivity, except for a small "summation" increase in the latter when the thresholds of the most sensitive two mechanisms approached equality. Even with this improved assumption, direct summation tests, first made in 1958 (see Paper XIII), reveal, in some situations, discrepancies which although small—of the order of 0·15 log units in threshold values—point to a more deep-rooted difficulty with the basic model. The handling of the difference between the extrafoveal and the foveal sensitivities was also misleading. Although the roles of the rod system at low levels and of the macular pigment at high levels in producing the observed differences were recognised, it was suggested that because their net effects for various conditioning stimuli appeared specifiable by a single parameter, they must somehow arise from a common cause. In fact all the evidence is that the macular pigment acts as an inert (photostable) filter while in the extrafoveal areas the rod system must be admitted as a fourth independently adaptable mechanism; thus the two factors appear completely unrelated.

The work with surrounds and backgrounds showed that similar adaptation effects on increment thresholds were obtained in the two cases, but that with a surround having a 1° diameter dark centre its intensity had to be some 10 to 20 times the equivalent background. Thus, in working with fairly narrow spectrum bands from monochromators for both test and field stimuli, it was decided to limit the latter to backgrounds as there is always a problem of light shortage and, in addition, a uniform background ensures a more level condition of adaptation in the neighbourhood of the test stimulus. At the same time, the size and flash duration of the test stimulus were kept constant. With these simplifications, attention was concentrated on finding out how, in the equilibrium case, the increment threshold U_λ of a monochromatic test stimulus of wavelength λ depended on the wavelength μ and the intensity W_μ of a monochromatic background field, U_λ and W_μ being both measured in energy units. (In later work, intensities of monochromatic stimuli were expressed in numbers of quanta instead of numbers of ergs.) The ulterior motive was to pursue further the idea that threshold sensitivity could be regarded as the resultant of three component sensitivities (foveal vision), or of four when the scotopic mechanism played a part (extrafoveal vision). The key to the method of attack was the independent variation of test and field colours and the method was later described as the "two-colour threshold technique". Paper III gives a full account of the work done before 1939. It may be noted that in this work the one test parameter varied—other than test wavelength—was the point of entry of the stimulus in the subject's pupil. Crawford (1937b) had shown that the sensitivity of rod vision to changes in retinal angle of incidence was much less than that of cone vision and, by exploiting this difference, the identification of scotopic response was much facilitated. It is also noteworthy that an anomaly had already appeared in the simple concept that for foveal vision just three fixed relative spectral sensitivities need to be invoked; this anomaly—called the "limited conditioning effect'—implicates the component system maximally sensitive at short wavelengths, which at high intensities of long-wave fields had apparently a constant threshold independent of any further increase in field intensity. After the interregnum of World War II, the results of Paper III were consolidated, and extended in various respects, in work described in Paper IV, VI and VII, which also reformulated in simpler terms the basic picture of increment threshold sensitivity as a resultant of the sensitivities of component mechanisms. However, new work reported in 1953 (Paper IX) pointed to considerable modifications of this picture, demanding, it appeared, (i) the admission in place of the original "blue-cone" system of a group of three response mechanisms (named π_1, π_2, π_3) maximally sensitive in the blue but having widely different sensitivities at longer wavelengths and, (ii) the recognition that each of the two longer wavelength mechanisms, corresponding respectively to the original "green-cone" and "red-cone" systems, may exist in two modifications, under different conditioning stimuli, with relatively small differences in spectral sensitivity (named π_4 and π_4', "green-cone"; π_5 and π_5', "red-cone"). A re-examination of the analysis of increment threshold sensitivity in terms of π-mechanisms in the light of work done up to 1958, is given in Paper XI.

I am devoting the rest of this paper to comments on several questions relating to the foregoing material and, particularly, to certain aspects of it on which interesting new results and insights have been obtained in the more recent investigations of a number of research workers. No approach to a comprehensive discussion of the numerous relevant papers is attempted. My choice of items and my comments on them are from the standpoint that the notion of π-mechanisms provides a useful starting-point and first approximation in mapping the whole domain of increment threshold sensitivities.

In what follows a general acquaintance with the papers collected in this volume will be assumed. But it may be of help to note here several abbreviations, symbols, etc., frequently used.

"t.v.i. or t.v.r. curve". This means a plot of log (increment threshold) versus log (intensity—or radiance—of a conditioning stimulus of fixed relative spectral composition to which the visual system is fully adapted).

"t.v.λ. curve". This means a plot of log (increment threshold for a monochromatic test stimulus) versus the wavelength λ or wavenumber $1/\lambda$ of the test stimulus for any particular conditioning stimulus and, in the dynamic case, at any specified epoch of that stimulus.

"Test sensitivity". Is defined as the reciprocal of increment threshold, so that a plot of log (test sensitivity) against λ or $1/\lambda$ is the corresponding t.v.λ. plot with the signs of the ordinates reversed.

"f.v.μ. curve". This means a plot of log (field intensity or radiance of a monochromatic background, which added under equilibrium conditions to a dark field, or any other steady existing field, raises the increment threshold of a test stimulus of fixed characteristics, including relative spectral composition, from its initial value to a prescribed constant multiple of that value) versus the wavelength μ or wavenumber $1/\mu$ of the added monochromatic field.

"Field sensitivity". Is defined as the reciprocal of the critical field intensity defined in the preceding definition; a plot of log (field sensitivity) against μ or $1/\mu$ is the f.v.μ. plot with the ordinate signs reversed.

The curves of these three species, as measured, are believed to be determined by the properties of several component mechanisms operating in the retinal area to which the test stimulus is applied. It is assumed that, in any experimental situation, it is meaningful to speak of the corresponding curves of the individual component mechanisms, i.e. the curves that would be obtained if, in turn, each specific mechanism were the only one contributing directly to the detection of the test stimulus. The qualification "directly" is inserted here to allow for the possibility—made more probable by the recent work of Pugh (1976)—that the condition of a particular mechanism may be modified by the conditions of other mechanisms resulting in changes in its field spectral sensitivity, while the relative test spectral sensitivity characterising its response to a near-threshold test stimulus may be unaffected. The symbols π_0, π_1, π_2, etc., are used to denote the component mechanisms inferred in applications of the two-colour threshold technique. For a particular mechanism π_i, the test and field sensitivities are commonly defined, respectively, as the reciprocal of the absolute threshold (symbol $\pi_{i\lambda}$ or, better, $\pi_i(\lambda)$) and as the reciprocal of the monochromatic field required to raise the increment threshold from the absolute threshold to ten times that value (symbol $\Pi_{i\mu}$ or, better, $\Pi_i(\mu)$). Table I of Paper XI (page 108) summarises a few salient properties of the π-mechanisms, and Tables A and B from Wyszecki and Stiles (1967), reproduced here, give, respectively, figures defining the mean shape of the t.v.r. curve of a foveal cone mechanism, and mean numerical values as measured or estimated for the field sensitivities $\Pi_i(\mu)$ of the various mechanisms. (See pp. 17-20 for Tables A and B.)

As my comments touch on a series of fairly distinct points, I have broken them up into sections numbered from 1 to 10.

1. THE BLUE-SENSITIVE RESPONSE MECHANISM π_2

This is the least well established of the three blue-sensitive mechanisms. It is not in evidence for every subject, notably for the subject (W.S.S.) of the original 1939 work. As shown for example in Fig. 2, p. 67 of Paper IX, π_2 in a subject for whom it appears is represented by the lowest branch of the t.v.r. curve for very short test wavelengths on a long-wave background, a branch which covers a range of threshold values of no more than 0·3 to 0·4 log units. This range, which corresponds to the difference in absolute thresholds for π_2 and π_1, varies with the subject and it is possible that where a subject does not show π_2, the π_2 mechanism may exist but may have an absolute threshold equal to or higher than that of π_1. For a test stimulus of fixed wavelength in the extreme blue (say 420 nm), the initial part of the t.v.r. curve for any field wavelength would be attributable to π_2 for any subject who with a long wavelength field showed a clear π_2 branch. Thus in theory the field sensitivity curve of π_2 throughout the whole spectrum should be determinable. In Paper IX only the moderate to long wavelength range of the curve was measured; among the difficulties in these observations was a certain instability of π_2 leading to small changes in the relative ordinate positions of π_2 and π_1. Of the several later workers who have confirmed the appearance of a π_2 branch, Watkins (1969a and b) reported that in his group of colour-normal subjects there was one whose original t.v.r. curves showed no π_2 branch, but who in later measurements obtained a "weak" π_2 contribution (presumably a branch with limited ordinate range). Mollon and Polden working at Cambridge have found subjects who show a clear π_2 branch but also report some instability in π_2 (private communication). Despite the difficulties, a full determination of the π_2 field spectral sensitivity curve would be of interest particularly because in the original incomplete determination (Paper IX) a curious feature of the curve appears in the range 540 to 610 nm, a feature which has some resemblance to the bands in the same region shown by the absorption spectra of haemoglobin, oxyhaemoglobin and cytochromes. While this feature may turn out to be an artifact of the original measurements, if confirmed it would represent a novel type of visual response curve with interesting possibilities.

2. FIELD SENSITIVITY OF π_1

The π_1 spectral sensitivity curve has a characteristic secondary lobe low down on the descending limb on the long-wave side of the peak, for which various explanations have been proposed: (i) that the "green-sensitive" π_4, or more probably the "red-sensitive" π_5 mechanism is somehow associated with a main "blue-sensitive" mechanism, π_3 perhaps, (ii) that receptors of π_1 contain a mixture of two or perhaps three visual pigments, (iii) that while the π_1 receptors contain just one pigment, this pigment has a secondary absorption band around 580 nm. It will be noted that the secondary lobe corresponds to a sensitivity no more than a few per cent of the peak sensitivity in the blue, and it would probably produce very little distortion of colour-matching data. It will also be noted that the secondary lobe occurs in much the same spectral region as the presumed special feature of the π_2 curve. Recently an important investigation by Pugh (1976) has shown that the π_1 field spectral sensitivity is not a simple additive function such that the adapting effect of any field with a power distribution $P_\mu d\mu$ is determined by an integral $\int \Pi_{1\mu} P_\mu d\mu = \Sigma_{\pi 1}$ (π_1-stimulus value). He established that for fields made up of mixtures of short wavelengths, $\mu < 450$ nm say, and long wavelengths, $\mu > 550$ nm say, the mixture produces effectively a higher π_1-stimulus value than would be expected from the π_1-stimulus values appropriate to the short- and long-wave constituents of the field's power distribution. To put the result more rigorously, if two monochromatic fields, one of short wavelength μ_1 and power P_1, the other of long wavelength μ_2 and power P_2, each produce when applied by itself the same effect in raising the π_1 increment threshold, then a mixture of the two of power $\sigma P_1 + (1 - \sigma) P_2$ where $0 < \sigma < 1$ produces a greater effect. Thus the breakdown in additivity of the field effects on sensitivity of short and long wavelengths corresponds to hyperadditivity. (As $\Pi_{1\mu}$ is defined in reciprocal quantum units, the power distributions P_μ in the above discussion must be supposed given in quantum units.)

Obviously Pugh's result favours the explanation (i) above, and Pugh elaborates this to a two-stage model of the π_1-mechanism whereby the factor by which a mixed field increases the increment threshold for π_1 above the zero field value, is the product of two factors, one determined by absorption in receptors (pigment) with peak sensitivity in the blue, the other by absorption in receptors (pigment) with peak sensitivity at longer wavelengths. For the blue peak sensitivity, the field sensitivity curve of π_3 suggests itself as a possibility and raises the interesting question whether the $\Pi_{3\mu}$ curve is additive in the sense used above.

3. ADAPTATION RECOVERY ANOMALY OF THE BLUE-SENSITIVE (π_1) MECHANISM (TRANSIENT TRITANOPIA)

The resolution of different cone mechanisms by measuring the increment threshold on zero field during recovery from exposure to high intensity fields was not accomplished until many years after their separation by the two-colour threshold technique using steady adapting fields. Auerbach and Wald (1954) first produced a kind of double branch in a foveal threshold recovery curve indicating the operation of a "violet" cone-receptor mechanism. This was obtained after a very intense conditioning field. Before that, Wright (1934) and Stiles (Paper VII) had observed that immediately after the removal of a long-wave field of moderate intensity to which the retina was adapted, the fovea becomes very insensitive to short-wave stimuli. Paper VII summarises some relevant observations. Increment thresholds were measured for test stimuli of various wavelengths when the retina was adapted to a moderately high level (20,000 trolands) of red light (640 nm). With test wavelengths below 500 nm, the test stimuli were detected by the π_1 mechanism. But immediately on the extinction of the field the threshold increased by a large factor of the order of 1 log unit and it was established, by the variation of this increment threshold with test wavelength, that the test flash was being seen by means of the green-sensitive π_4 and not the blue-sensitive π_1 mechanism which remained temporarily "blind" for many seconds. Das (1964) substantially confirmed this observation. A quite different result was obtained by Du Croz and Rushton (1966) who, by using very high intensity adapting fields of different colours ("spectrum" interference filters), were able to show that the recovery curves (log (increment threshold) against time) after extinction of the field displayed branches identifiable as parts of independent recovery curves of the various mechanisms, and that, in particular, after a long-wave adaptation the initial branch of the recovery curve for a blue test stimulus was attributable to π_1, so that the anomaly described above was not observed. A similar if less striking separation in the recovery curve of branches corresponding to π_4 and π_5 was also established. This remarkable extension of the concepts of independent component mechanisms was obtained by adaptations to fields (of the order of a million trolands exposed for 20 seconds) which were known by the fundus reflection work of Rushton to bleach nearly all the cone pigment. The apparent discrepancy between the Du Croz and Rushton results concerning the recovery of the π_1 mechanism and those of Stiles has been elucidated by recent work by Mollon and Polden (1975a and b, 1977b), adding many new insights into what may be happening. They found in fact that at high, but not too high, adapting field intensities (up to 10^5 trolands) of yellow light the extinction, or even the reduction of the field intensity to one-tenth, produced the anomalous rise of the increment threshold of a short-wave test stimulus, but that if very high intensities were used of the order of 10^6 or more, the anomalous rise did not occur and the Du Croz and Rushton type of recovery supervened. Their initial interpretation of the anomaly was that the recovering π_4 mechanism exerts a strong inhibitory effect on the π_1 mechanism. The problem is then why this ceases at very high fields. Their further results and comments (Mollon and Polden, 1977b) suggest that the change may be connected with the switch from π_1 to π_3 in the steady state t.v.r. curves. Clearly this is potentially a fruitful line of attack on the inter-relations of mechanisms. Professor Pugh has also made observations on the anomaly which both confirm and extend some of the results noted above.

According to another early observation of a special dynamic property of the blue-sensitive as compared with the green- and red-sensitive cone mechanisms, the former takes a much longer time to become adapted to a high intensity coloured background of long wavelength. Tests with backgrounds of different wavelengths suggest that the agency producing this delay in light adaptation has maximal sensitivity, not in the blue where the blue-cone (π_1) mechanism is most sensitive, but at a much longer wavelength (Paper VI). The whole question of increment threshold sensitivity during the early adaptation period on exposing a high intensity background was examined by Boynton and his collaborators (1956, 1959). Their t.v.λ. curves in these early stages of light adaptation were resolved into component spectral sensitivities differing considerably from those indicated for π-mechanisms by steady-state measurements. Just as in the earlier phases of dark adaptation there are complicating factors still needing to be elucidated.

4. RELATIONSHIP OF BLUE-SENSITIVE CONE MECHANISMS π_1, π_2, π_3

The connection between these supposed distinct mechanisms raises certain questions. Originally all the mechanisms were based on increment thresholds measured on fields to which the retina was fully adapted. If for a particular conditioning field (given spectral composition) and a particular test wavelength the t.v.r. curve shows two branches assigned to distinct mechanisms, A and B, we should like to know that when the field intensity is such that the observed threshold lies on the A branch, then if the response to the test stimulus of the A mechanism could in some way be blocked we should observe a threshold on the B branch (produced), attributable to the B mechanism. If A is π_4 and B is π_1, and the field has wavelength 600 nm we can change the test wavelength say from 475 nm to 510 nm—without disturbing in any way the adaptation condition—so that the observed threshold for a particular field intensity, which initially could be identified as the threshold of π_1, becomes for the new test wavelength the threshold for π_4. Arguments of this kind justify the conclusion that for all intensities of the 600 nm field both mechanisms are present, and we can draw a complete branch for each. But this test fails for π_1, π_2 and π_3 because for the test and field wavelength combinations such that distinct branches of the t.v.r. curve corresponding to these mechanisms can be obtained, the test wavelength must always be in the short-wave region below about 510 nm, where it seems that the relative test sensitivities of π_1, π_2, π_3 remain fixed; i.e. the log (spectral sensitivity) curves have the same shape and relative position in this spectral range. Changing test wavelength then merely moves the three branches up or down as a whole without altering their relative positions. This being so, an alternative to treating π_1, π_2, π_3 as distinct mechanisms would be to say that they correspond to a single mechanism which when it is fully adapted in turn to each of a series of increasing levels of the adapting field—of some fixed colour—undergoes at a certain level, dependent on the field colour, a fairly abrupt change in threshold response properties, a change that has previously been attributed to π_1 taking over the detection of the test stimulus from π_2. At still higher levels a further abrupt change occurs, previously attributed to a switch from π_1 to π_3. We could speculate that in the transition from π_2 to π_1, the mechanism jettisons its association with the visual receptors responsible for the high field sensitivity of π_2 at medium and long wavelengths (and involving possibly the special feature noted in Section 1), and in the transition from π_1 to π_3 a further jettisoning of associations with medium and long-wave receptors is taking place. This general conception would be consistent with the new work of Pugh on the field sensitivity of π_1, because we should not expect light absorbed in the main receptors and light absorbed in the associated receptors to yield a truly additive spectral sensitivity curve. As far as the π_1 to π_3 transition is concerned it is noteworthy that the π_1 and π_3 branches intersect at a field intensity (long-wave field) in the range where the bleaching of the pigments of the π_4 and π_5 mechanisms is well advanced, and it is reasonable to suppose that receptors containing these pigments, or one of them, are those associated with short-wave receptors in the π_1 form of the mechanism. Of course, as the pigment-kinetics work of Rushton shows, the range of partial bleaching—say 10 to 90 per cent—is fairly extensive, probably more than 10 to 1 in field intensity. This extended range must present something of a problem in quantitative explanations of the π_1 to π_3 transition that rest on the bleaching of the long-wave pigment. Granting this, J. Mollon has suggested (private communication) that it is probably unnecessary to introduce difficult ideas of switching from one modification to another by the jettisoning or re-acquiring of long-wave receptors, because the bleaching of the pigments in the latter as the intensity of the long-wave field is raised will of itself reduce and finally make negligible the contribution of the signals from these receptors to the action of the field in raising the increment threshold. His view is of a permanent association of short- with moderate- or long-wave receptors in the mechanism, leading to the following conception of the t.v.r. curve for a short-wave test stimulus—say, 435 nm—on a long-wave field—say, 600 nm. It is assumed for the purposes of this explanation that the t.v.r. curve shows no π_2 branch. Starting from zero field and increasing progressively the field intensity, the rise in threshold produced is attributed initially to a field response resulting from quantum absorptions in the mechanism's long-wave receptors only, because for the pigment of the short-wave receptors the absorption coefficient for long-wave light is very small. In this way a rising section of the t.v.r. curve is generated corresponding to the π_1 branch, until the bleaching of the pigment in the longer wave receptors becomes so considerable that the "quantum catch" of these receptors flattens out to a constant value—this follows from Rushton's kinetics—and as a result the corresponding threshold curve exhibits a similar flattening. Finally a third, rising, section of the t.v.r. curve is produced when, despite the smallness of the relevant absorption coefficient, the quantum catch of the short-wave receptors reaches sufficiently large values to contribute to the field response and consequent raising of the threshold. The second and third sections correspond to the π_3 branch. It has been tacitly assumed that the pigment of the short wave-length receptors is not bleached in the field range concerned. It may also be noted that, unlike the distortion of t.v.r. curves due to bleaching considered in Section 5 and Fig. 2, the theory just given does not depend on the pigment of the long-wave receptors being present in high density.

Mollon's concept of the π_1 to π_3 transition appears to me a promising one, although an adequate quantitative development of the idea remains to be carried out. Any explanation of the transition π_2 to π_1 on the same lines seems to require moderate or long-wave receptors with pigment that, compared with the pigments of π_4 and π_5, is more easily bleachable in the equilibrium situation, i.e. has a higher photosensitivity or a lower regeneration rate or both.

The results of further work on the adaptation recovery anomaly of the blue-sensitive system are likely to be highly pertinent to the alternative conception of π_1, π_2, π_3, here considered, and the whole relationship sets attractive problems.

5. Problems of the "Green-sensitive" and "Red-sensitive" Mechanisms (π_4, π_4', π_5, π_5')

The difficulties of separating π_4 and π_5 by identifying branches in t.v.r. curves are discussed in Paper IX, p. 90, which also gives the first evidence for distinguishing low and moderately high intensity states for both π_4 and π_5. The higher intensity states are referred to as π_4' and π_5' respectively, while π_4 and π_5 are retained to represent the two mechanisms when the conditioning stimuli are low, i.e. such as not to raise the threshold of the mechanism to more than about ten times its value on zero field. A first idea was that the distinction between π_4 and π_4', or π_5 and π_5', evident in the increment threshold data, might arise because of the bleaching of the pigment in the cones. This bleaching can modify the shape of the t.v.r. curve if the pigment density is sufficiently high. Figure 2 shows how the t.v.r. curve of a particular mechanism, π_4, which has the standard shape (Table A) when the test and field wavelengths are the same, will be modified when different test and field wavelengths are used if the receptors of the mechanism contain high density pigment which is bleached as the field intensity to which the retina is adapted is raised. If the test

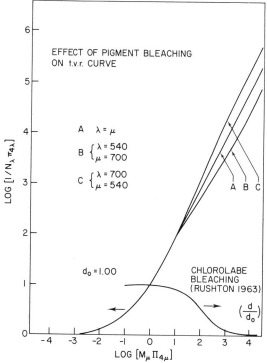

FIG. 2. Curves A, B and C show the shape of the t.v.r. curve of a single mechanism whose cone receptors are activated by absorption in the visual pigment chlorolabe with an effective optical density, in the dark, of 1·0 at the wavelength of maximum absorption coefficient—540 nm. The fourth curve shows how the pigment density is reduced as the field intensity $M\mu$ to which the retina is adapted is raised.

wavelength lies at the peak of the spectral absorption curve and the field wavelength near the "tail" of the curve, then as the pigment is bleached the receptor's sensitivity to the test wavelength will increase with respect to its sensitivity to the field. The t.v.r. will then develop a dip over a certain range of field intensities that could be interpreted as the intrusion of a new mechanism, with a modified spectral sensitivity curve. On the other hand if the spectral positions of test and field wavelengths are reversed, the t.v.r. curve will develop an elevation over the bleaching range, a distortion quite unlike the expected effect of a new mechanism. In Paper XI the possibility that the transitions π_4 to π'_4 and π_5 to π'_5 might be attributable to this effect is rejected (a) because the transition seems to occur at levels where insufficient bleaching has occurred and (b) because in one case, π_5 to π'_5 the bleaching would produce an elevation and not a dip. However, if the presence of rather high densities (say greater than 0·5) of pigments in cone receptors is confirmed, some distortion of the shape of t.v.r. curves for the same mechanism for different combinations of test and field wavelengths would have to be admitted. So far, in the interpretation of t.v.r. curves, a constant shape of the branches attributable to individual cone mechanisms has seemed adequate. (However, see Section 6 below). This may be so in part, (i) because the distortion effects may be rather small and, (ii) because it is not easily possible in many instances to follow the t.v.r. curves over the range where the pigment bleaching would be expected to produce distortion. However, a re-examination of this whole argument with respect especially to π_4/π'_4 and π_5/π'_5 is required. As regards the blue-sensitive mechanisms, we know virtually nothing about the kinetics of bleaching of the visual pigment in the receptors. Rushton's fundus reflection methods have not in fact been successful in demonstrating the presence of a bleachable "blue-absorbing" pigment.

There are few increment threshold studies providing evidence on the existence or properties of the duality π_4/π'_4 and π_5/π'_5 in the "green" and "red" sensitive systems. Watkins (1969a and b) claims that his measurements at a limited number of test and field wavelengths and for groups of normal, deutan and protan subjects are consistent with π_4 and π'_4, π_5 and π'_5, but with certain identifiable differences in the shapes of the spectral sensitivity curves for the colour-defective subjects. As Watkins used only a limited number of test and field wavelengths it is difficult to assess how compelling his conclusions may be. The most significant recent contribution on the π_4/π'_4 and π_5/π'_5 systems is that of Whittle (Whittle and Challands, 1969; Whittle, 1973, 1974; Whittle and Swanson, 1974), who measured, not increment thresholds, but suprathreshold brightness matches obtained by a haploscopic (binocular-matching) method in which two test flashes (40 msec, exposed simultaneously) seen respectively by the left and right eyes on backgrounds, also exposed only to the respective eyes, were matched in brightness. Generally a white field of 1·76 log trolands and a white test flash were used for the left eye, these being kept constant. For the right eye different combinations of test and field wavelengths, λ and μ respectively, and a complete range of field intensities were used. Thus the procedure had a certain analogy with the two-colour technique, except that the test flash (seen by the right eye) was adjusted not to threshold but to match the apparent brightness of a constant reference flash on a constant background seen by the left eye. In this way a series of curves of log (matching flash intensity) versus log (field intensity) for each λ/μ combination could be obtained, one corresponding to the actual t.v.r. curve, the others to progressively increasing apparent flash-brightness levels.

The results showed a rather close correspondence with the increment threshold analysis for π_4 and π'_4, and π_5 and π'_5, even though the apparent flash-brightness levels correspond to flashes of intensity from 1 to 3 log units above the increment threshold. For the blue-sensitive mechanism, however, the π_1 branch shown by the increment threshold curve is not in evidence when flash-brightness matches are made at some one or more log units above increment threshold. Whittle concludes, in conformity with well-established viewpoints, that the blue-sensitive mechanism carries little weight as a brightness-producing system (see Marks, 1974, on this point). Whittle's work is perhaps most interesting for the persistent appearance of a π_4/π_4' and π_5/π_5' transition in the suprathreshold measurements.

As explained in the footnote to Table B (above), the values given for the spectral sensitivities of π_4 and π_5 are true field sensitivities but those for π_4' and π_5' were obtained by applying to the $\Pi_{4\mu}$ and $\Pi_{5\mu}$ values "corrections" based respectively on the change of test spectral sensitivity values in going from below to above the field intensities of the transition region. This procedure implies that for each of the four modifications—π_4, π_4', π_5, π_5'—the test and field relative spectral sensitivities in the relevant spectral regions are identical. (See Paper XI for some details of these correcting ratios.) At the time of the original measurements (1953) and using the same subjects, direct determinations of the field sensitivities $\Pi_{4\mu}'$ and $\Pi_{5\mu}'$ were attempted, but some difficulty was experienced from imperfect adaptation to the moderately high monochromatic field intensities required to raise the increment threshold above the zero field value by about 2 log units. The effect of inadequate adaptation showed itself in a hysteresis effect in the results when, in the same observing session, the wavelength of the adapting field was shifted in steps from red to blue, and then back from blue to red. Although the full results have not survived, the means of the red to blue and blue to red observations were in general agreement with the corrections based on the test sensitivity data; i.e. $\Pi_{4\mu}'$ lower than $\Pi_{4\mu}$ by some 0·2 to 0·3 log units in the red and little different in the green, $\Pi_{5\mu}'$ about the same as $\Pi_{5\mu}$ in the red and 0·1 to 0·2 log units higher in the green. However, these means are not acceptable as substitutes for true equilibrium values, and unfortunately other work prevented the planned repeats with more adequate adaptation time.

In a limited application of the two-colour threshold technique to the determination of t.v.λ. curves, making no use of the more powerful t.v.r. and f.v.μ. approaches, Wald (1964) obtained spectral sensitivity results for normals which are substantially in agreement with the earlier t.v.λ. measurements and f.v.μ. sensitivities of Stiles, except that for the "red-sensitive" process, corresponding to π_5 or π_5', the data of Wald suggest considerably lower values than for π_5, for wavelengths shorter than about 560 nm, provided the curves are superimposed at longer wavelengths where they have similar shape. This point is illustrated in Fig. 8 of Enoch's informative discussion of Wald's data (Enoch, 1972). This raises the question whether in the shorter-wave half of the spectrum (λ less than 560 nm, say), the test sensitivity (t.v.λ.) of π_5 or π_5', measured by Wald, may not in fact deviate from the field sensitivity measured by Stiles. Recently Cavonius and Estévez (1975a) obtained field spectral sensitivities for π_5 which agree with those of Stiles rather than with the shape found by Wald using the t.v.λ. method. (See also Ingling, 1969, in particular, his Fig. 12, p. 1145.)

Important further applications of the t.v.λ. procedure to the vision of colour-

TABLE A *Function $\zeta(x)$ defining the average shape of the t.v.r. curve of an individual foveal cone mechanism*

log x	log $\zeta(x)$	log x	log $\zeta(x)$
$\bar{3}$·00	0	$\bar{2}$·80	$\bar{1}$·67
$\bar{3}$·05	0	$\bar{2}$·85	$\bar{1}$·65
$\bar{3}$·10	0	$\bar{2}$·90	$\bar{1}$·63
$\bar{3}$·15	0	$\bar{2}$·95	$\bar{1}$·61
$\bar{3}$·20	$\bar{1}$·99	$\bar{1}$·00	$\bar{1}$·59
$\bar{3}$·25	$\bar{1}$·99	$\bar{1}$·05	$\bar{1}$·57
$\bar{3}$·30	$\bar{1}$·98	$\bar{1}$·10	$\bar{1}$·55
$\bar{3}$·35	$\bar{1}$·98	$\bar{1}$·15	$\bar{1}$·52
$\bar{3}$·40	$\bar{1}$·98	$\bar{1}$·20	$\bar{1}$·50
$\bar{3}$·45	$\bar{1}$·97	$\bar{1}$·25	$\bar{1}$·48
$\bar{3}$·50	$\bar{1}$·96	$\bar{1}$·30	$\bar{1}$·45
$\bar{3}$·55	$\bar{1}$·96	$\bar{1}$·35	$\bar{1}$·43
$\bar{3}$·60	$\bar{1}$·95	$\bar{1}$·40	$\bar{1}$·40
$\bar{3}$·65	$\bar{1}$·94	$\bar{1}$·45	$\bar{1}$·37
$\bar{3}$·70	$\bar{1}$·94	$\bar{1}$·50	$\bar{1}$·34
$\bar{3}$·75	$\bar{1}$·93	$\bar{1}$·55	$\bar{1}$·32
$\bar{3}$·80	$\bar{1}$·92	$\bar{1}$·60	$\bar{1}$·28
$\bar{3}$·85	$\bar{1}$·92	$\bar{1}$·65	$\bar{1}$·26
$\bar{3}$·90	$\bar{1}$·91	$\bar{1}$·70	$\bar{1}$·22
$\bar{3}$·95	$\bar{1}$·90	$\bar{1}$·75	$\bar{1}$·19
$\bar{2}$·00	$\bar{1}$·89	$\bar{1}$·80	$\bar{1}$·15
$\bar{2}$·05	$\bar{1}$·88	$\bar{1}$·85	$\bar{1}$·12
$\bar{2}$·10	$\bar{1}$·87	$\bar{1}$·90	$\bar{1}$·08
$\bar{2}$·15	$\bar{1}$·86	$\bar{1}$·95	$\bar{1}$·04
$\bar{2}$·20	$\bar{1}$·85	0·00	$\bar{1}$·00
$\bar{2}$·25	$\bar{1}$·84	0·05	$\bar{2}$·96
$\bar{2}$·30	$\bar{1}$·83	0·10	$\bar{2}$·92
$\bar{2}$·35	$\bar{1}$·82	0·15	$\bar{2}$·88
$\bar{2}$·40	$\bar{1}$·80	0·20	$\bar{2}$·83
$\bar{2}$·45	$\bar{1}$·79	0·25	$\bar{2}$·79
$\bar{2}$·50	$\bar{1}$·77	0·30	$\bar{2}$·74
$\bar{2}$·55	$\bar{1}$·76	0·35	$\bar{2}$·70
$\bar{2}$·60	$\bar{1}$·74	0·40	$\bar{2}$·65
$\bar{2}$·65	$\bar{1}$·72	0·45	$\bar{2}$·61
$\bar{2}$·70	$\bar{1}$·70	0·50	$\bar{2}$·56
$\bar{2}$·75	$\bar{1}$·69		

Notes. For log $x > 0.5$, log $\zeta(x) = \bar{1}\cdot06 - \log x$. The average shape of the t.v.r. curve is obtained by plotting $-\log \zeta(x)$ against log x. Small differences, probably not significant, in the shapes of mean experimental of different mechanisms (see Paper IX), have been averaged out to give a mean function $\zeta(x)$. Text stimulus characteristics: $1°$ diameter, 0.2 sec flash.

W. S. STILES

TABLE B *Field sensitivities of component visual mechanisms at the fovea*

Wave no. $\frac{1}{\mu}$ (cm^{-1})	log $\Pi_{1\mu}$	log $\Pi_{2\mu}$	log $\Pi_{3\mu}$	log $\Pi_{4\mu}$	log $\Pi'_{4\mu}$	log $\Pi_{5\mu}$	log $\Pi'_{5\mu}$
14,250		$\overline{12}$·060					
500		($\overline{12}$·380)		$\overline{11}$·211		$\overline{11}$·946	$\overline{11}$·960
750	$\overline{14}$·970	$\overline{12}$·700		$\overline{11}$·595		$\overline{10}$·332	$\overline{10}$·313
15,000	($\overline{13}$·235)	($\overline{11}$·010)		$\overline{11}$·957		$\overline{10}$·686	$\overline{10}$·682
250	$\overline{13}$·500	$\overline{11}$·620		$\overline{10}$·304	$\overline{10}$·006	$\overline{10}$·974	$\overline{10}$·991
500	($\overline{13}$·740)	$\overline{11}$·840		$\overline{10}$·594	$\overline{10}$·290	9·233	9·226
750	$\overline{13}$·980	($\overline{10}$·060)		$\overline{10}$·893	$\overline{10}$·571	9·435	9·430
16,000	($\overline{12}$·170)	$\overline{10}$·270		9·150	$\overline{10}$·850	9·632	9·641
250	$\overline{12}$·360	($\overline{10}$·370)		9·335	9·137	9·763	9·759
500	$\overline{12}$·610	$\overline{10}$·650		9·511	9·318	9·860	9·857
750	$\overline{12}$·800	$\overline{10}$·910		9·607	9·523	9·896	9·832
17,000	$\overline{12}$·840	$\overline{10}$·990		9·758	9·682	9·905	9·871
250	$\overline{12}$·800	$\overline{10}$·620	$\overline{13}$·160	9·824	9·778	9·931	9·834
500	$\overline{12}$·850	$\overline{10}$·980	($\overline{13}$·420)	9·909	9·856	9·944	9·879
750	$\overline{12}$·910	9·240	($\overline{13}$·670)	9·963	9·916	9·910	9·813
18,000	$\overline{11}$·130	$\overline{10}$·990	($\overline{13}$·920)	9·981	9·965	9·910	9·787
250	$\overline{11}$·160	$\overline{10}$·880	$\overline{12}$·140	8·005	9·962	9·912	9·796
500	$\overline{11}$·390	$\overline{10}$·870	($\overline{12}$·370)	8·003	8·002	9·888	9·727
750	$\overline{11}$·599		($\overline{12}$·670)	8·005	8·026	9·875	9·741
19,000	$\overline{11}$·860		($\overline{12}$·950)	8·007	8·006	9·878	9·742
250	$\overline{10}$,054		($\overline{11}$,230)	9·948	9·910	9·804	9·698
500	$\overline{10}$·257		$\overline{11}$·528	9·888	9·893	9·749	9·589
750	$\overline{10}$·424		$\overline{11}$·756	9·786	9·791	9·634	9·472
20,000	$\overline{10}$·528		$\overline{11}$·873	9·660	9·668	9·517	9·366
250	$\overline{10}$·647		$\overline{10}$·031	9·556		9·392	9·254
500	$\overline{10}$·775		$\overline{10}$·227	9·463		9·325	
750	$\overline{10}$·922		$\overline{10}$·345	9·395		9·241	
21,000	9·051		$\overline{10}$·499	9·322		9·138	
250	9·154		$\overline{10}$·622	9·233		9·081	
500	9·237		$\overline{10}$·652	9·161		$\overline{10}$·994	
750	9·268		$\overline{10}$·723	9·059		$\overline{10}$·910	
22,000	9·354		$\overline{10}$·745	$\overline{10}$·950		$\overline{10}$·804	
250	9·410		$\overline{10}$·870	$\overline{10}$·922		$\overline{10}$·794	
500	9·478		$\overline{10}$·892	$\overline{10}$·922		$\overline{10}$·719	
750	9·454	9·700	$\overline{10}$·903	$\overline{10}$·855		$\overline{10}$·694	
23,000	9·460	9·650	$\overline{10}$·880	$\overline{10}$·810		$\overline{10}$·644	
250	9·433	9·620	$\overline{10}$·868	$\overline{10}$·742		$\overline{10}$·560	
500	9·372	9·540	$\overline{10}$·778	$\overline{10}$·680		$\overline{10}$·506	
750	9·296	9·470	$\overline{10}$·731	$\overline{10}$·587		$\overline{10}$·418	
24,000	9·232	9·280	$\overline{10}$·595	$\overline{10}$·426		$\overline{10}$·336	
250	9·035	9·080	$\overline{10}$·456	$\overline{10}$·332		$\overline{10}$·257	
500	$\overline{10}$·854	$\overline{10}$·960		$\overline{10}$·163		$\overline{10}$·136	
750	$\overline{10}$·664						

Note. The quantity tabulated for each mechanism represents the logarithm of the reciprocal of the field radiance of a monochromatic field that raises the increment threshold for a given mechanism to ten times its value on zero field, the retina being assumed always to be fully adapted to the field. The radiance of the uniform monochromatic adapting field is expressed in terms of the number of quanta per second entering the observing eye per sq. deg. of field.

The values given are derived from the results of experimental work summarily described in Paper IX and published in graphical form in that paper and in Paper XI and a later contribution (Stiles, 1964). The following additional details give a rather fuller account of the measurements and the derivation of the field sensitivities.

Test stimulus: $1°$ diameter; 0.2 sec. flash period; monochromatic of wavelength λ.

Field: $10°$ diameter; continuously exposed with test flash superimposed at the centre; monochromatic of wavelength μ, or mixture of a main monochromatic field, wavelength μ, with an auxiliary field (filtered light, narrow spectral band).

Foveal observation of the test stimulus: equilibrium conditions.

Subjects: (1) P.B., (2) E.K., (3) P.F., (4) W.S.; subjects (1), (2) and (3) all female and in age range 20-30, subject (4) male aged 51.

$\Pi_{5\mu}$: the relative values of $\Pi_{5\mu}$ were determined for each subject in two blocks of measurements using a test stimulus of wavenumber $15,000$ cm^{-1} ($\lambda = 666.7$ nm) throughout and monochromatic fields of wavenumbers $14,500$ cm^{-1} by 250 cm^{-1} steps to $20,250$ cm^{-1} (Block A), and $19,250$ cm^{-1} by 250 cm^{-1} steps to $24,500$ cm^{-1} (Block B). In the first run of Block A the field intensity at each field wavenumber was set at an intensity that it was estimated from preliminary measurements would raise the log (threshold) by a fixed amount (about one log unit or rather less) above the zero field value. In the run the thresholds for all field wavenumbers were measured, and from the deviation of the value at each field wavenumber from the mean for all field wavenumbers, an estimate was made of the change in the corresponding field intensity that would be expected to produce a threshold exactly equal to the mean. This correction was made using the relation between threshold and field intensity defined by the standard shape of a component t.v.r. curve (Table A). The reciprocals of the field intensities so corrected provided a first determination of the relative values of $\Pi_{5\mu}$ in the wavenumber range of Block A. In the next run the field intensities were pre-set at the corrected values obtained in the first run, and then proceeding as before a second determination of the relative values of $\Pi_{5\mu}$ was derived. At least four runs on different days, traversing the field wavelengths in alternating order in successive runs, were made for each subject, and the means of the logarithms of the relative values at each wavenumber were computed. To find absolute values of $\Pi_{5\mu}$, further threshold measurements (Block C) were made for fixed test and field wavenumbers both equal to $15,000$ cm^{-1}, (a) with zero field intensity, (b) with a field intensity estimated to raise the threshold by not more than about one log unit. The standard t.v.r. shape was again used to determine from the mean measured threshold values the field intensity to raise the threshold exactly one log unit above the zero field value. This gave the absolute value of $\Pi_{5\mu}$ at $(1/\mu) = 15,000$ cm^{-1} and by comparison with the relative value found earlier for this wavenumber, the factor for converting all the relative values of Block A to absolute values was derived. For converting the mean relative values for the wavenumbers covered by the Block B measurements, the factor used was derived by comparing the mean relative values obtained respectively in Blocks A and B in their common wavenumber range. The final values of log $(\Pi_{5\mu})$ in the Table, are the means of the log absolute values for all four subjects.

$\Pi_{4\mu}$: the values given in the Table were obtained by a precisely similar procedure to that described for $\Pi_{5\mu}$, except that test wavenumber used was $20,000$ cm^{-1}, and the factor for conversion of relative to absolute values was obtained for $(1/\mu) = 20,000$ cm^{-1}.

$\Pi_{1\mu}$: all measurements were made with a test stimulus of wavenumber $23,000$ cm^{-1}. For obtaining relative values of $\Pi_{1\mu}$ in the shorter wavelength range, a fixed yellowish-green auxiliary field (effective wavelength around 555 nm) was used of sufficient intensity to raise the threshold onto the lower part of the π_1 branch of the t.v.r. curve. The main (monochromatic) field had wavenumber $18,750$ cm^{-1} increasing by 250 cm^{-1} steps to $24,750$ cm^{-1}. The intensities of the main fields of different wavenumbers required to increase the log threshold by a constant amount above the value for the auxiliary field only, were determined by the same indirect procedure used for finding relative values of $\Pi_{5\mu}$ and $\Pi_{4\mu}$, ignoring the presence of the auxiliary field. In a second block of measurements, complete t.v.r. curves were determined for monochromatic fields (no auxiliary field) of wavenumber $14,250$ cm^{-1}, increasing in 16 steps to $20,250$ cm^{-1}. For each field wavenumber the π_1 branch of the curve was fitted with the standard component t.v.r. shape, from the position of which along the log (field intensity) axis the absolute value of $\Pi_{1\mu}$ could be at once derived. The relative values of $\Pi_{1\mu}$ obtained in the shorter wavelength range were then converted to absolute values by a factor chosen to give best agreement at the join with the absolute values found at longer wavelengths by the direct method. The tabulated values are again the means for all four subjects; the brackets indicate a value obtained by graphical interpolation.

$\text{II}_{3\mu}$: test stimulus wavenumber, 23,000 cm^{-1} throughout. For finding $\text{II}_{3\mu}$ in the shorter wave-length range, an orange auxiliary field (effective wavelength around 600 nm) was used of intensity just sufficient to bring the threshold onto the initial flat range of the π_3 branch of the t.v.r. curve, so that the observed threshold could be taken as the absolute threshold for the π_3 mechanism. Thus, after determining as for $\text{II}_{1\mu}$ the relative values of $\text{II}_{3\mu}$ for main (monochromatic) fields of wavenumbers 19,500 cm^{-1} by 250 cm^{-1} steps to 24,250 cm^{-1}, the factor for converting to absolute values was readily obtained from the observed increase in threshold above the value for the auxiliary field only. For longer field wavelengths complete t.v.r. curves showing a well-developed π_3 branch were determined for monochromatic fields (no auxiliary field) provided by the green and yellow lines of a high intensity mercury arc, and the corresponding absolute values of $\text{II}_{3\mu}$ deduced by fitting with the standard t.v.r. curve. As before, the Table gives final means for four subjects, with brackets round graphically interpolated values.

$\text{II}_{2\mu}$: test stimulus wavenumber 23,000 cm^{-1} used throughout. Subject (4) had to be omitted from these determinations as his t.v.r. curves showed no, or at most an extremely shallow π_2 branch. The other subjects gave π_2 branches with an absolute threshold on the average 0·25 log units lower than the absolute threshold for π_1. All determinations of $\text{II}_{2\mu}$ were made by fitting the standard t.v.r. shape to the rather small portion of the π_2 branch visible in t.v.r. curves for different field wavenumbers, and the fitting errors were materially greater than in the determinations of $\text{II}_{1\mu}$ and $\text{II}_{3\mu}$. Identifying and fitting the π_2 branch proved most difficult for short-wavelength fields, and satisfactory mean values of log $\text{II}_{2\mu}$ by the direct method were not obtained in this spectral region. The boxed-in values between 22,750 cm^{-1} were derived on the assumptions (i) that in this spectral region the test sensitivity and field sensitivity of π_2 stand in a fixed ratio, and (ii) that the Weber Fraction of π_2 has the same value—0·087—as for the other blue-sensitive mechanisms π_1 and π_3. The boxed values can then be derived from the absolute thresholds for test stimuli of different wavelength exposed on zero field, which in this short wavelength range and for the three subjects concerned can be identified with π_2 thresholds. The boxed values are of course speculative only. All tabulated values are means for three subjects.

$\text{II}_{5\mu}$, $\text{II}'_{4\mu}$: for reasons explained in Section 5 of the present paper, the direct measurements made of these field sensitivities were unacceptable because true equilibrium conditions were not achieved. The boxed values given in the Table were obtained by a speculative and indirect method—described in Paper XI, pp. 106-108—which reduces in practice to multiplying the $\text{II}_{5\mu}$ and $\text{II}_{4\mu}$ values by respective wavelength-dependent factors derived from the change in test sensitivity of the appropriate mechanism on raising the adaptation level. For mechanism π_5, the factor was taken as proportional to the ratio of the test sensitivity for a blue-green field (20,000 cm^{-1}) of intensity 1552 trolands to that for a field of similar colour but of intensity 43 trolands (curves F and D in the mean test spectral sensitivity data for the same group of subjects reproduced in Stiles, 1964). For mechanism π_4 the factor was assumed proportional to the ratio of the test sensitivity for a red field (15,000 cm^{-1}) of intensity 2506 trolands, to that for a field of similar colour but of intensity 29 trolands (curves M and L in Stiles, 1964). The constants of proportionality involved in the two factors have been taken so that the values of $\text{II}'_{5\mu}$ and $\text{II}_{5\mu}$ are approximately the same at long wavelengths $(1/\mu)$(less than about 17,000 cm^{-1}), while $\text{II}'_{4\mu}$ and $\text{II}_{4\mu}$ agree approximately in the medium wavelength range $((1/\mu)$ greater than about 18,000 cm^{-1}) but there is an arbitrary element in these normalisations.

defectives have been made by Wald and collaborators (1966, 1967 and some later papers), and these have a bearing on the shape of the test spectral sensitivity curve of the "red-sensitive" mechanism.

6. CONE SATURATION

The t.v.r. curve for the extrafoveal retina of the normal eye corresponds to rod vision of the test stimulus up to high field intensities if the two-colour threshold method is used with a red field and a green test stimulus. It then shows the well-known "rod-saturation" effect (Aguilar and Stiles, 1954); but, if in the same figure there is also shown the fraction of the rod rhodopsin bleached at each field level as derived from Rushton's data, it is apparent that rod response is already saturated when no more than a few per cent bleaching has occurred. For foveal (cone) vision on the other hand, the t.v.r. curve, at least for the π_4 and π_5 branches, can be followed to very high field levels at which nearly all the cone pigment is bleached, and yet shows no upward turn away from the constant Weber fraction line, which might be taken as an indicator of incipient saturation. (See Figs. 6 and 7 of Paper XII). In the last decade, Alpern, Rushton and Torii (1970a, b, c and d) in an outstanding series of papers, have thrown much additional light on the saturation property by measurements of threshold sensitivities for brief, intense conditioning stimuli rather than for fields to which the retina has become adapted. Initially they were concerned with rod vision and, by experiments employing the so-called after-flash effect (Alpern, 1965; Alpern and Rushton, 1965), they found a new kind of saturation in which it is the inhibitory effect of a light flash exposed on a steady field, namely, its action in raising the increment threshold in a neighbouring retinal area, that is subject to saturation. Later they applied a similar method to cone vision, and for this they also established a saturation of the inhibitory effect. Their work also included measurements on cone vision by a method more closely akin to the procedure used originally to establish rod saturation. This work, confirmed and extended by King-Smith and Webb (1974) and Shevell (1977), showed that cone mechanisms, notably π_4 and π_5, saturate in the original sense—the increment threshold increases indefinitely when the conditioning stimulus (a background) is progressively raised towards a (finite) saturation level—provided however that the test stimulus is applied before the mechanism has had time to adapt to the background. Thus in the first measurements by this method, the adapting field was exposed on the previously dark field for just 180 msec during which the 20 msec test flash was superimposed. A plot of log (increment threshold) against log (background intensity in trolands) then showed the characteristic upturn from the 45° line, to asymptote to a vertical saturation line at a background of the order of 4·1 log trolands (red test stimulus to isolate π_5) or 4·5 log trolands (green test stimulus, to isolate π_4), a white conditioning field being used in both cases. The fact that cone saturation is observable by using a flashing conditioning field but not by a field to which the retina has become adapted is explained by noting that in the former situation the flashed field generates, by absorption in the visual pigment, a strong surge of neural responses before the light has time to bleach more than a very little pigment. Thus, attributing the saturation to congestion in the further transmission of the neural response, this can occur when the number of quanta absorbed and the consequent neural traffic approaches a certain limit. In the equilibrium situation, however, this limit may never be reached, because the more intense the adapting field, the more the pigment is bleached and the smaller its capacity for absorbing quanta. As noted above, the discovery of cone saturation was first made by Alpern, Rushton and Torii by the more involved method in which an annular stimulus surrounding the foveal test stimulus is flashed on for 100 msec at a fixed time (50 msec) after the test flash exposure (10 msec), its intensity being such that it raises the threshold of the test flash. The effect of the annular after-flash is reduced if, in the annulus a steady field is applied all the time, on which the annular flash is superimposed. Measurements can then be made of the way the after-flash intensity which produces a given effect on the test flash threshold varies with the intensity of the steady field. Even if the annular flash is not exposed, the steady annular field will itself raise the threshold of the test stimulus. To take account of this, the after-flash intensity is raised until it increases the test threshold by some prescribed fixed factor above the value obtained with the steady field acting alone, the assumption being that when this is done at all steady fields the after-flash itself will be producing always the same inhibitory effect on the detectability of the test stimulus. The curves, log (flash intensity) versus log (steady field intensity), so obtained show the characteristic saturation shape. The after-flash method and the simpler field flashing method of observing cone saturation, are strictly concerned with different effects although no doubt they have a common root cause. It is perhaps not surprising therefore that the field intensity to produce saturation is widely different—by some two log units—in the two cases.

Until recently, evidence of saturation properties for blue-sensitive mechanisms (π_1, π_2, π_3) had not been reported. Mollon and Polden (1977a) have now found that if the auxiliary field method is applied to follow to high intensities the t.v.r. curve of these mechanisms, using a short-wave test stimulus and a short-wave main field of progressively increased intensity mixed with a constant long-wave auxiliary field, then the curve, log (increment threshold) versus log (main field intensity), bends upwards from the constant Weber fraction line towards a vertical asymptote in a way indicative of saturation. They point out, quite correctly, what I had failed to observe, that a curve in Paper IX (Fig. 11), determined under similar conditions to theirs, shows at high intensities an increase of gradient that already suggests an approach to saturation for mechanism π_1. According to Mollon and Polden's new work, it appears that the short-wave cone mechanisms not only saturate but also, unlike π_4 and π_5, they do so in the equilibrium case.

7. Properties of Individual Mechanisms Studied by Working on Branches of Response Curves Associated with Them

The first application of this concept to cone vision was in the determination of t.v.r. curves showing π_4 and π_1 branches (i) with the test stimulus entering the subject's pupil through the centre or (ii) through a peripheral point of the pupil. The effect of retinal directional sensitivity is to raise the threshold for the latter case, but the rise is slightly larger in the branch attributable to π_1, indicating therefore a difference in directional properties of the receptors of the two mechanisms. Differences in other properties may similarly be found by varying other test parameters, such as test flash period or angular area. This has been done for area of test flash to study spatial integrating properties (Paper VII; Brindley, 1954; Green, 1968) and for period of test flash to compare temporal integrating properties (Krauskopf, 1969; Krauskopf and Mollon, 1971; Mollon and Krauskopf, 1973). More sophisticated test tasks have also been employed in which, for example, the critical flicker frequency is determined for a test stimulus of intensity not so high that the response to it ceases to be attributable to the mechanism that the two-colour technique is designed to isolate (Brindley et al., 1966; Green, 1969; Estévez and Spekreijse, 1974; Cavonius and Estévez, 1975a). The interesting special case when the test stimulus is allowed to spread over a large proportion of the visual field (Ganzfeld studies) has been examined by Kelly (1962), who measured critical frequency characteristics. Such interesting global data do not of course pinpoint response properties of mechanisms in localised retina areas. Visual acuity of individual colour mechanisms has been investigated by similar two-colour methods (Paper VII, Brindley, 1970; Cavonius and Estevez, 1975b). They have also been extensively used in work where the response to stimuli is determined by electrophysiological methods. On the whole the concepts of π mechanisms have proved of value in interpreting results (Krauskopf, 1973; Estévez and Cavonius, 1975; Padmos and Norren, 1975; Estévez et al, 1975, Harwerth and Sperling, 1975). The use of contrast evoked potentials in both humans and animals (primates) is noteworthy.

Reverting to the usual psychophysical application of the two-colour method for humans, it has become clear that by the use of test stimuli with different characteristics, especially wavelength, imaged on different retinal points in the foveal, parafoveal and extrafoveal areas, the way the "absolute" sensitivity and other properties of individual mechanisms change in traversing the retina can be investigated for both normal and colour-defective subjects (Paper VII; Wald, 1966 and 1967).

One factor in the general usefulness of the method is no doubt the fact that it is based on the criterion of minimal detectable disturbance of a continually repeated standard stimulus situation, and that to determine the threshold value of the test variable appropriate to this criterion, any other indicators may substitute for the transition from "yes" to "no" in a subject's answers in a psychophysical experiment on humans. In electrophysiological work the indicator may be some fixed small excess over random fluctuations in a feature of the electrical record, and in animal behaviour experiments a similarly agreed small deviation. In certain cases, increment thresholds in similar external stimulus situations, obtained in psychophysical, electrophysiological and behaviour experiments may be comparable; presumably this could occur where the factors determining the threshold are peripheral to the indicator mechanisms called into play in the different experimental techniques.

8. Rod and Cone Interactions

The extent to which a visual response to light is determined exclusively by the quanta absorbed in the rod receptor system (absorption in rhodopsin), or exclusively by those absorbed in one of the cone receptor systems (absorption in one of the cone pigments, erythrolabe, chlorolabe, cyanolabe) or, in some way, by contributions from absorptions of more than one of these kinds, is a wide-ranging and controversial question. The following remarks deal with the more limited question of the extent to which increment thresholds (including thresholds on zero fields or absolute thresholds) reveal interaction between different component mechanisms.

Where, in determining an increment threshold, the response to the test stimulus may arise through two different receptor mechanisms, an apparent summation of their effects may be produced by what is known as probability summation, even though there is the highest degree of independence of the mechanisms consistent with their both being capable of activating a common indicator signal. This is now a familiar concept—discussed, for example, in Wyszecki and Stiles (1967), pp. 543 and 552—which leads to the general rule that if the thresholds of the independent component mechanisms when acting alone have infinitely sharp values, there is no probability summation—the observed threshold is the lower of the component thresholds—but if a threshold is simply the value to give a certain probability of detection, the lowering of the resultant threshold will be determined by the steepness of the probability-of-detection curves given by the component mechanisms, acting alone. In recent years the more sophisticated approach of signal detection theory, typified by an article of Nachmias (1972), may modify the details of the probability summation concept, without I think changing the essential point.

Where the observed threshold cannot be identified as the resultant of the thresholds of independent component mechanisms, the summation is described as physiological summation and is evidence of some interaction in the threshold responses of the mechanisms. This concept is not of course limited to threshold responses of component colour mechanisms for test stimuli of fixed characteristics. In the case of a large test stimulus, the resultant threshold may be regarded as arising from similar mechanisms operating in the various small parts of the retinal area on which the test stimulus is imaged. The same distinction between probability and physiological summation can be drawn.

In the increment threshold analysis used in most papers of the present volume, it is assumed that the component mechanisms are independent so that only probability summation operates, or that any physiological summation effects are small enough to be ignored. While this is still probably acceptable as a crude first approximation, small but significant deviations have been found. Dutch workers (Van der Velde and Bouman, 1948) tested the probability summation at threshold of rod and cone systems (extrafoveal vision) and found a slightly greater probability of detection than would be consistent with independent mechanisms. The first direct study of the summation of threshold responses from different colour mechanisms (foveal vision) was made much later in 1958. By the use of a suitable coloured field (background) a condition was set up in which a test stimulus consisting of a mixture of two wavelengths was such that for each wavelength constituent in the absence of the other, the threshold could be attributed to a single mechanism, different for the two wavelengths. By threshold measurements with varying proportions in the mixture, the way the responses from the two mechanisms were summating could be determined. Results, all obtained with 1° foveal test stimuli, showed that in certain cases, the resultant threshold did not agree with the prediction of probability summation, but the deviation (0·1 to 0·2 log units) was in the direction of less summation, indicating apparently a physiological inhibitive rather than summative effect. A series of figures summarising the results of this work are included in Paper XIII, p. 118. Repetition and extension of the work, using, however, smaller—10 min diam.—test stimuli and making measurements for negative as well as positive test increments, showed many similar and rather complicated summation or inhibition effects of the same order of magnitude (Boynton, Ikeda and Stiles, 1964; Ikeda, 1963 and 1964). Ikeda, for example, showed that with very brief test flashes the inhibitive effect did not appear. While perhaps none of the deviations is large enough to affect the threshold analysis as a first approximation, their incorporation in a broader and more precise scheme presents problems.

In the special case of increment thresholds on a dark field, Guth (1967) and collaborators have observed summation anomalies of much the same kind as those referred to above. In interpreting his results Guth has been preoccupied with questions of brightness additivity and with difficult concepts of heterochromatic brightness-matching on which I would not wish to comment in the present context.

So far, interactions have been considered from a position that assumes each mechanism to be brought independently to a certain state by the conditioning stimulus, the actual interaction occurring in the processes by which the signals produced by the test flash in the respective mechanisms are combined at some higher level to determine a detectable or not detectable resultant. Interaction of a different kind might fairly be said to occur if the condition of a particular mechanism were dependent not only on light absorbed in its "proper receptors" but also in the "proper receptors" of other mechanisms. Originally (Paper III) it was postulated that any radiation modifying the condition of a particular mechanism, i.e. any conditioning stimulus, and any radiation producing a threshold response, i.e. any test stimulus, would do so as far as variations of wavelengths were concerned in accordance with a spectral sensitivity curve unique to the mechanism and the same for both test and conditioning stimulus. It was also implied—and the formulae proposed assumed this—that for non-monochromatic stimuli, their effects on the mechanism would be determined by a simple integration over the spectrum of the product of its spectral sensitivity and the spectral power of the stimulus; thus an initial linear stage in the effect was assumed. Most of the earlier studies used mono-chromatic stimuli, and for these it was concluded (Paper IX) that, in the spectral regions where the relative spectral sensitivities both to test stimuli and to conditioning stimuli could be determined, they were the same. The considerations of Section 2 and before all the crucial work of Pugh indicate that the π_1 field spectral sensitivity curve must be composite and dependent on two—possibly three—sensitivities associated probably with the proper receptors of other mechanisms. If we admit two sensitivities for each of which the initial stage of stimulation is linear with respect to spectral power distribution, the basic formula for the increment threshold given in Wyszecki and Stiles (1967), p. 574,

$$\frac{1}{N_{i\lambda}} = \pi_{i\lambda}\, \zeta_i(M_\mu \Pi_{1\mu})$$

must be modified for mechanism ($i = 1$) to

$$\frac{1}{N_{1\lambda}} = \pi_{1\lambda}\, Z_1(M_\mu \Pi'_{1\mu},\, M_\mu \Pi''_{1\mu})$$

where the function $Z_1(\ldots, \ldots)$ depends on two arguments, where $\Pi'_{1\mu}$ and $\Pi''_{1\mu}$ are the two component field sensitivities and where if the field stimulus is not monochromatic, the products $M_\mu \Pi'_{1\mu}$ and $M_\mu \Pi''_{1\mu}$ must be replaced by integrals over the spectrum of the field stimulus power M_μ. Pugh showed that the function $Z_1(x, y)$ does not reduce simply to a function of $(x+y)$, which would correspond to the original theory, and he proposes tentatively on the basis of his data that it might have the product form: $Z'_1(x) \cdot Z''_1(y)$, where both $Z'_1(\ldots)$ and $Z''_1(\ldots)$ may approximate to the original $\zeta_1(\ldots)$ (Table A).

In the case of π_1 the test and field sensitivity curves obtained for monochromatic stimuli agree in their common spectral range, and there is, I think, no evidence of a breakdown of additivity for test stimulus mixtures confined to wavelengths in that range. There is the possibility that the relative test sensitivity curve $\pi_{1\lambda}$ corresponds to one of the functions $\Pi'_{1\mu}$, $\Pi''_{1\mu}$, but not to the other, in the accessible range, and we should then be justified in identifying that function with the "proper receptors" of the π_1 mechanism.

The possibility of a rather similar breakdown of additivity in field sensitivity with reference particularly to π_4 and π_5 was also envisaged by Boynton, Daş and Gardiner (1966) and although the measurements themselves are not entirely satisfactory and are difficult to interpret, the idea of the kind of interaction between mechanisms at the level of field conditioning, as considered here, was certainly clearly enunciated.

The important modification in the mechanism concept necessary to accommodate the non-additivity of the field sensitivity of π_1, must not obscure the fact that in certain experimental situations, the mechanisms preserve a considerable degree of independence. Thus Alpern and Rushton (1965) have concluded from their measurements that after-flash phenomena are consistent with the view that the π-mechanisms are behaving independently, even though in these cases it is frequently a stimulus applied not only at a different time but also in a part of the retina that merely adjoins the area on which the test flash is imaged, which is producing a "field" increase in test threshold. It is also relevant to note that much of the initial analysis of increment thresholds does not depend on the test and field sensitivities of a mechanism being the same everywhere in the spectrum.

The possibility of a modification of the t.v.r. curve of the rod mechanism as a result of a contribution from the cone systems, has been raised by Makous and Boothe (1974) from the results of increment threshold studies that apparently contradict the results of Flamant and Stiles (1948). However, in later work Makous and Peeples (1975) report that using the same conditions they find no conflict in the two sets of data, but that when sufficiently high intensity adapting fields (higher than those of Flamant and Stiles) are used, the t.v.r. function for backgrounds of long wavelength differs from that for backgrounds of shorter wavelength, the former having more effect at high field levels in raising the rod threshold even though the fields are scotopically balanced. It certainly seems that the results of Makous and his co-workers present a problem. Using material summarised in Paper III, Fig. 3,

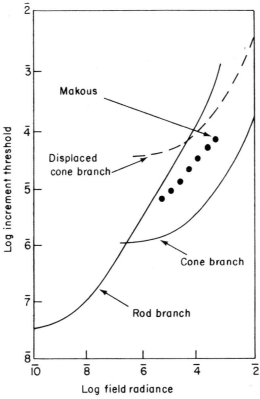

FIG. 3. Diagram illustrating the problem raised by the results of Makous and collaborators on the possible effect of cone stimulation on the form of the t.v.r. curve of parafoveal rod vision.

shows the t.v.r. curve for 5° parafoveal vision for the combination $\lambda = 580$ nm, $\mu = 500$ nm. From the test spectral sensitivity data in the same paper, it appears that changing λ from 580 nm to 490 nm would lower the rod branch by some 0·6 log units. On the other hand, if parafoveal cones behaved just like foveal cones, the same change of λ would raise the cone branch by an estimated 0·9 log units. In fact, the increase is likely to be less for the parafoveal cones than for the foveal cones. Probably, therefore, the net effect of changing λ from 580 to 490 nm would be to raise the cone branch with respect to the rod branch by not more than 1·5 log units, and the broken line curve in the figure shows the new (relative) position. Clearly if this approximate prediction of the situation is valid, for the combination $\lambda = 490$

nm, $\mu = 500$ nm, the cone branch will take over at a certain high scotopic level. But with a deep red field the scotopic level at which take-over occurs will certainly be higher, so that the t.v.r. curves for green (500 nm) and deep red fields will deviate in shape at a certain level that will coincide with the take-over level for the green field. In Fig. 3, I have tried to indicate by the dotted curve, using the Makous and Peeples results, where they find the break-away point. It is clearly at a lower level than that predicted for cone intervention according to the usual theory. Makous and Peeples determined the approximate position of the absolute cone threshold experimentally from the break in dark-adaptation recovery curves, and established by a direct method that there is a problem. It is not altogether clear the kind of rod-cone interaction that could be in action. If it is a contribution of cones to a rod-cone pool, through which the effect of the field in raising the threshold is produced, one might expect a red field with its relatively high cone effect, to bend an ideal straight line rod branch upwards at high field intensities, rather than for short-wave fields to bend the branch downwards at high levels. Alternatively the cone contribution might be assumed to inhibit the effect of rod stimulation in raising the threshold. Clearly, further work on this question will be required. (See also a contribution by Sternheim and Glass, 1975.)

9. π-MECHANISMS AND COLOUR-MATCHING FUNCTIONS

A first comparison of π-mechanism spectral sensitivities with colour-matching functions (Paper IX, Figs. 18 and 19) indicated (a) that the field sensitivities of π_1, π_4 and π_5 could be represented to a rough approximation by linear combinations of C.I.E. 1931 colour-matching functions, or rather better, in the short-wave range, by the modified C.I.E. functions of Judd and, (b) that the chromaticity coordinates of the spectral colours in a W.D.W. system derived on the hypothesis that the colour-matching functions are some linear combinations of the field sensitivities, $\Pi_{1\mu}$, $\Pi_{4\mu}$, $\Pi_{5\mu}$, show certain deviations from Wright's directly, measured chromaticities. (The C.I.E. 1931 Colorimetric System is largely based on these chromaticities of Wright.) The deviations were taken rather seriously at the time, particularly the largest one, namely, the too small amount of negative red chromaticity in the spectral range 19,000 to 22,000 cm^{-1} approx. But it was later realised that the modification of the relative shapes of the field sensitivities, particularly of π_4 and π_5, to eliminate this discrepancy would be rather small. Recently Estévez and Cavonius (1977) made a much more satisfactory comparison in which the field sensitivities of π_1, π_4, π_5 and of the relative colour-matching functions for the same subjects were determined. They found there was no significant discrepancy. They noted too that the field sensitivities of π_1, π_4 and π_5, quoted in the accompanying Table B, would yield good agreement with Wright's mean spectral chromaticities if the comparatively small distortion of less than 0·1 log unit were made in the π_5 curve in the blue-green region. Estévez and Cavonius found no evidence in any of their work for the modified sensitivities $\Pi'_{4\mu}$ and $\Pi''_{5\mu}$ and, in particular, no support for the suggestion that they would be needed rather than $\Pi_{4\mu}$ and $\Pi_{5\mu}$ in explaining their colour-matching data which were made at moderately high intensities. Their results in this respect emphasise the unsatisfactory position as regards the existence or properties of the modified forms, π'_4 and π'_5.

Most information on the increment threshold spectral sensitivities of cone mechanisms has been obtained for foveal vision using test stimuli not generally exceeding 1° in angular diameter. The availability now of colour-matching data representing cone vision in a 10° field, and probably most representative of the cone mechanisms a few degrees away from the foveal centre, suggests that it would be useful to have for comparison the threshold spectral sensitivities of cone mechanisms for these areas. However, to obtain these by the usual increment threshold analysis is likely to prove difficult (i) because of the intrusion of rod response and (ii) because the device of working in the early stages of recovery situations to avoid this intrusion will be complicated, at least for the short-wave mechanisms, by the anomalies considered in Section 3.

10. Increment Threshold Analysis of Colour Defectives

The exploitation of increment threshold analysis for clinical testing of colour-defectives was initiated by Boynton and Wagner (1961). Their work rests essentially on the idea that if a single mechanism, π_4 or π_5, is alone operative and if the increment thresholds as measured for the following four cases are, respectively:

N_{11}: flash of wavelength λ_1 on field of wavelength λ_1 and radiance M_1
N_{12}: flash of wavelength λ_1 on field of wavelength λ_2 and radiance M_2
N_{21}: flash of wavelength λ_2 on field of wavelength λ_1 and radiance M_1
N_{22}: flash of wavelength λ_2 on field of wavelength λ_2 and radiance M_2

then,

$$p = \frac{N_{11}}{N_{12}} \bigg/ \frac{N_{21}}{N_{22}} = 1$$

provided the field intensities M_1 and M_2 are such that the corresponding points on the t.v.r. curve lie on the upper section where increment threshold is proportional to field intensity (Weber range). If, however, two or more mechanisms are in operation and λ_1 and λ_2 are such that the relative spectral sensitivities of these two wavelengths are different for the two mechanisms, then p will be different from unity. If λ_1 and λ_2 lie in the red and green respectively, then the contribution of blue-sensitive mechanisms can be ignored and the value of the ratio should distinguish dichromats from trichromats. More specific information on the character of any defect is obtained by considering the ratios N_{12}/N_{21}, N_{11}/N_{21}, etc. The method while rather satisfactory for sorting out protanopes and deuteranopes proved of limited value in separating these from the protanomalous and deuteranomalous.

Probably of the more recent work, that of Wald (t.v.λ. curves only) and of Watkins has yielded most information on increment threshold applications to colour-defectives (Wald, 1964 and 1966; Cole and Watkins, 1967; Watkins, 1969a and b). The problems of anomalous trichromats seem to turn on small differences that are not easily revealed by the relatively coarse increment threshold methods. In this connection, the new and valuable method of 'exchange thresholds" developed by Rushton, Powell and White (1973a, b and c) is particularly interesting. While this method uses a conditioning stimulus and a test stimulus, the latter is not simple but consists of an alternating presentation of two light patches of different spectral compositions imposed in turn on an identical retinal area, the test variable being a single parameter controlling the patch intensities, and the test criterion, the detectability of the alternation of the two patches. The method has been successful in determining the spectral sensitivities of the longer wave mechanisms of protanopes and deuteranopes, and in throwing light on the spectral response systems of anomalous trichromats. It will certainly have further applications.

Concluding Remarks

It is remarkable that in the understanding of increment threshold sensitivity and its dependence on different colour-sensitive mechanisms one can progress so far without appeal to the concepts of opponent-colour theory, especially the scheme of ideas developed over the years by Hurvich and Jameson, which in other areas of visual psychophysics has been found so stimulating and helpful, particularly by those whose approach is through psychology. However, it has become increasingly evident that among the necessary modifications and extensions of the simple model of threshold discrimination by colour mechanisms mainly used in this book, there must be included the introduction of some kind of colour-differencing mechanisms. Two of the factors imposing this development are (i) experimental data on threshold summation anomalies, referred to in Section 8, and certain related difficulties in constructing more precise and satisfactory resultant t.v.λ. curves from component fixed spectral sensitivities, a group of problems worked on directly by Boynton, Sperling, King-Smith and their collaborators as well as indirectly by a number of others and, (ii) the very limited success achieved by a colorimetric line-element, based on the simple model, in explaining colour-discrimination data (see Paper V), and the fact that most of the formulae arrived at by colorimetrists to reproduce precisely such empirical data are cast in a form based on the ideas of colour-differencing or opponent-colour mechanisms.

In relation to this last point I would say that an important modern trend is the attempt to embody much of our knowledge of colour mechanisms in a so-called "inductive" line element, that is, one concerned less with the exact fitting of particular blocks of discrimination data and more with providing a mathematical model which, though reproducing such data only approximately, nevertheless, by its structure and by the meanings of the terms and constants appearing in it, shows how the threshold is related to the properties of the component mechanisms responsible for discrimination. A good example of an inductive line-element is the zone-fluctuation model put forward by Vos and Walraven (1972). Like most line-elements so far proposed it is limited in the sense that it applies only to the equilibrium case and does not include parameters to express the effects of surrounds. The production of a line-element to cover the complexities of threshold sensitivity, even in the simpler dynamic and surround situations, presents formidable problems. However, in my opinion, attempts at such quantitative formulations—incomplete though they must be—are often of value in clarifying merely qualitative ideas on colour mechanisms and their properties.

References

Aguilar, M. and Stiles, W. S. (1954). Saturation of the rod mechanism at high levels of stimulation. *Optica Acta* **1**, 59.

Alpern, M. (1965). Rod-cone independence in the after-flash effect. *J. Physiol.* **176**, 462.

Alpern, M. and Rushton, W. A. H. (1965). The specificity of the cone interaction in the after-flash effect. *J. Physiol.* **176**, 473.

Alpern, M., Rushton, W. A. H. and Torii, S. (1970a). The size of rod signals. *J. Physiol.* **206**, 193.

Alpern, M., Rushton, W. A. H. and Torrii, S. (1970b). The attenuation of rod signals by backgrounds. *J. Physiol.* **206**, 209.

Alpern, M., Rushton, W. A. H. and Torii, S. (1970c). The attenuation of rod signals by bleaching. *J. Physiol.* **207**, 449.

Alpern, M., Rushton, W. A. H. and Torii, S. (1970d). Signals from cones. *J. Physiol.* **207**, 463.

Auerbach, E. and Wald, G. (1954). Identification of a violet receptor in human color vision. *Science* **120**, 401.

Barlow, H. B. and Sparrock, J. M. B. (1964). The role of after-images in dark-adaptation. *Science* **144**, 1309.

Blakemore, C. B. and Rushton, W. A. H. (1965). Dark adaptation and increment threshold in a rod monochromat. *J. Physiol.* **181**, 612.

Boynton, R. M. (1956). Rapid chromatic adaptation and the sensitivity functions of human colour vision. *J. Opt. Soc. Am.* **46**, 172.

Boynton, R. M., Das, S. and Gardiner, J. (1966). Interaction between photopic visual mechanisms revealed by mixing conditioning fields. *J. Opt. Soc. Am.* **56**, 1775.

Boynton, R. M., Ikeda, M. and Stiles, W. S. (1964). Interactions among chromatic mechanisms as inferred from positive and negative increment thresholds. *Vis. Res.* **4**, 87.

Boynton, R. M., Kandel, G. and Onley, J. W. (1959). Rapid chromatic adaptation of normal and dichromatic observers. *J. Opt. Soc. Am.* **49**, 654.

Boynton, R. M. and Wagner, M. (1961). Two-colour threshold as test of color vision. *J. Opt. Soc. Am.* **51**, 429.

Brindley, G. S. (1954). The summation areas of human colour-receptive mechanisms at increment threshold. *J. Physiol.* **124**, 400.

Brindley, G. S. (1970). Physiology of the Retina and Visual Pathway, 2nd Edition. Edward Arnold (London).

Brindley, G. S., Du Croz, J. J. and Rushton, W. A. H. (1966). The flicker fusion frequency of the blue-sensitive mechanism of colour vision. *J. Physiol*. **183**, 497.

Cavonius, C. R. and Estévez, O. (1975a). Contrast sensitivity of individual colour mechanisms of human vision. *J. Physiol*, **248**, 649.

Cavonius, C. R. and Estevéz, O. (1975b). Sensitivity of human colour mechanisms to gratings and flicker. *J. Opt. Soc. Am*. **65**, 966.

Cole, B. L. and Watkins, R. D. (1967). Increment thresholds in tritanopia. *Vis. Res*. **7**, 939.

Crawford, B. H. (1937a). The change of visual sensitivity with time. *Proc. Roy. Soc*. **B123** 69.

Crawford, B. H. (1937b). The luminus efficiency of light entering the eye pupil at different points and its relation to brightness threshold measurements. *Proc. Roy. Soc*. **B124**, 81.

Crawford, B. H. (1947) Visual adaptation in relation to brief conditioning stimuli. *Proc. Roy. Soc*. **B134**, 283.

Das, S. R. (1964). Foveal increment thresholds in dark adaptation. *J. Opt. Soc. Am*. **54**, 541.

Du Croz, J. J. and Rushton, W. A. H. (1966). The separation of cone mechanisms in dark adaptation. *J. Physiol*. **183**, 481.

Enoch, J. M. (1972). *In* "Handbook of Sensory Physiology" (Eds. D. Jameson and L. M. Hurvich.), Vol. VII/4, p. 552. Springer-Verlag, Berlin, Heidelberg and New York.

Estévez, O. and Cavonius, C. R. (1975). Flicker sensitivity of the human red and green cone mechanisms. *Vis. Res*. **15**, 879.

Estévez, O. and Cavonius, C. R. (1977). Human color perception and Stiles' Π mechanisms. *Vision Res*. **17**, 417.

Estévez, O. and Spekreijse, H. (1974). A spectral compensation method for determining the flicker characteristics of the human colour mechanisms. *Vis. Res*. **14**, 823.

Estévez, O., Spekreijse, H., Van den Birg, J. T. P. and Cavonius, C. R. (1975). The spectral sensitivities of isolated human color mechanisms determined from contrast evoked potentials. *Vis. Res*. **15**, 1205.

Flamant, F. and Stiles, W. S. (1948). The directional and spectral sensitivities of the retinal rods to adapting fields of different wavelengths. *J. Physiol*. **107**, 187.

Green, D. G. (1968). The contrast sensitivity of the colour mechanisms of the human eye. *J. Physiol*. **196**, 415.

Green, D. G. (1969). Sinusoidal flicker-characteristics of the color-sensitive mechanisms of the eye. *Vis. Res*. **9**, 591.

Guth, S. L. (1967). Non-additivity and inhibition among chromatic luminances at threshold. *Vis. Res*. **7**, 319.

Harwerth, R. S. and Sperling, H. G. (1975). Effects of intense visible radiation on the increment threshold spectral sensitivity of the rhesus monkey eye. *Vis. Res*. **15**, 1193.

Ikeda, M. (1963). Study of interrelations between mechanisms at threshold. *J. Opt. Soc. Am*. **53**, 1305.

Ikeda, M. (1964). Further use of the summation index for the study of colour vision. *J. Opt. Soc. Am*. **54**, 89.

Ingling, C. R. (1969). A tetrachromatic hypothesis for human colour vision. *Vis. Res*. **9**, 1131.

Kelly, D. H. (1962). Visual responses to time-dependent stimuli. IV. Effects of chromatic adaptation. *J. Opt. Soc. Am*. **52**, 940.

King-Smith, P. E. and Webb, J. R. (1974). The use of photopic saturation in determining the fundimental spectral sensitivity curves. *Vis. Res*. **14**, 421.

Krauskopf, J. (1969). Variation of critical duration of red and green cone receptors with chromatic adaptation. *J. Opt. Soc. Am.* **59**, 504 (Abstract).

Krauskopf, J. (1973). Contributions of the primary chromatic mechanisms to the generation of visual evoked potentials. *Vis. Res.* **13**, 2289.

Krauskopf, J. and Mollon, J. D. (1971). Variation of the temporal integration properties of individual chromatic mechanisms in the human eye. *J. Physiol.* **219**, 611.

Makous, W. and Boothe, R. (1974). Cones block signals from rods. *Vis. Res.* **14**, 285.

Makous, W. and Peeples, D. (1975). Rod-cone interaction: Reconciliation with Flamant and Stiles. Personal communication; published paper not traced.

Marks, L. E. (1974). Blue-sensitive cones can mediate brightness. *Vis. Res.* **14**, 1493.

Mollon, J. D. and Krauskopf, J. (1973). Reaction time as a measure of the temporal response properties of individual colour mechanisms. *Vis. Res.* **13**, 27.

Mollon, J. D. and Polden, P. G. (1975a). Some properties of the blue cone mechanism of the eye. *Proc. Physiol. Soc.* 19-20 Sept. (Describes a demonstration).

Mollon, J. D. and Polden, P. G. (1975b). Transient Tritanopia: evidence for interaction between cone mechanisms. *Proc. Physiol. Soc.* 19-20 Sept. (Brief communication).

Mollon, J. D. and Polden, P. G. (1977a). Saturation of a retinal cone mechanism. *Nature* **265**, 243.

Mollon, J. D. and Polden, P. G. (1977b). An anomaly in the response of the eye to light of short wavelengths. *Phil. Trans. Roy. Soc.* **B278**, 207.

Nachmias, J. (1972). "Handbook of Sensory Physiology" Eds. D. Jameson and L. M. Hurvich), Vol. VII/4, p. 56. Springer-Verlag, Berlin, Heidelberg and New York.

Padmos, P. and Norren, D. V. (1975). Increment spectral sensitivity and colour discrimination of the primate, studied by means of graded potentials from the striate cortex. *Vis. Res.* **15**, 1103.

Piantanida, T. P. and Sperling, H. G. (1973a). Isolation of a third chromatic mechanism in the protanomalous observer. *Vis. Res.* **13**, 2033.

Piantanida, T. P. and Sperling, H. G. (1973b). Isolation of a third chromatic mechanism in the deuteranomalous observer. *Vis. Res.* **13**, 2049.

Pugh, E. (1976). The nature of the π_1 mechanism of W. S. Stiles. *J. Physiol.* **257**, 713.

Rushton, W. A. H., Powell, D. S. and White, K. D. (1973a). Exchange thresholds in dichromats. *Vis. Res.* **13**, 1993.

Rushton, W. A. H., Powell, D. S. and White, K. D. (1973b). Spectral sensitivity of "red" and "green" cones in the normal eye. *Vis. Res.* **13**, 2003.

Rushton, W. A. H., Powell, D. S. and White, K. D. (1973c). Pigments in anomalous trichromats. *Vis. Res.* **13**, 2017.

Shevell, S. K. (1977). Saturation in human cones. *Vis. Res.* **17**, 427.

Sternheim, C. E. and Glass, R. A. (1975). Evidence for rod and cone contributions to common adaptation pools. *Vis. Res.* **15**, 277.

Stiles, W. S. (1964). Foveal threshold sensitivity on fields of different colors. *Science* **145**, 1016.

Stiles, W. S. and Crawford, B. H. (1933). The liminal brightness increment as a function of wavelength for different conditions of the foveal and parafoveal retina. *Proc. Roy. Soc.* **B113**, 496.

Stiles, W. S. and Crawford, B. H. (1934). The liminal brightness increment for white light for different conditions of the foveal and parafoveal retina. *Proc. Roy. Soc.* **B116**, 55.

Van der Velde and Bouman, M. A. (About 1948). Reference not known.

Vos, J. J. and Walraven, P. L. (1972). An analytical description of the line element in the zone-fluctuation model of colour vision. *Vis. Res.* **12**, 1327.

Wald, G. (1964). The receptors of human colour vision. *Science* **145**, 1007.

Wald, G. (1966). Defective color vision and its inheritance. *Proc. Nat. Acad. Sci.* **55**, 1347.

Wald, G. (1967). Blue blindness in the normal fovea. *J. Opt. Soc. Am.* **57**, 1289.

Watkins, R. D. (1969a). Foveal increment thresholds in normal and deutan observers. *Vis. Res.* **9**, 1185.

Watkins, R. D. (1969b). Foveal increment thresholds in protan observers. *Vis. Res.* **9**, 1197.

Whittle, P. (1973). The brightness of coloured flashes on backgrounds of various colour and luminances. *Vis. Res.* **13**, 621.

Whittle, P. (1974). Intensity discrimination between flashes which do not differ in brightness; some new measurements on the "blue" cones. *Vis. Res.* **14**, 599.

Whittle, P. and Challands, P. D. C. (1969). The effect of background luminance on the brightness of flashes. *Vis. Res.* **9**, 1095.

Whittle, P. and Swanston, M. T. (1974). Luminance discrimination of separated flashes: the effect of background luminance and the shape of t.v.i. curves. *Vis. Res.* **14**, 713.

Wright, W. D. (1934). The measurement and analysis of colour adaptation phenomena. *Roy. Soc. Proc.* **B115**, 49.

Wyszecki, G. and Stiles, W. S. (1967). "Color Science". John Wiley and Sons, Inc., New York.

Paper II: Reprinted from The Physical and Optical Societies Report, Joint Discussion on Vision, 1932.

EQUIVALENT ADAPTATION LEVELS IN LOCALIZED RETINAL AREAS

By W. S. STILES, Ph.D. and B. H. CRAWFORD, B.Sc., A.Inst.P.

ABSTRACT. The paper shows how the notion of retinal adaptation can be placed on a quantitative basis. The state of a localized retinal area under an arbitrary conditioning stimulation is specified by reference to a standard scale of stimulations—the equivalent background brightness scale or the equivalent surround brightness scale. The équivalent background (or surround) brightness should be independent of the test used to determine it, and experiment shows this to be true for the equivalent background, but with the equivalent surround certain unexplained deviations are observed. The use of the equivalent background brightness as a foundation upon which theories of the mechanism of retinal adaptation can be based is illustrated by examples. A practical application of the equivalent background brightness to the definition of a coefficient measuring the reduction of visibility due to glare is mentioned.

---

§1. THE GENERAL PROBLEM

THE visual phenomena of adaptation, temporal and spatial induction, disability glare, etc., show that what we perceive at a particular place in the visual field and at a given time depends not only on the immediate stimulation at that place, but also on the previous stimulation of the whole field and on the immediate stimulation in the region surrounding the selected area. The hypothesis which may be put forward as the first step in the explanation of many of these effects is the following. For a given immediate stimulation of a localized retinal area, the latter can exist in different states depending on the previous stimulation of the whole retina and on the immediate stimulation of the retina external to the given area*. Variations in the perceptions in the given area and at the given time are due to changes in state of this kind.

We may call this the "generalized adaptation hypothesis." To the extent that visual perceptions are reproducible phenomena it is certainly true that, if the complete stimulation remains the same, then any change in the corresponding perceptions must be due to some change in the condition of the percipient. The essential point in the adaptation hypothesis is therefore the introduction of "localization," i.e. the assumption that each small patch of the retina is at each instant in a particular state, and that the perceptions there depend only on the light incident and on the state of the patch, although many widely different conditions of stimulation of the whole retina may cause the selected area to assume the state in question.

---

* We have to admit, also, day-to-day variations in the state of the retina, which appear to be unconnected with its "light history."

In this paper the implications of the adaptation hypothesis are examined critically, and experiments are described designed to test a certain equivalence principle which appears as a necessary consequence of the hypothesis.

To follow changes in the state of a given retinal area due to changes in the conditioning stimulation*, use is made of a visual test, such as the determination of the brightness difference threshold for white light, the critical flicker frequency for red light, the *Empfindungszeit*, etc. Each such test gives in a sense a quantitative measure of the state of the retinal area. Each test, however, yields a different measure, and although in some cases there is a general resemblance between the types of curve obtained there is no exact correspondence and it is difficult to know what meaning is to be attached to a resemblance of this kind. All kinds of tests have been devised, some giving a critical flicker frequency, others a threshold brightness or a wave-length limen, and so on, and there is no reason to expect these numbers to be proportional or simply related one to another. Moreover, quantitative measures obtained with different tests sometimes exhibit very different characteristics. To sum up, the result of a test depends not only on the state of the retinal area but also on the mechanism called into play by the test, and these two factors are associated, in a way we do not know, to determine the numerical result.

To overcome this difficulty and to be able to evaluate the state of a retinal area in a way which shall be independent of the test, the obvious course is to choose a scale of standard conditioning stimulations (for example, a series of steady, uniform brightnesses occupying the whole visual field external to the selected area) and define the quantitative measure of the state of a given retinal area under a given conditioning stimulation as the scale number of the standard stimulation for which the retinal state is the same as under the given conditions. To apply this method we must be able to discover whether the states of the given retinal area for two different conditioning stimulations are identical. The visual test enters at this stage: if a particular visual test X_1 gives the same numerical result under the arbitrary conditioning stimulation and under the standard stimulation α, then it follows from the adaptation hypothesis that the state of the retinal area must be the same in the two cases. If this method is valid we should expect the following experimentally verifiable principle to hold good. If α_1, α_2, etc., are the values of the standard stimulation which with different visual tests X_1, X_2, etc., give the same numerical result as the arbitrary conditioning stimulation, then $\alpha_1 = \alpha_2 = \alpha_3$, etc. In other words, whatever visual test is employed as indicator, the same value of the standard stimulation equivalent to the given arbitrary condition must be obtained.

In the experimental tests of this equivalence principle, described below, two scales of standard stimulations have been worked with—the equivalent surround brightness scale and the equivalent background brightness scale. The *equivalent surround brightness* α is a steady uniform brightness of white light of intensity α

* By "conditioning stimulation" we shall mean the previous stimulation of the whole retina and the immediate stimulation in the area external to the localized area under consideration.

candles/ft.²*, filling the whole visual field with the exception of a circular patch of diameter 1°, representing the local area under test, in which the test stimulus is applied. The *equivalent background brightness*† is a steady uniform brightness of white light of intensity β cdl./ft.², filling the whole visual field including the test area. (In this case the test stimulus is superposed on the brightness β.) The invariance of the equivalent surround brightness with change in the test will be termed the equivalent surround principle. The equivalent background principle is similarly defined. Although the equivalent surround principle can be deduced from the adaptation hypothesis, the equivalent background principle seems to require an additional assumption, namely that the superposition of a uniform background brightness on the whole field including the test area affects the numerical result of the test only indirectly by altering the state of the retina in the test area. This point is dealt with in § 4.

Assuming for the moment the validity of the equivalence principle, we have in α (or whatever variable is used to define the scale of standard stimulations) a quantitative measure of the state of a retinal area at a given time, which is independent of the visual tests used in determining it. To each value of α corresponds a different condition of the retinal area concerned. The change of condition may correspond to variations in the concentration c of a photochemical substance in the rod-and-cone layer, to the setting up of an electrical polarization p in the end receptors, to the presence or absence of scattered light, or to some other change in the physical condition of the retina. It must, however, be true that α is a function of c or of p. Thus $\alpha = f(c)$, $\alpha = g(p)$, or some other similar relation must hold good. In the absence of definite knowledge of the physical factors determining the state of the retina, we must continue to use α as a measure of the retinal condition. When we can correlate with the different standard stimulations specified by α, a specific change in physical condition, then knowing α for a given retinal area at a given time under an arbitrarily prescribed conditioning stimulation we shall also know the concentration c or the polarization p, or such other physical condition as has been introduced in the correlation.

Up to now it has been assumed for simplicity that the condition of a retinal area can be fixed by one variable. This is definitely not true when we admit the most general retinal stimulations involving coloured lights. Our method of specifying retinal condition can, however, be extended to the general case. It is probable that three or perhaps four variables are required to define completely the state of

---

* Here and elsewhere in the paper we speak of a stimulation as a brightness of white light of x cdl./ft.² A visual stimulation however must be expressed in energy units, and the energy distribution over the spectrum should be specified. Our units are, in fact, energy units in which one unit is equivalent to a brightness of 1 cdl./ft.² If we take a fraction $1/x$ of this energy unit we speak of "a brightness of $1/x$ cdl./ft.²" All the white-light brightnesses used in the present experiments were obtained from gas-filled filament lamps run at their rated efficiencies. The energy-distribution corresponds therefore to a black-body distribution at a temperature of the order 2750° K. The low brightnesses were obtained by interposing diaphragms and neutral filters.

† The equivalent background brightness is not strictly a conditioning stimulation because it includes a part of the immediate stimulus in the test area.

the retina in a given area at a given time. Work on these lines gives promise of providing a new angle of attack on the problem of the tripartite mechanism evidenced in colour-matching equations.

§ 2. EXPERIMENTAL*

The general object of the experiments was to take an arbitrary conditioning stimulation and determine the equivalent surround and equivalent background brightness using different tests. In the arbitrary conditioning stimulation selected, the brightness was zero throughout the field with the exception of a small patch, situated 6° above the localized retinal area under test. The test area itself was viewed either directly (foveal vision) or indirectly (parafoveal vision). In the latter case a weak point-source of light 5° to the right of the test area served as fixation point. The tests employed were all variants of brightness difference threshold determinations.

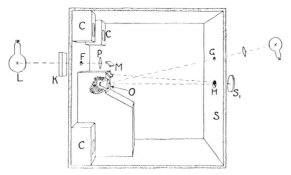

Fig. 1. Experimental cube with side wall removed.

In figure 1 is shown a sketch of the apparatus. This consists of a large hollow wooden cube painted white inside. The back wall S is illuminated to any desired brightness level by four lamp boxes C, in the windows of which diaphragms and filters can be placed. The subject sits in a wooden cabin constructed inside the cube and views the screen S by applying his eye to an eye-hole O. (In all the experiments monocular observation, with the idle eye dark-adapted, was used. The eye-hole O is sufficiently large for the natural pupil to be operative.) In a small hole in the screen S the image G of the plate of a pointolite lamp is focussed, and produces a vertical illumination E ft.-cdl. at the ocular O. In determining the equivalent surround brightness a circular hole H in the screen S, of angular diameter 1°, is exposed, and behind it is placed a small screen S_1 which receives no light from the lamp boxes C. This 1° patch constitutes the test field. A test spot is focussed on the test field by the lens P via the mirrors M. The test spot is merely the image of an illuminated aperture in a diaphragm F, the light being obtained from a lamp L which moves on a photometer bench. The lamp L is motor-driven at a variable

* No attempt is made to give full details of these experiments, which will be described in a further publication elsewhere.

t

τ

speed so chosen that the brightness *t* of the test spot projected on to S_1 varies with time *τ* in accordance with the law $t^{-1}.dt/d\tau = \text{constant} = 0\cdot01 \text{ sec.}^{-1}$ An automatic shutter *K* enables the test spot to be exposed periodically and for a variable flash period. When the equivalent background brightness is being determined, the hole *H* is covered with a white card and the brightness due to the lamp boxes *C* is continuous over the whole of the screen *S*. The test spot is then in effect focussed on the screen *S*.

T

In all the visual tests used, what is determined is the minimum brightness *T* of the test spot, at which it is just perceived by the subject. The general test of this type can be varied in four principal ways by changing (*a*) the size of the test spot, (*b*) the flash period, (*c*) the colour of the test spot and (*d*) the brightness and colour of the 1° test field on which the test spot is projected. Variations of the type (*d*) have not yet been investigated because the higher the brightness in the test field the less the threshold value *T* is affected by the conditions in the surrounding field, and this makes the determination of equivalent surround or equiva-

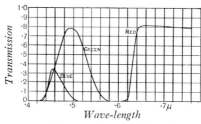

Fig. 2. Transmissions of colour filters.

δ, p

W, R, G

B

lent background subject to an increasing error. We have therefore confined our attention to the case when the test field brightness is zero. The size of the test spot has been varied in angular diameter *δ* from 0·1° to 0·8°, the flash period *p* has been varied from 0·05 sec. to 1 sec. and four colours, white (*W*), red (*R*), green (*G*), and blue (*B*) have been used. The transmission curves of the colour filters used to obtain the red, green and blue test spots are shown in figure 2. Although the flash period itself is varied, the period for the complete cycle flash-darkness has been maintained constant at 3 seconds. The assumption is that the effect of the previous flash will be negligible under these conditions. The subject seated in the cabin hears the click of the shutter when the test spot is flashed on. He is supplied with two keys one or other of which he depresses according as he does, or does not see the test spot. The keys operate an electric recorder device mounted on the carriage of the lamp *l*, which shows a black spot for "seen" and a red spot for "not seen" on a tape placed along the photometer bench. The record obtained shows a series of black spots when the test spot is visible with certainty, a region where both black and red spots occur, and a series of red spots where the test spot is certainly not visible. The threshold *T* is taken to be the value of the test spot brightness at the point on the record where there are as many red spots on the main black spot series side as there are black spots on the main red spot series side.

Figure 3 * shows two typical curves representing the variation of $\log_{10} T$ ($\delta = 0.4°$, $p = 0.05''$, W) with $\log_{10}\beta$ (where β is the background brightness), at the fovea and at the parafoveal point ($5°$ left of fovea). The curves were obtained by taking measurements of the threshold for a series of backgrounds of increasing brightness, the subject having previously sat in total darkness for 1 hour to become completely dark-adapted. The brightness range can be divided into two regions, the high-brightness region in which fovea and parafovea behave similarly although the parafoveal threshold is always higher than the foveal threshold, and the low-brightness region in which the foveal threshold is nearly constant whereas the parafoveal threshold drops continuously to a much lower value. For the arbitrary conditioning stimulation, the intensity of the bright patch at $6°$ above was chosen to give an illumination $E = 2.28$ cdl./ft.², which corresponds to an equivalent background in the high brightness range of about 0.5 cdl./ft.² (position A, figure 3), or an illumina-

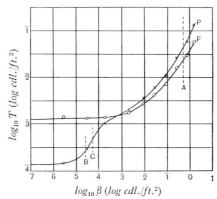

Fig. 3. Subject: B.H.C. using right eye, left eye dark adapted throughout.
Curve P: threshold for parafovea. Test area $5°$ to left of fixation point.
Curve F: threshold for fovea centralis.
Test spot: angular diameter $\delta = 0.4°$. Flash period $\tau = 0.05$ sec. White.

tion $E = 2.0 \times 10^{-4}$ or 1.0×10^{-4} cdl./ft.² giving equivalent backgrounds in the low brightness range of about 4.8×10^{-5} and 2.5×10^{-5} cdl./ft.² (positions C and B, figure 3). It is obvious from figure 3 that the equivalent background is indeterminate for the fovea at low brightnesses because of the constancy of the threshold. No attempt was therefore made to determine the equivalent background or surround for these conditions.

The experimental procedure adopted was the following. Four background (or surround) brightnesses were chosen which were known from preliminary work to give threshold values in a range containing the threshold value for the arbitrary conditioning stimulation (a bright patch at $6°$ above the test area on a dark field). The threshold values for three variants of the test were then determined at each

* As in most visual work, it is convenient to plot the logarithms of the brightnesses rather than the brightnesses themselves. Speaking generally, the reason for doing this is that the range of brightnesses is usually very large (β varies over the range 1 to 10^{-6} in figure 3) whereas the percentage accuracy of measurement is of the same order throughout.

of the four background brightnesses and also for the arbitrary conditioning stimulation. By plotting the threshold for each test against background brightness, the value of the background brightness corresponding to the threshold obtained with the selected conditioning stimulation could be determined. Thus a run of this kind gave three values for the equivalent background brightness which, if the principle holds good, should be the same. For readings in the parafovea at low brightnesses it was necessary to keep the subject in total darkness for an hour prior to the commencement of the measurements. A parafoveal run occupied about 3 hours, a foveal run about $2\frac{1}{4}$ hours.

§ 3. RESULTS

The following tables give the main results obtained with the exception of the measurements for $\log_{10} E = \overline{4}\cdot31$, which are similar in general character to those for $\log_{10} E = \overline{4}\cdot01$ and are omitted to economize space. The arbitrary stimulation condition with a bright patch at 6° above the test area, producing a vertical illumination of the eye, E, is indicated as "conditioning stimulation A" when $E = 2\cdot28$, $\log_{10} E = 0\cdot36$; and as "conditioning stimulation B" when $E = 1\cdot02 \times 10^{-4}$, $\log_{10} E = \overline{4}\cdot01$. In each table, the figures on one line refer to a single run. The 1st, 3rd and 5th columns of figures are values of $\log_{10} \alpha$ or $\log_{10} \beta$, the 2nd and 4th columns give the differences between the 1st and 3rd, and between the 3rd and 5th columns respectively.

Values of $\log_{10}$ (equivalent background brightness), or $\log_{10} \beta$.

Table 1. Fovea. Conditioning stimulation A.

(a) Test spot white.

Subject	Diameter of test spot, and flash period				
	$0\cdot4°$ $0\cdot05$ sec.		$0\cdot1°$ $0\cdot05$ sec.		$0\cdot1°$ $0\cdot75$ sec.
B.H.C.	$\bar{1}\cdot74$	$0\cdot06$	$\bar{1}\cdot68$	—	—
,,	$\bar{1}\cdot67$	$-0\cdot04$	$\bar{1}\cdot71$	—	—
,,	—	—	$\bar{1}\cdot81$	$-0\cdot02$	$\bar{1}\cdot83$
,,	$\bar{1}\cdot65$	$-0\cdot12$	$\bar{1}\cdot77$	$0\cdot01$	$\bar{1}\cdot76$
F.W.C.	$\bar{1}\cdot50$	$0\cdot05$	$\bar{1}\cdot45$	—	—
,,	—	—	$\bar{1}\cdot76$	$-0\cdot08$	$\bar{1}\cdot84$
,,	$\bar{1}\cdot60$	$-0\cdot11$	$\bar{1}\cdot71$	$-0\cdot05$	$\bar{1}\cdot76$
W.S.S.	$\bar{1}\cdot82$	$-0\cdot04$	$\bar{1}\cdot86$	$-0\cdot15$	$0\cdot01$
,,	$\bar{1}\cdot76$	$-0\cdot10$	$\bar{1}\cdot86$	$0\cdot03$	$\bar{1}\cdot83$
Mean differences		$-0\cdot04$		$-0\cdot04$	

(b) Diameter of test spot, $0\cdot4°$. Flash period, $0\cdot05$ sec.

Subject	Colour of test spot				
	White		Red		Green
B.H.C.	$\bar{1}\cdot63$	$0\cdot11$	$\bar{1}\cdot52$	$0\cdot01$	$\bar{1}\cdot51$
F.W.C.	$\bar{1}\cdot59$	$0\cdot07$	$\bar{1}\cdot52$	$-0\cdot18$	$\bar{1}\cdot70$
W.S.S.	$\bar{1}\cdot73$	$-0\cdot15$	$\bar{1}\cdot88$	—	—
,,	$\bar{1}\cdot89$	$0\cdot12$	$\bar{1}\cdot77$	$-0\cdot07$	$\bar{1}\cdot84$
Mean differences		$0\cdot04$		$-0\cdot08$	

Table 2. Parafovea—5°. Conditioning stimulation *A*.

(*a*) Test spot white.

Subject	Diameter of test spot, and flash period				
	0·4° 0·05 sec.		0·1° 0·05 sec.		0·1° 0·75 sec.
B.H.C.	$\bar{1}$·66	− 0·02	$\bar{1}$·68	0·06	$\bar{1}$·62
F.W.C.	$\bar{1}$·56	− 0·06	$\bar{1}$·62	0·05	$\bar{1}$·57
W.S.S.	$\bar{1}$·60	0·08	$\bar{1}$·52	0·04	$\bar{1}$·48
Mean differences	0·00		0·05		

(*b*) Diameter of test spot, 0·4°. Flash period, 0·05 sec.

Subject	Colour of test spot				
	White		Red		Green
B.H.C.	$\bar{1}$·62	− 0·01	$\bar{1}$·63	0·03	$\bar{1}$·60
W.S.S.	$\bar{1}$·63	− 0·06	$\bar{1}$·57	− 0·05	$\bar{1}$·62
F.W.C.	$\bar{1}$·60	− 0·06	$\bar{1}$·66	− 0·01	$\bar{1}$·67
Mean differences	0·00		− 0·01		

Table 3. Parafovea—5°. Conditioning stimulation *B*.

(*a*) Test spot white.

Subject	Diameter of test spot, and flash period				
	0·4° 0·05 sec.		0·1° 0·05 sec.		0·1° 0·75 sec.
B.H.C.	$\bar{5}$·36	0·08	$\bar{5}$·28	− 0·09	$\bar{5}$·37
"	$\bar{5}$·45	0·10	$\bar{5}$·35	− 0·16	$\bar{5}$·51
F.W.C.	$\bar{5}$·44	− 0·11	$\bar{5}$·55	− 0·09	$\bar{5}$·64
"	$\bar{5}$·58	0·03	$\bar{5}$·55	0·09	$\bar{5}$·46
W.S.S.	$\bar{5}$·68	0·22	$\bar{5}$·46	− 0·27	$\bar{5}$·73
"	$\bar{5}$·55	0·01	$\bar{5}$·54	0·03	$\bar{5}$·51
Mean differences	0·06		− 0·08		

(*b*) Diameter of test spot, 0·4°. Flash period, 0·05 sec.

Subject	Colour of test spot				
	White		Green		Blue
B.H.C.	$\bar{5}$·37	− 0·17	$\bar{5}$·54	0·09	$\bar{5}$·45
"	$\bar{5}$·46	− 0·01	$\bar{5}$·47	0·00	$\bar{5}$·47
F.W.C.	$\bar{5}$·45	− 0·11	$\bar{5}$·56	− 0·08	$\bar{5}$·64
"	$\bar{5}$·65	0·12	$\bar{5}$·53	0·12	$\bar{5}$·41
W.S.S.	$\bar{5}$·42	− 0·18	$\bar{5}$·60	0·01	$\bar{5}$·59
"	$\bar{5}$·55	0·01	$\bar{5}$·54	0·03	$\bar{5}$·51
Mean differences	− 0·06		0·03		

If the equivalent background brightness has the same value whatever the character of the test spot, the mean differences in the above tables should all approximate to zero. Actually the mean differences in no case exceed 0·10 (which corresponds to a variation in β of about 25 per cent.) and it may be concluded that the equivalent-background principle is valid for the conditioning stimulations and the range of tests here considered.

Values of $\log_{10}$ (equivalent surround brightness) or $\log_{10}\alpha$.

Table 4. Fovea. Conditioning stimulation A.

(a) Test spot white.

Subject	Diameter of test spot, and flash period				
	0·4° 0·05 sec.		0·1° 0·05 sec.		0·1° 0·75 sec.
W.S.S.	—	—	1·09	0·00	1·09
,,	0·92	− 0·24	1·16	—	—
,,	—	—	1·21	0·04	1·17
,,	0·87	− 0·14	1·01	− 0·13	1·14
B.H.C.	0·80	− 0·19	0·99	− 0·10	1·09
	—	—	1·29	0·07	1·22
,,	0·93	− 0·34	1·27	—	—
,,	0·75	− 0·53	1·28	—	—
,,	—	—	1·32	0·05	1·27
,,	0·94	− 0·22	1·16	− 0·10	1·26
F.W.C.	0·86	− 0·34	1·20	− 0·17	1·37
	—	—	1·03	0·00	1·03
,,	0·69	− 0·55	1·24	—	—
,,	—	—	1·13	− 0·02	1·15
,,	0·72	− 0·08	0·80	− 0·12	0·92
,,	0·60	− 0·35	0·95	0·00	0·95
Mean differences		− 0·30		− 0·04	

(b) Diameter of test spot, 0·4°. Flash period, 0·05 sec.

Subject	Colour of test spot				
	White		Red		Green
B.H.C.	0·91	− 0·08	0·99	0·05	0·94
,,	1·11	0·24	0·87	− 0·21	1·08
,,	0·71	− 0·12	0·83	− 0·05	0·88
F.W.C.	0·79	− 0·01	0·80	− 0·09	0·89
,,	0·84	0·06	0·78	− 0·03	0·81
,,	0·53	− 0·04	0·57	0·07	0·50
W.S.S.	0·83	− 0·01	0·84	− 0·03	0·87
,,	0·69	− 0·26	0·95	0·11	0·84
,,	0·79	0·00	0·79	− 0·11	0·90
Mean differences		− 0·02		− 0·03	

Table 5. Parafovea—5°. Conditioning stimulation *A*.

(a) Test spot white.

Subject	Diameter of test spot, and flash period				
	0·4° 0·05 sec.		0·1° 0·05 sec.		0·1° 0·75 sec.
B.H.C.	—	—	0·71	0·18	0·53
,,	0·76	− 0·13	0·89	0·12	0·77
,,	0·79	− 0·17	0·96	0·10	0·86
F.W.C.	0·49	− 0·21	0·70	0·30	0·40
,,	0·51	− 0·25	0·76	0·25	0·51
W.S.S.	0·68	− 0·19	0·87	0·26	0·61
,,	0·63	− 0·25	0·88	0·37	0·51
Mean differences		− 0·20		0·23	

(b) Diameter of test spot, 0·4°. Flash period, 0·05 sec.

Subject	Colour of test spot				
	White		Red		Green
F.W.C.	0·52	0·00	0·52	0·01	0·51
B.H.C.	0·68	− 0·02	0·70	0·05	0·65
W.S.S.	0·56	− 0·07	0·63	0·05	0·58
Mean differences		− 0·03		0·04	

A number of measurements were made under conditioning stimulation *B* for the parafoveal point. Considerable difficulty was experienced by two of the subjects owing to the fading in and out of the 1° test field, which at the low brightness level in question presented a contrast not much above the threshold. For the third subject the test field was visible throughout, and he experienced no particular difficulty in taking the measurements. Nevertheless the results for this case are erratic and scarcely good enough to serve as a test of the equivalence principle.

It is clear from the mean differences in tables 4 and 5 that changing the colour of the test spot has no appreciable effect on the equivalent surround. This is not true, however, for changes in the size and flash period of the test spot. For the fovea, the equivalent surround for the large spot (0·4°) is definitely smaller than for the small spot (0·1°). For the parafoveal point, the equivalent surround for the small spot with short flash period (0·05 sec.), differs from the value derived by the use of the other test spots. Thus these experiments show that the equivalent-surround brightness principle is not verified for all variations of the test. Possible reasons for this breakdown will be mentioned in the next section, which gives a careful statement of the assumptions involved in deriving the principle.

§4. ANALYSIS OF THE NOTION OF RETINAL ADAPTATION

We shall treat vision as though it were essentially monocular. The illumination of a given area of the retina would be proportional to the brightness at the corresponding point in the external field if it were not for variations in pupil diameter and scattering of light in the eye. Knowing the pupil diameter we can reduce the external brightnesses to the values appropriate to a fixed pupil. The illumination of a retinal area by light scattered from the cones of rays converging on to other areas, may be regarded as an interaction between different areas of the retina, and the effects produced in this way may for the present purpose be grouped together with effects due to coupling of a strictly physiological character between retinal elements. Thus by the stimulation of a retinal area we shall mean its illumination due to light regularly refracted by the optical system of the eye. This illumination is proportional to the brightness at the corresponding point in the external field, reduced to the value appropriate to a fixed pupil.

The general type of quantitative visual test used in investigating the retina may be described briefly as follows. The stimulation of the retina is completely prescribed (it can of course be variable with time in a definite way). A statement depending upon what the subject sees is propounded, which he can assert or deny. One of the parameters (the test parameter) determining the physical stimulus is variable. By successive repetitions of the complete experiment, a "yes" or "no" answer is associated with each value of the test parameter. A conventional method of fixing one or more critical values of the test parameter from the distribution of "yes" and "no" answers is laid down, and these critical values represent the numerical result of the test.

To follow the phenomena of adaptation, spatial and temporal induction, etc., the tests employed must be effectively "localized" or confined to a small area of the retina and to a restricted time interval. The existence of localized tests is usually taken for granted, and no difficulty arises so long as the qualitative aspects of the effects are alone in question. For our purpose, however, it is necessary to adopt a more precise statement of the assumption involved, and as the idea of localized tests is inseparably connected with the adaptation hypothesis the two concepts are best introduced together.

S

τ

It is assumed: That a given small retinal area S in a given brief interval of time τ may exist in different states depending upon the stimulation both within and without the given area, during and before the prescribed time interval. The

ξ

state of the retina in the cell $S\tau$* is specifiable in terms of one variable (ξ) or in terms of several variables ($\xi_1, \xi_2, \ldots \xi_n$). ......(1).

That, given a cell $S\tau$, there exist so-called localized tests, in which the subject's statement refers to what he sees in the test cell $S\tau$, in which the test variable concerns the stimulation in the test cell, and which are such that the numerical result of the test depends (*a*) on the complete specification of the stimulation in the test cell (the test stimulus), on the subject's statement and on the

* The cell $S\tau$ is an abbreviation for "the retinal area S during the interval τ."

conventional method used to obtain the numerical result; and (*b*) on the state of the retina in the test cell; while the numerical result in question does not depend on the stimulation of the retina outside the test cell (the conditioning stimulation) except in so far as this plays a part in determining the state of the retina inside the test cell. ......(2).

Let σ be the numerical result of any localized test. Then assumption (2) is expressed symbolically by the equations,

$$\sigma = f(\mu, \xi) \qquad \text{(retinal state specifiable by one variable)} \qquad ......(3),$$

$$\sigma = f(\mu, \xi_1 \ldots \xi_n) \qquad \text{(retinal state specifiable by several variables)} \qquad ......(4).$$

Here μ is used to represent all the parameters specified in assumption (2) (*a*) above.

In what follows we confine ourselves to the case in which the retinal state is specifiable by one variable, ξ, which may be termed the adaptation level.

The state of the retina in the test cell depends on the stimulation in the test cell and on the stimulation in other areas and at other times. If the stimulation in the test cell were zero, the other conditions remaining the same, the adaptation level would be ξ_0. If the stimulation outside the test cell were reduced to zero, the test stimulation being unchanged, the adaptation level would be ξ_T. We now make the further assumption that the adaptation in the actual case, ξ, depends only on ξ_0 and ξ_T, i.e.

$$\xi = g(\xi_0, \xi_T) \qquad ......(5).$$

Combining (3) and (5) we have,

$$\sigma = f\{\mu, g(\xi_0, \xi_T)\} \qquad ......(6).$$

It is clear from this equation that if the same test is repeated for two different conditioning stimulations and the same result σ is obtained, then since σ, μ and ξ_T have by hypothesis the same values, ξ_0 must also be the same in the two cases.

We now take a standard scale of conditioning stimulations, for example a series of uniform steady brightnesses α (white light) surrounding the test cell. To each value of α corresponds a value of ξ_0, i.e. $\xi_0 = h(\alpha)$, and since we have assumed nothing about ξ_0 except that it is some variable expressing the state of the retina, we may take ξ_0 as equal to α. Thus given a conditioning stimulation and a localized test, the value of α for which the result of the test is the same as in the prescribed conditions, is the adaptation level in the test cell, appropriate to the given conditioning stimulation. The essential point and one which is subject to direct experimental test is the equivalent surround brightness principle, namely that *the adaptation level α is independent of the localized test used in its determination.*

The above definition of the adaptation level is relative to the dimensions of the test cell ($S\tau$) originally fixed.

In an important class of cases which are particularly amenable to measurement, the conditioning stimulation does not vary with time. It is then appropriate to work with tests which are localized in space only, the time interval being unrestricted. The test cell becomes a test cylinder with the time as its long axis. It is useful to

σ

f

μ

ξ_0
ξ_T

g

α
h

refer in such cases to space-localized tests. The equivalent surround method suffers from this restriction. It can only give ξ_0, the adaptation level of a retinal area which, at the time, is not subject to direct stimulation.

An alternative scale of standard stimulations may be adopted which presents certain advantages although it involves an additional important assumption. Sup-pose, the test stimulus having been fixed, a series of uniform steady brightnesses β (white light) are imposed over the whole field *including the test cell*. As the stimu-lation in the test cell has changed, μ has altered and the argument developed above breaks down. We now make the additional assumption:

That the effect of imposing a steady uniform brightness (white light) over the whole field affects the numerical result of a localized test only by changing the state of the retina in the test area.   ......(7).

Thus in place of assumption (3) we have,

$$\sigma = f'(\mu', \xi) \qquad\qquad ......(8),$$

where μ' includes all the variables represented by μ with the exception of any stimulation in the test field which forms part of a steady uniform brightness imposed over the whole field. Again we postulate,

$$\xi = g'(\xi_0', \xi_T') \qquad\qquad ......(9)^*,$$

where ξ_0' is the state of the retina in the test cell when the test stimulus is removed (leaving the superposed uniform field brightness intact), and ξ_T' is the retinal state due to the test stimulus acting alone. It follows from (8) and (9) that

$$\sigma = f'\{\mu', g'(\xi_0', \xi_T')\}.$$

For the standard scale of uniform brightnesses β, ξ_0' will be a definite function of β so that $\xi_0' = h'(\beta)$, and we may take ξ_0' equal to β. As before, we deduce the *equivalent background principle*, that *the adaptation level β is independent of the localized test used in its determination*.

The results given in § 3 have shown that for the static conditioning stimu-lations investigated, the equivalent-background principle is approximately verified. This is evidence in favour of the assumptions from which we have derived the principle, including the particularly interesting assumption (7). On the other hand, the experiments on equivalent surrounds give somewhat different values depending on the test employed. We must enquire then in what way the assumptions made break down. There are two main reasons which may explain why our experi-ments fail to confirm the equivalent surround principle.

It has been assumed in effect in (2) that the state of the retina is sensibly the same at all points of the test cell, so that we can ascribe to it a unique value. ...(10). In figure 4 a sketch is given showing three conceivable ways in which ξ might vary across the 1° test field in our equivalent surround measurements. If case *A* or case *C* corresponds to reality we should be justified in taking a unique value for ξ, but with case *B* it is likely that large and small test spots would give different values

---

* This equation and equation (5) are not required for the tests used in our experiments. For these tests, $\xi = \xi_0$ (equivalent surround), $\xi = \xi_0'$ (equivalent background).

of the equivalent surround. For the fovea the deviations found were in the direction to be expected if ξ varied across the test field in some such way as that shown in curve B. On the other hand the deviations for the parafovea are not consistent with this explanation.

The assumption that the retinal condition is specifiable by a single variable may break down, even in the restricted case here considered, where all conditioning brightnesses in the field are white. ...(11).

It might be the case that the adaptation of the rods and cones can vary independently, and some tests may depend more on the cones, others more on the rods. It is not, however, easy to see why effects of this kind should not equally invalidate the equivalent-background principle.

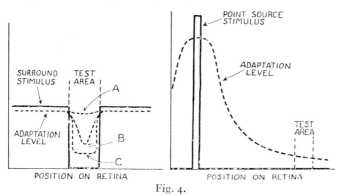

Fig. 4.

Thus in the case of the equivalent surround brightness there are discrepancies between theory and experiment, whose explanation is at the moment obscure. Nevertheless we believe that the specification of retinal condition in terms of equivalent background or equivalent surround brightness is substantially sound, and in the next section we shall show how equivalent background brightness serves as the foundation for possible theories of retinal action.

Even though it may be necessary to modify more or less radically the analysis reproduced above, some similar scheme of ideas must be developed if the notion of retinal adaptation is to be raised to a quantitative status.

§5. APPLICATIONS

In table 6 the mean values, for the several observers, of log (equivalent background) and log (equivalent surround) for the conditioning stimulations A and B are collected together. The means include all determinations irrespective of the test used. Mean values are included for the log (equivalent surround) at the parafoveal point, condition B. Although the determinations under these conditions were too difficult to give information as to the validity of the equivalent surround principle, the mean values introduced here give some idea of the order of magnitude of log (equivalent surround). The following points are of interest: (*a*) For the fovea and parafovea in the high brightness condition A, the equivalent surround is about 13 times the equivalent background; that is to say, stimulation over the whole field including the test area is 13 times as effective as stimulation outside the test area, in raising the retina to a given level of adaptation. At the low-brightness level, on the other hand, at the parafoveal point the equivalent surround is only of the order twice the equivalent background. Thus the high-brightness level corresponds more to curve C, figure 4, the low-brightness level to curve A, the coupling between the retinal elements being much closer at low brightnesses. (*b*) The difference between the $\log_{10}\beta$ values for the parafoveal point at conditions A and B respectively is equal to about $\bar{4}\cdot10$, the difference between the $\log_{10}E$ values for these cases equalling $\bar{4}\cdot30$. Thus, over this very wide range of intensities E (1 to 10,000) the equivalent background is approximately proportional to E, the constant of proportionality varying only from about 1 to 1·6.

Table 6. *Mean values of* $\log_{10}\alpha$ *and* $\log_{10}\beta$ *for different observers.*

	Conditioning stimulation	Retinal position	Observer		
			W.S.S.	B.H.C.	F.W.C.
$\log_{10}\beta$	A	fovea	$\bar{1}\cdot84$	$\bar{1}\cdot69$	$\bar{1}\cdot64$
	A	5° parafovea	$\bar{1}\cdot57$	$\bar{1}\cdot64$	$\bar{1}\cdot61$
	B	5° parafovea	$\bar{5}\cdot55$	$\bar{5}\cdot42$	$\bar{5}\cdot54$
$\log_{10}\alpha$	A	fovea	$0\cdot98$	$1\cdot08$	$0\cdot86$
	A	5° parafovea	$0\cdot68$	$0\cdot76$	$0\cdot57$
	B	5° parafovea	$\bar{5}\cdot60$	$\bar{5}\cdot57$	$\bar{4}\cdot03$
$\log_{10}\alpha$ $-\log_{10}\beta$	A	fovea	$1\cdot14$	$1\cdot29$	$1\cdot22$
	A	5° parafovea	$1\cdot11$	$1\cdot12$	$0\cdot96$
	B	5° parafovea	$0\cdot05$	$0\cdot15$	$0\cdot49$
$(\log_{10}\beta)_A$ $-(\log_{10}\beta)_B$		5° parafovea	$\bar{4}\cdot02$	$\bar{4}\cdot21$	$\bar{4}\cdot07$

A possible theory of the effect of a bright source of light in lowering the sensitivity at surrounding points, is that light is scattered in the eye, from the cone of rays converging on to the image of the bright source. The scattering may occur in the optic media of the eye or in the retinal layer. A calculation can be made of the illumination of a retinal element distant θ from the image of the bright source, and it appears that this illumination is proportional to E/θ, where E is the vertical illumination at the eye due to the source. If the addition of scattered light is the only effect which the bright source has on the state of the neighbouring retinal elements, then the equivalent background brightness for a retinal element distant θ from the image of the source should be proportional to E/θ. We have just seen that for $\theta = 6°$, β is proportional to E. Other measurements have shown, however, that with change of θ, β varies more rapidly than as θ^{-1}, and the scattering theory breaks down*.

---

* For a discussion of this scattering theory, in the light of measurements of equivalent background brightness, see W. S. Stiles, *Proc. R.S.* B, **105**, 132 (1929).

To consider another application of the equivalent background brightness in testing proposed theories of retinal mechanism, let us suppose that the condition of a retinal area is determined by the concentration C of a photochemical substance P which under the effect of light is transformed to a modified form P', there being a natural recovery process from P' to P. Assuming the total concentration of P and P' to be constant and equal to unity, the variations of C are determined by the differential equation,

$$- dc/dt = kBC - a\,(1 - C) \qquad \ldots\ldots(12),$$

where B is the stimulus brightness which is assumed to be uniform over the whole visual field, and k and a are constants with precise physical meanings. If B has a steady value equal to β then for equilibrium

$$0 = k\beta C - a\,(1 - C),$$

$$C = \frac{a}{k\beta + a} = \frac{1}{1 + k\beta/a}.$$

This gives the relation between the concentration C and the corresponding uniform steady background brightness β.

If at $t \leqslant 0$, $B = B_0$ and for $t > 0$, $B = 0$, we shall have at $t = 0$, $C_0 = \dfrac{1}{1 + kB_0/a}$ and integrating equation (12),

$$(C - 1) = (C_0 - 1)\,e^{-at}.$$

We cannot determine directly the variation of C with t, but we can find the equivalent background brightness corresponding to different times after switching off the initial brightness B. Substituting for C and C_0 their values in terms of equivalent background brightness we have,

$$\left(\frac{1}{1 + k\beta/a} - 1\right) = \left(\frac{1}{1 + kB_0/a} - 1\right) e^{-at},$$

or

$$\beta = \frac{B_0 e^{-at}}{1 + k\,(1 - e^{-at})\,B_0/a} \qquad \ldots\ldots(13).$$

We have commenced the experimental determination of the variation of equivalent background brightness with time, after switching off a steady uniform brightness. The subject views a field of brightness $B_0 = 1 \cdot 5$ cdl./ft.² for five minutes. At the end of this period the brightness is reduced to zero and determinations of the threshold at the $5°$ parafoveal point are made at intervals for an hour. A series of increasing background-brightnesses are then imposed for each of which the threshold is determined. In this way the variation of $\log_{10}$ (equivalent background) with $\log_{10}$ (time) is easily deduced. Six runs of this kind (three each for two subjects) have been made and the curves showing the variation of $\log_{10}\beta$ with $\log_{10}t$ are reproduced in figures 5 and 6. These are only preliminary results and in the case of one subject (W.S.S.) the three curves exhibit considerable deviations. Nevertheless we can obtain some idea whether the above theory is likely to fit the facts.

C

B
k, a

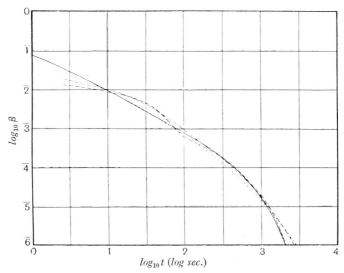

Fig. 5. Subject: B.H.C. using right eye, left eye dark adapted throughout.

- - - - - - - -⎫
———— ⎬ Curves for test spot 0·4° diam., 0·05 sec. flash period.
—·—·—·—   Curve for test spot 0·1° diam., 0·05 sec. flash period.

———————   Curve computed from formula: $\beta = \dfrac{1 \cdot 5 e^{-\cdot 00275\, t}}{\{1 + 6000\,(1 - e^{-\cdot 00275\, t})\}}$.

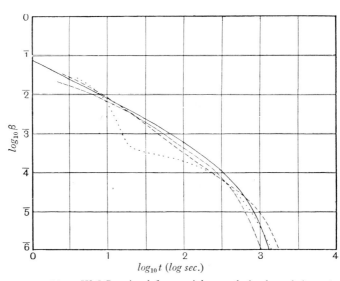

Fig. 6. Subject: W.S.S. using left eye, right eye dark adapted throughout.

- - - - - - - -⎫
———— ⎬ Curves for test spot 0·4° diam., 0·05 sec. flash period.
—·—·—·—   Curve for test spot 0·1° diam., 0·05 sec. flash period.

———————   Curve computed from formula: $\beta = \dfrac{1 \cdot 5 e^{-\cdot 0044\, t}}{\{1 + 4500\,(1 - e^{-\cdot 0044\, t})\}}$.

The continuous lines in figures 5 and 6 represent theoretical curves computed from formula (13) above with the following values of the constants:

Subject B.H.C. $k = 11 \cdot 0$ Subject W.S.S. $k = 13 \cdot 2$,

$a = 0 \cdot 00275$. $a = 0 \cdot 0044$.

The agreement is fair, bearing in mind the uncertainty in the experimental curves. Further measurements including variation of B_0 are necessary before judgment can be passed on the variant of the photochemical theory of adaptation here suggested. The main point, however, is that the equivalent background brightness method enables the theory to be tested *without the aid of delicate assumptions as to the mechanism of threshold perception and of the way in which this is controlled by the concentration of the photochemical substance.*

Finally we may mention an application of the equivalent background brightness, of another kind. The presence of bright sources in the field of view affects the visibility of objects and light-signals. It is convenient to have a method of specifying the deleterious effect of such glare sources, independently of the particular object viewed. If β is the equivalent background brightness when looking in a given direction with the glare-sources exposed, and β_0 is the value with the glare-sources screened, the glare effect is expressible as $G = \beta/\beta_0$ which, by the equivalent-background principle, is independent of the visual task involved.

       G

Errata

Page 208. Lines 1 and 2: 13 should be 18.
Line 9: $\overline{4} \cdot 10$ should be $4 \cdot 10$.
Line 10: $\overline{4} \cdot 30$ should be $4 \cdot 30$.
Table 6, 6th row of figures: $1 \cdot 29$ should be $1 \cdot 39$; 7th row of figures: replace $\overline{4} \cdot 02 : \overline{4} \cdot 21 : \overline{4} \cdot 07$ by $4 \cdot 02 : 4 \cdot 21 : 4 \cdot 07$.

Paper III: Reprinted from the Proceedings of the Royal Society of London, Series B, Vol. 127, 1939.

612.843.6

The directional sensitivity of the retina and the spectral sensitivities of the rods and cones

By W. S. STILES, *The National Physical Laboratory*

(*Communicated by Sir Herbert Parsons, F.R.S.—Received* 27 *October* 1938—
Revised 28 *November* 1938)

1. INTRODUCTION

It is now well established that light rays of the same spectral character and physical intensity entering the eye through different points of the pupil may produce visual impressions which differ in brightness and colour even though the patch of retina stimulated (the fovea) is kept the same.* Rays entering the eye through different points of the pupil and terminating on the same point of the retina are incident on the retina in different directions. Also, they have traversed different paths in the refractive media of the eye and may have suffered different losses by absorption, scattering or reflexion. It has been shown, however, that differences in the light losses in the refractive media do not account for the observed variations in visual response, which must therefore be attributed to variations in the reaction of the retina to light incident on it in different directions or, briefly, to a

---

* See Stiles and Crawford (1933), Dziobek (1934), Wright and Nelson (1934), Goodeve (1936), Stiles (1937) and Crawford (1937).

directional sensitivity of the retina. Further evidence that this is so is given later in the paper (p. 81).

The first measurements of the directional sensitivity of the retina were made by photometric methods. The rays from one part of a photometric matching field entered the eye as a narrow pencil through a fixed point of the pupil. The point of entry of the pencil of rays from the other part could be varied. The intensity of this pencil could also be varied so as to bring the two parts to equality of brightness. Thus it was possible to determine the relative physical intensities of rays entering through different points of the pupil and producing the same subjective brightness. The *relative luminous efficiency* η of a ray entering through a particular point of the pupil was defined to be inversely proportional to the physical intensity required to produce a given subjective brightness. It was found (*a*) that the relative luminous efficiency is maximal for a certain point of entry P_M which is generally situated near the centre of the pupil, (*b*) that if η is put equal to unity for a ray entering at P_M then its value for a ray entering at a point P displaced r mm. from P_M is given approximately by the expression $\eta = 10^{-pr^2}$, where p is a constant equal to about 0·05, (*c*) that the value of p shows a small systematic variation with wave-length, being greatest in the blue, less in the red and least in the yellow. It was also found that the colour impression produced by monochromatic light of given wave-length varies as the point of entry of the ray is traversed across the pupil.

The results summarized above all refer to foveal vision of a photometric or colorimetric matching field. A different approach to the problem of retinal sensitivity is provided by the measurement of absolute thresholds and difference thresholds. In recent work a type of threshold measurement has been developed on the following lines. The eye views a given distribution of brightness (the conditioning stimulation) and at a given instant, an *additional* stimulus (the test stimulus) is applied over a given area of the field for a given time. The subject signifies whether or not the application of the test stimulus calls forth any visual impression. ˙No analysis of the visual impression by the subject is required. He has not to decide, for example, whether he perceives a change of brightness or of colour. By successive trials using different intensities of the test stimulus, it is possible to determine the intensity at which the subject has a 50 % chance of perceiving the test stimulus. The intensity so obtained is termed the *liminal brightness increment* (l.b.i.). Usually the test stimulus is a small patch of light exposed for a brief interval of time. With the same conditioning stimulation, the variation of the l.b.i. with a property of the test stimulus, such as its angular size, its exposure time or, for a monochromatic test stimulus, its wave-length, can be studied. In addition the effect of changes in *the conditioning stimulation* may be determined. For the purposes of this paper retinal sensitivity will be defined as the reciprocal of the l.b.i.

Measurements of the l.b.i. are much less, precise than photometric measurements of brightness. On the other hand, the l.b.i. can be determined for any retinal area, foveal or extrafoveal, and the eye need not be in a steady state. The test stimulus will not in general disturb appreciably the state of adaptation of the retina. This is a valuable feature of the method, enabling us to determine, for example, the sensitivity of the retina to light of one wave-length when it is adapted to light of another wave-length.

In the present investigation the directional sensitivity of the retina has been studied by determining the variation of the l.b.i. as the position in the pupil of the point of entry of the rays constituting the test stimulus is varied. Both foveal and parafoveal vision of the test stimulus were employed. The conditioning stimulation consisted of a uniformly bright circular patch of light at the centre of which the test stimulus was applied. The case in which both test stimulus and conditioning stimulation are of white light has already been examined by Crawford (1937). In the present measurements, small bands of the spectrum were used for both test stimulus and conditioning stimulation. Crawford's results and those of the present paper show that the directional sensitivity of the parafoveal retina is **very** different for conditioning stimulations of high and low brightnesses respectively. This difference is here attributed to a transition from rod to cone vision as the brightness of the conditioning stimulation is raised. For many of the observations we are able to say whether the test stimulus was perceived by rod or by cone vision by considering the way in which the l.b.i. varies with the wave-length of the test stimulus and the intensity and wave-length of the conditioning stimulation.

The directional sensitivity of the foveal retina shows small but definite variations with the brightness of the conditioning stimulation which appear only for certain combinations of the wave-lengths of test stimulus and conditioning stimulation. These variations are attributed to transitions from vision by one type of cone to vision by another type. It proves possible to distinguish between perception of the test stimulus by different types of cone in foveal vision in much the same way as we distinguish between perception by rods and by cones in parafoveal vision. In the process, we obtain information about the spectral sensitivities of the different types of cone.

2. The subject's conditions of observation

The subject sat in a curtained enclosure and maintained his head in a fixed position by biting on a sealing-wax bit which was rigidly attached to the apparatus. He observed with one eye only, the other eye being covered with an eye shade. His field of view for parafoveal and foveal observation of the test stimulus is shown diagrammatically in figs. 1a and 1b respectively. For parafoveal observation, he directed his gaze at one of the two feeble points of light F_1 and F_2 (fixation points), the one not in use being removed from the field. For foveal observation, he looked towards the centre of the square of 3° side defined by the four feeble points of light N_1, N_2, N_3, N_4 (orientation points). The test stimulus S appeared to him as a square patch of light of 1·04° side, exposed for 0·063 sec. at regular intervals once in every 3·6 sec. For foveal observation, the test stimulus appeared at the centre of the square $N_1 N_2 N_3 N_4$ and for parafoveal observation at a point separated by 5° from the appropriate fixation point and in the position S shown in the figure. An audible signal, repeated just after each exposure, marked time for the subject. The subject held in his hand two keys, one of which he operated when he perceived the test stimulus and the other when he failed to do so.

The conditioning stimulation appeared to the subject as a uniformly bright and approximately circular patch of light of diameter 10° (the central field C), outside which the brightness of the field was zero. In an important special case the brightness of this central field was also zero. The test stimulus always appeared in the centre of the central field.

Prior to the commencement of a series of measurements the subject remained in the dark for a period up to 1 hr. depending on the nature of the measurements. The pupil of his observing eye was dilated when necessary by administering a few drops of a 5 % solution of euphthalmine hydrochloride about 1 hr. before the measurements.

3. Apparatus and method

The main principle of the apparatus is made clear by fig. 2. A parallel beam of light provided by spectrometer II is partially transmitted by the cube C and is brought to a focus ω_2 in the plane of the subject's pupil at O by the lens L_3. This beam is seen by the subject as a uniformly bright patch of light which forms the central field of the conditioning stimulation. A parallel beam from spectrometer I is delimited by a square aperture in the diaphragm T_3, is partially reflected at the diagonal surface in the cube C

and is finally brought to a focus ω_1 in the plane of the subject's pupil by the lens L_3. The diaphragm T_3 is so placed that the subject sees a virtual image of the square aperture at infinity. This image forms the test stimulus. It is important to note that in the area of the field of view occupied by the test stimulus, the eye receives radiation from both the test stimulus and the conditioning stimulation; thus in this sense, the test stimulus is added to or superposed on the conditioning stimulation. The fixation and orientation points are introduced from the side by reflexion in a thin plain glass plate M inserted in the parallel beam from spectrometer II. The rays forming a particular fixation or orientation point are reflected by M to form a real image in the plane K which is the focal plane of the lens L_3. This real image when seen through the lens L_3 appears to the subject as a virtual image at infinity.

By slight rotations of the cube C the test stimulus beam can be sent into the eye through different points of the pupil, while the point of entry of the beam forming the central field remains practically unchanged. After such a rotation of cube C, the diaphragm T_3 must be readjusted by a displacement in its own plane to restore the test stimulus to its original position in the subject's field of view.

A diagram of the complete apparatus is shown in fig. 3. As the apparatus differs little from that described in a previous paper (Stiles 1937), it will suffice to indicate its main features and such changes and additions as have been made.

Images of the ribbon filament source S_1 are formed on the entrance slits of the two spectrometers I and II. The rays from the exit slit of spectrometer I pass through the continuous wedge W_1 and the step-wedge W_2 and are rendered parallel by the lens L_2. The rays from the exit slit of spectrometer II pass through the continuous wedge W_3 and are rendered parallel by lens L_4. The two parallel beams from the spectrometers are then focused to give images ω_1 and ω_2 of the respective exit slits at the subject's eye, as already explained. The auxiliary optical system $L_7 - G - E$ enables the relative positions of the slit images to be determined without disturbing the subject.

At R_1 a shutter is interposed in the beam of spectrometer I. The shutter consists of two rotating disks geared together so that one rotates three times for each rotation of the other. There is an indentation in the periphery of each disk and light is passed by the shutter only when the two indentations come into coincidence opposite the entrance slit of the spectrometer. The width of the indentation in the faster disk, the radius of this disk and its speed of rotation determine the exposure time of the test

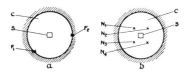

FIG. 1. Subject's field of view (*a*) for parafoveal, (*b*) for foveal observation.

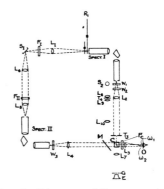

FIG. 3. Diagram of the apparatus (not to scale).

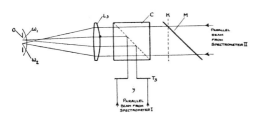

FIG. 2. Diagram showing the principle of the measurements.

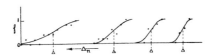

FIG. 4. Derivation of Δ.

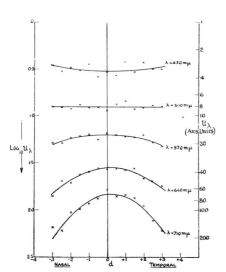

FIG. 5. Directional sensitivity of the dark-adapted parafovea (fixation point F_1).

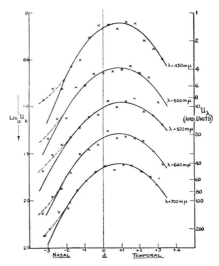

FIG. 6. Directional sensitivity of the dark-adapted fovea.

stimulus. The use of two disks in this way, rather than a single disk, gives a shutter of higher efficiency. The slower disk carries contacts operating a buzzer once in every 3·6 sec.

The thread controlling the position of the step wedge W_2 is connected to a carriage moving on rails across a wide strip of recording paper which is given a slow motion in the direction of its length. Two pens, marking in different colours and operated by the keys in the subject's hands, are fixed to the carriage. Between successive exposures of the test stimulus the carriage is moved to bring different steps of the wedge W_2 into the beam so that on the paper a record is obtained of the subject's responses to different intensities of the test stimulus.

Stray light filters and neutral filters can be inserted in the beam of spectrometer I, of spectrometer II or in the common beam at F_I, F_{II}, F_c respectively.

The fixation or orientation points are obtained in the following manner. An opal lamp S_2 placed at the focus of lens L_8 is imaged at the focus of the similar lens L_9, the image being at the focus of lens L_{10}, so that finally an image of the lamp is formed on the eye by the lens L_3. Between lenses L_8 and L_9 a metal diaphragm T_4 is inserted containing one or four small holes (fixation or orientation points respectively). The images of these holes formed by lens L_{10} are arranged to lie in the focal plane of lens L_3 (allowing for reflection in M) so that the subject sees the fixation or orientation points at infinity. A resistance enables the subject to adjust the intensity of the lamp S_2 and colour filters can be inserted in the beam if required.

The positioning of the eye with respect to the slit images ω_1 and ω_2 and the measurement of the separation of ω_1 and ω_2 were carried out by methods similar to those previously described. When filters were inserted at F_c, a slight displacement of the images ω_1 and ω_2 usually occurred. The images were restored to their correct positions by a suitable shift of the lens L_3 in its own plane.

The method of calculating the intensities of the areas of the subject's field of view illuminated by the two spectrometers was the same as in the previous investigation. The calculations yield the values of the following quantities:

U'_λ = the flux of radiant energy of wave-length λ, expressed in ergs/sec., received by the eye from spectrometer I during the exposure of the test stimulus, *divided by* the angular area of the test stimulus expressed in square degrees. (For brevity U'_λ will be referred to as the "energy" of the test stimulus.)

W_μ = the flux of radiant energy of wave-length μ, expressed in ergs/sec., received by the eye from spectrometer II *divided by* the area in square degrees of the field illuminated by spectrometer II. (W_μ will be referred to as the energy of the central field.)

Corresponding to U'_λ and W_μ, the conventional photometric brightnesses B'_U and B_W of the test stimulus and central field are derived from the relations:

$$B'_U = 2 \cdot 02 \times 10^3 \ U'_\lambda V_\lambda,$$

$$B_W = 2 \cdot 02 \times 10^3 \ W_\mu V_\mu,$$

where V_λ and V_μ are the values of the standard relative luminosity factor for wave-lengths λ and μ respectively. B'_U is defined as the brightness in candles per square foot which, if viewed through an artificial pupil of area 10 sq. mm. by an eye possessing the standard curve of relative luminosity, would match in brightness the test stimulus as seen by a similar eye in the actual apparatus. B_W is similarly defined.*

The spectral purity of the light in test stimulus or central field is specified by the wave-length difference $\Delta\lambda$ or $\Delta\mu$ between the extreme limits of the spectrum band passed by the spectrometer. In general, $\Delta\lambda$ and $\Delta\mu$ had values of the order of 15 and 30 mμ respectively. Parasitic light of wave-length lying outside the desired band was reduced to an unimportant amount by the use of coloured stray-light filters.

For the exit slit of spectrometer I a fixed slit of height 0·50 mm. and width 0·48 mm. was used for all the measurements. The image ω_1 of this slit had the same dimensions. For the entrance slit, fixed slits of various widths were used. The slit height of spectrometer II was either approx. 0·50 or 2·20 mm. The continuously variable symmetrical slits were adjusted as required.

The calculations of U'_λ and W_μ were made assuming the slit widths so small that slit-width corrections could be neglected.

4. DERIVATION OF THE LIMINAL BRIGHTNESS INCREMENT FROM THE RECORD OF THE SUBJECT'S RESPONSES

The logarithm of the energy of the test stimulus during a measurement of the l.b.i. may be expressed in the form

$$\log_{10} U'_\lambda = \log_{10} (U'_\lambda)_0 - \Delta_n,$$

* B'_U and B_W can be obtained in terms of photons by replacing the factor $2 \cdot 02 \times 10^3$ by $2 \cdot 18 \times 10^5$.

where $(U'_\lambda)_0$ is the energy when the step wedge W_2 was removed from the beam the other conditions remaining unchanged, and Δ_n is the optical density for wave-length λ of the nth step of wedge W_2. If the subject recorded "seen" M times, and "not seen" $N-M$ times when a particular step of W_2 was in the beam then $f = M/N$ may be regarded as an approximation to the probability of seeing the test stimulus for that particular energy. Determinations of f for a series of consecutive values of n gave a graph of f against Δ_n from which the l.b.i. could be derived. Examples of such graphs are shown in fig. 4. In each case five exposures were made at each step, i.e. $N = 5$. The density difference between consecutive steps equalled approximately 0·07 but varied slightly with wave-length. The S-shaped curves drawn in fig. 4 are all of the form:

$$f = \tfrac{1}{2}[1 - P\{h(\Delta_n - \Delta)\}] \text{ for } \Delta_n > \Delta$$
$$= \tfrac{1}{2}[1 + P\{h(\Delta_n - \Delta)\}] \text{ for } \Delta_n < \Delta,$$

in which Δ_n is allowed to vary continuously, Δ and h are constants, and $P\{x\}$ is the probability integral $\dfrac{2}{\sqrt{\pi}}\displaystyle\int_0^x e^{-x^2}\,dx$. A relation between f and Δ_n of this form is to be expected if the following conditions hold:

(i) when the test stimulus is exposed there is a critical intensity which must be exceeded if the subject is to record "seen",

(ii) the critical intensity varies from exposure to exposure in a random manner about an average value corresponding to a density in the beam equal to Δ,

(iii) if Δ', Δ'', Δ''', etc. are the densities corresponding to the critical intensities at the instants of different exposures, then Δ', Δ'', Δ''', etc., form a Gaussian distribution about a mean value Δ with a modulus of precision h.

In most cases an S-shaped curve of the above form could be fitted to the plot of f against Δ_n with the measure of agreement illustrated in fig. 4.

In practice, tracings of the theoretical S-shaped curve corresponding to different values of h were prepared. The traced curves could be placed in turn over the experimental graph of f against Δ_n and the pair of values of h and Δ giving the best fit could be determined "by inspection".

The energy U_λ of the test stimulus corresponding to the density value Δ is given by the relation

$$\log_{10} U_\lambda = \log_{10} (U'_\lambda)_0 - \Delta.$$

U_λ is the energy of the test stimulus at which the subject's response is as likely to be "seen" as "not seen". U_λ is accepted as the value of the l.b.i. yielded by the measurement. Corresponding to each determination of U_λ

we obtain in h an estimate of the sharpness of the liminal value, or of the extent to which the critical intensity referred to in (i) above varies from exposure to exposure.

In the first measurements a determination of the l.b.i. was based on sixty exposures, made up of five exposures each of nine consecutive steps of wedge W_2, which were known from a preliminary rough setting by the subject to embrace the liminal value, together with fifteen blanks (test stimuli of zero intensity). The sixty exposures were presented in random order. It was soon found that a "seen" response to a blank was obtained only very rarely. For the bulk of the measurements the stimuli were presented in order of decreasing or increasing intensity, the step wedge being moved one step after each exposure. Each succession of exposures covered the range from "certainly seen" to "certainly not seen" or vice versa. Three successions of exposures with increasing intensity and two with decreasing intensity completed the measurement. No blanks were included. Tests showed that this method gave about the same values of the l.b.i. as the first method but the precision was a little better; it imposed less strain on the subject and called for a less precise preliminary setting. It was adhered to for all the subsequent measurements.

5. SPECIFICATION OF THE DIRECTION OF INCIDENCE OF A RAY ON THE RETINA

The direction of incidence on the retina is the effective variable determining the change in retinal response when a ray enters the eye through different points of the pupil. As in previous work, this direction will be specified indirectly by giving the position of the point of entry of the ray in the pupil or rather in the apparent pupil, i.e. the pupil seen from outside the eye. The ray entering through the centre of the apparent pupil. and terminating on a given retinal point may be regarded as defining the normal to the retina at that point. Any other ray entering the apparent pupil at a point d mm. from the centre and terminating on the same retinal point will strike the retina at an angle of incidence (i.e. at an angle with the normal ray) equal to $2 \cdot 4d$ deg. This result is only a rough approximation applicable for an average normal eye and for retinal points at or near the fovea. Since for the fully dilated pupil d may have a value up to about 4 mm., we are dealing with the effects of changing the angle of incidence from 0° to about 10°.

There are practical advantages in keeping the point of entry on the horizontal diameter of the apparent pupil and this has been done in all the present measurements. Thus we require only one variable, namely d, the distance in mm. from the point of entry to the centre of the apparent pupil, d is taken as positive when the point of entry is on the temporal and negative when it is on the nasal side of the centre. It is easy to show that when the relative luminous efficiency η can be represented by the expression 10^{-pr^2}, where r is the distance in mm. of the actual point of entry from the point of entry P_M giving maximal luminous efficiency, then the variation of η across the horizontal diameter is represented by the analogous expression $10^{-p(d-d_m)^2}$, where p has the same value as before and d_m defines the position of the point of entry which gives a greater luminous efficiency than any other point on the horizontal diameter.

The pupil is not a fixed structure in the eye. Its diameter and, possibly, the position of its centre change with the lighting conditions. It appears from the present measurements that, when dilated with a mydriatic, the pupil does not always assume the same diameter. The centre of the dilated pupil has been found to shift slightly ($\frac{1}{10}$ to $\frac{2}{10}$ mm.) during the course of a series of measurements. These vagaries are unfortunate for the present purpose.*

6. Results. Central field of zero brightness

All the measurements reported refer to the writer's left eye. This is a slightly hypermetropic eye ($+0\cdot5$ Sph. $-0\cdot25$ Cyl. $130°$) and a normal trichromat belonging to Abney and Watson's Class I (rod-free fovea). The examination of other eyes was deferred until the results of the present work should have indicated the points meriting special study.

We consider first the case in which the subject's field of view was completely dark save for the fixation or orientation points and the flashes of the test stimulus. Prior to every series of measurements the subject remained for about 1 hr. in the dark. Thus the observations were made with the dark-adapted eye. Fig. 5 shows, for five wave-lengths of the test stimulus, the variation of the logarithm of the l.b.i. for $5°$ parafoveal vision (fixation point F_1) as the point of entry of the rays was moved across the horizontal diameter of the apparent pupil. Each plotted point is the mean of two or more values obtained in independent runs. In each run half the points were obtained in a traverse from nasal to temporal, the other half in a traverse in the reverse sense. At present we are concerned only with the

* A method of specifying point of entry independently of the pupil has been suggested to the writer by Professor Hartridge. The proposal is to use as a fixed point of reference in the eye the reflected image in the cornea of a distant light on which the subject fixates.

variation of $\log_{10} U_\lambda$ and an arbitrary constant has been added to the absolute values for each curve to give a convenient spacing of the different curves in the figure. In the figure the scale of $\log_{10} U_\lambda$ has been taken to be increasing in the downwards direction, so that the curves represent the variation of $(-\log_{10} U_\lambda) = \log_{10} 1/U_\lambda$ with respect to a similar scale increasing in the upwards direction. The curves show that the sensitivity of the dark-adapted parafoveal retina is practically non-directional for test stimuli in the blue-green but exhibits a slight directional effect in the yellow, which becomes well defined in passing through orange to red. In the violet there appears to be a slight effect in the reverse sense.

Similar measurements for foveal vision of the test stimulus are given in fig. 6. The familiar difficulties in measuring the foveal threshold (save in the red end of the spectrum), due to the greater sensitivity of the parafovea, are accentuated when the rays enter near the edge of the pupil. This is so because the parafoveal sensitivity is maintained while the foveal sensitivity falls off as the point of entry moves from centre to periphery of the pupil.

Fortunately with practice the subject can tell from the appearance of the test stimulus whether his fixation has wandered so that he is using parafoveal instead of foveal vision. When this occurred, the subject operated neither key and the exposure was repeated. It sometimes happened when the test stimulus was correctly fixated, that the light scattered or irregularly reflected in the eye could be seen parafoveally although the normal image of the test stimulus produced no response. This was not accepted as vision of the test stimulus.

The curves of fig. 6 show that the sensitivity of the dark-adapted foveal retina exhibits a pronounced directional effect whatever the wave-length of the test stimulus.

It is appropriate to compare the variation of $\log_{10}(1/U_\lambda)$ with point of entry and the corresponding variation of $\log_{10}\eta$, where η is the relative luminous efficiency obtained in brightness matching measurements. The variation of $\log_{10}(1/U_\lambda)$ can in fact be represented to a first approximation by the empirical formula:

$$\log_{10}(1/U_\lambda) = \log_{10}(1/U_\lambda)_m - p_\lambda(d - d_m)^2, \qquad (1)$$

where $\log_{10}(1/U_\lambda)_m$ is the maximum value of $\log_{10}(1/U_\lambda)$ which is attained at $d = d_m$, and p_λ is a constant. This formula is of the same form as that previously found for $\log_{10}\eta$ and there can be little doubt that the same cause is operative in the two types of experiment. The continuous curves drawn in figs. 5 and 6 have been computed from the above formula with suitable choice of the constants p_λ and d_m. For the foveal measurements, the data show a tendency (very marked for $\lambda = 430$ mμ) to deviate from the fitted curve for $(d - d_m)$ greater than 3 mm. A similar deviation was observed in the curves of $\log_{10}\eta$ against d. The values of p_λ for foveal vision come out to be about 15 % lower than those derived from the $\log_{10}\eta$ curves obtained for the same eye in the brightness matching experiments with monochromatic light (Stiles 1937). The position of the maximum d_m is also displaced from about 0·6 mm. temporal to about 0·9 mm. temporal.

To see whether these differences were due to a difference in the luminous efficiencies operative for the threshold measurements and for the brightness matching measurements, or to an actual change in the eye, brightness matching traverses were made for $\lambda = 500$ mμ and for $\lambda = 700$ mμ (foveal vision). The results gave values of p_λ and d_m in substantial agreement with those found from the corresponding threshold curves. It must be concluded that for this eye the direction of incidence on the retina of the ray giving maximal luminous effect and the magnitude of the directional effect specified by p_λ have changed. Changes of the same kind are in evidence if the measurements of η made with monochromatic light (Stiles 1937) are compared with the original measurements made with white light (Stiles and Crawford 1933). It appears that in the course of about six years the point of entry in the horizontal diameter giving the greatest value of η has shifted for this eye from about 0·2 mm. nasal to about 1·0 mm. temporal. Whatever the actual mechanism giving rise to the directional properties of the retina, we are probably justified in regarding the direction of incidence which gives the greatest value of η as defining in some manner the direction in which the end organs of the retina are pointing. It is possible therefore that for the eye in question the end organs at the fovea are being gradually sheared over. During about the same period of time the refraction of the eye has changed from emmetropic to $+0\cdot5$ Sph. $-0\cdot25$ Cyl. 130° but no other symptom which might possibly be correlated with the changes in d_m has been noted.

The values of d_m for several eyes studied by Crawford and the writer are given in Table I. In some cases the point of entry was varied on the vertical diameter of the pupil and d_m then defines the position on the vertical diameter giving the greatest value of η. The values of d_m for extrafoveal points were obtained from measurements of the l.b.i.

Unfortunately the pupil centre is not a perfectly stable reference point and the value of d_m is subject to some ambiguity on this account. However, the figures in the table show that d_m varies appreciably for different eyes, and for different retinal points of the same eye. The systematic

TABLE I. POSITION OF THE POINT OF ENTRY ON THE HORIZONTAL OR
VERTICAL DIAMETER OF THE PUPIL OF THE RAY GIVING THE GREATEST
VISUAL EFFECT

Subject L.E. = left eye, R.E. = right eye	Date of measurement and refer- ence		Method of measurement	Retinal patch	Diam. of pupil traversed	d_m in mm.
W.S.S. (L.E.)	1932	(1)	Brightness matching	Fovea	Hor.	− 0·2 (nasal)
,,	1932	(1)	,,	,,	Vert.	− 0·5 (upper)
,,	1932*	(1)	,,	,,	Hor.	0
,,	1932	(1)	,,	,,	Vert.	− 0·2 (upper)
,,	1936	(2)	,,	,,	Hor.	+ 0·6 (temp.)
,,	1936	(2)	,,	,,	Vert.	− 0·5 (upper)
,,	1937–8	(4)	,,	,,	Hor.	+ 0·9 (temp.)
,,	1937–8	(4)	l.b.i. measurements	,,	,,	+ 0·9 (temp.)
,,	1937–8	(4)	,,	5° parafovea (fixation point F_1)	,,	+ 0·2 (temp.)
,,	1937–8	(4)	,,	5° parafovea (fixation point F_2)	,,	+ 1·5 (temp.)
B.H.C. (L.E.)	1932	(1)	Brightness matching	Fovea	,,	− 0·5 (nasal)
,,	1932	(1)	,,	,,	Vert.	+ 0·6 (lower)
B.H.C. (R.E.)	1932	(1)	,,	,,	Hor.	− 0·5 (nasal)
,,	1932	(1)	,,	,,	Vert.	+ 0·2 (lower)
B.H.C. (L.E.)	1937	(3)	l.b.i. measurements	,,	Hor.	− 0·5 (nasal)
,,	1937	(3)	,,	5° parafovea	,,	− 1·5 (nasal)
,,	1937	(3)	,,	14° parafovea	,,	− 1·7 (nasal)
R.H.S. (L.E.)	1937	(3)	,,	Fovea	,,	− 1·4 (nasal)
,,	1937	(3)	,,	5° parafovea	,,	− 1·8 (nasal)
F.W.C. (R.E.)	1932	(1)	Brightness matching	Fovea	,,	+ 0·5 (temp.)
,,	1932	(1)	,,	,,	Vert.	0

* Six weeks later.
References: (1) Stiles and Crawford (1933); (2) Stiles (1937); (3) Crawford (1937);
(4) Stiles (present work).

determination of d_m in the vertical and horizontal diameters for a large
number of eyes would be of considerable interest.

Further measurements of the effect of wave-length on the directional
sensitivity were made by the *two-point method*, in which $\log_{10}U_\lambda$ is determined for two points of entry, P_o, at or near the point giving maximal
sensitivity (central entry) and P_p, near the periphery of the pupil (peripheral entry). Measurements were made for a series of wave-lengths span-
ning the spectrum in one run. From the two values of $\log_{10}U_\lambda$ obtained for

each wave-length and from the co-ordinates d_o and d_p of the points P_o and P_p, the value of p_λ was computed using formula (1). It was necessary to assume the value of d_m obtained earlier from the curves of figs. 5 and 6.

Figs. 7 and 8 give the mean values of p_λ obtained from five two-point determinations for parafoveal vision and from three such runs for foveal vision. For parafoveal vision, p_λ is not very different from zero for λ less than 600 mμ. As λ increases from 600 to 700 mμ, p_λ increases to approximately 0·045 and finally it appears to drop again slightly. For foveal vision p_λ lies in the range 0·045 to 0·065 and shows a variation with wave-length similar to that found previously in the brightness-matching experiments. The values of p_λ obtained from new measurements by the brightness-matching method (two point determinations) are shown as the circles in fig. 9 which also gives the values obtained in the earlier investigation. Apart from the shift in absolute value already noted, the new determinations of p_λ by the brightness-matching method show the same variation with wave-length as the old and this variation is closely followed by the values of p_λ derived from the l.b.i. determinations.

Determinations of p_λ at a second parafoveal point, again at 5° from the fovea, but in a different meridian, are plotted in fig. 10. For these measurements the fixation point F_2' was used. Save for the point at $\lambda = 450$ mμ, p_λ shows a similar variation with wave-length to that obtained for the other parafoveal point. For this parafoveal point, d_m had the value 1·5 mm. (temporal).

We may sum up the above results as follows: the sensitivity of the dark-adapted parafovea is nearly independent of the direction of incidence of the light on the retina except for wave-lengths in the orange and red. The sensitivity of the dark-adapted fovea shows a pronounced variation with direction of incidence for all wave-lengths. The magnitude of the directional effect for the fovea varies to a limited extent with wave-length and the variation resembles that found in the earlier experiments by the brightness-matching method.

In parafoveal observation of a coloured test stimulus, the fact that the test stimulus is coloured can be appreciated only when its intensity exceeds a certain multiple of the threshold value. This multiple, known as the photochromatic ratio, was observed to be greater for peripheral entry than for central entry of the light rays in the pupil. For example, at 700 mμ it had on the average the value 1·4 for central, and 2·5 for peripheral entry. At shorter wave-lengths, the values were of course very much larger but showed a difference in the same sense between central and peripheral entry.

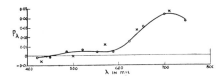

Fig. 7. Variation of p_λ with λ for the dark-adapted parafovea (F_1). ⊙, Two-point determinations; ×, from data of fig. 5.

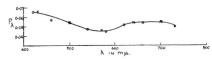

Fig. 8. Variation of p_λ with λ for the dark-adapted fovea. ⊙, Two-point determinations; ×, from data of fig. 6.

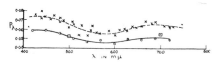

Fig. 9. Variation of p_λ with λ by brightness-matching method. ⊙, New values by two-point method; ⊡, new values from traverses; ×, old values, Stiles (1937).

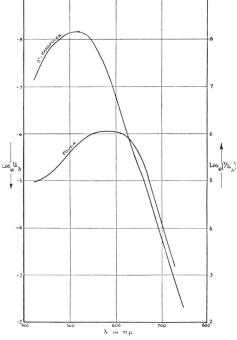

Fig. 11. Spectral sensitivities of dark-adapted fovea and parafovea (F_1). Central entry.

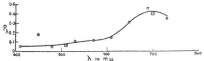

Fig. 10. Variation of p_λ with λ for the dark-adapted parafovea (F_2). ⊙, Two-point method (single determination); ⊡, from traverses.

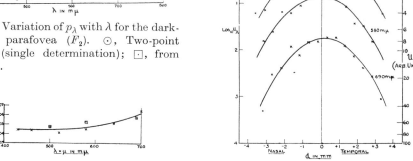

Fig. 13. Variation of p_λ with λ for the light-adapted parafovea (F_1). $\lambda = \mu$; ×, Single determination by two-point method; $\log_{10} W_\mu$ round about $\bar{2} \cdot 5$. ⊡, From traverses of fig. 12.

Fig. 12. Directional sensitivity of the light-adapted parafovea (F_1). $\lambda = \mu$; $\log_{10} W_\mu = \bar{3} \cdot 2$ (500 mμ), $\bar{3} \cdot 6$ (580 mμ), $\bar{2} \cdot 7$ (690 mμ).

In foveal observation of the test stimulus, the photochromatic ratio does not depend on the point of entry and, in fact, it has the value 1 for all colours except yellow.

The mean values of $\log_{10} U_\lambda$ for central entry, obtained in the two-point determinations, are plotted against wave-length in fig. 11. The actual values are given and not the values plus an arbitrary constant as in figs. 5 and 6. The curves of fig. 11 are of the type first obtained by Abney and Watson (1916) and they can be interpreted in terms of the duplicity theory of vision in the following manner. Foveal vision of the test stimulus is served solely by the cones since rods are absent from the fovea. Thus the foveal curve represents the variation with wave-length of the logarithm of the l.b.i. of the foveal cone system. The parafovea contains both rods and cones. For any wave-length of the test stimulus the parafoveal rods acting alone would give one value of the l.b.i., $(U_\lambda)_s$, and the parafoveal cones acting alone would give another value $(U_\lambda)_p$. The l.b.i. of the parafoveal cones may be assumed to vary with wave-length in much the same way as the l.b.i. of the foveal cones so that the graph of $\log_{10}(U_\lambda)_p$ against λ will have the same form as the foveal curve of fig. 11 although it may be displaced parallel to the axis of $\log_{10} U_\lambda$. In reality the rods and cones are in action together and although we do not know how their respective effects "add up" we may safely assume that the resultant parafoveal l.b.i. will not be greater than either $(U_\lambda)_s$ or $(U_\lambda)_p$. Thus since for λ greater than 630 mμ the parafoveal l.b.i. exceeds the foveal l.b.i., it follows *a fortiori* that $(U_\lambda)_p$ will exceed the foveal l.b.i. This means that the parafoveal cone system is less sensitive than the foveal cone system. On the other hand for λ less than 600 mμ, the parafoveal l.b.i. is much smaller than the foveal l.b.i. and, *a fortiori*, much smaller than $(U_\lambda)_p$. Thus in this region of the spectrum we .can identify the parafoveal l.b.i. with $(U_\lambda)_s$, the l.b.i. of the parafoveal rod system. As λ increases beyond 600 mμ it is probable that the ratio of $(U_\lambda)_p$ to $(U_\lambda)_s$ tends to diminish, until at 700 mμ the two quantities are not very different. This is suggested by the fact that the photochromatic ratio for parafoveal vision diminishes for λ greater than 600 mμ, until at $\lambda = 700$ mμ it equals approximately 1·4. Thus, the parafoveal cones may participate to an increasing degree in determining the parafoveal l.b.i. as we pass from 600 mμ to the extreme red end of the spectrum.

If we accept the above interpretation, then in fig. 8 the values of p_λ measure the directional sensitivity of the foveal cones. In fig. 7 the values of p_λ for λ less than 600 mμ measure the directional sensitivity of the parafoveal rods. The increase in p_λ at longer wave-lengths may be due (a) to an increase in the directional sensitivity of the parafoveal rods with increase in wave-length, (*b*) to the participation of the parafoveal cones which, like the foveal cones, may show a large directional sensitivity at all wave-lengths, (*c*) to a combination of these two causes.

7. Central field illuminated: parafovea

For all the observations described in this section, the light rays forming the central field entered the subject's eye through the centre of the pupil. The test stimulus was observed parafoveally using fixation point F_1. With a central field of high brightness and of the same wave-length as the test stimulus, the variation of $\log_{10} U_\lambda$ with point of entry of the test stimulus was determined for wave-lengths 500, 580 and 690 mμ (fig. 12). The values of p_λ obtained from two-point determinations under similar conditions are plotted against λ in fig. 13. These results show that when the parafoveal retina is adapted to a high brightness of given wave-length, it exhibits a well-developed directional sensitivity to a test stimulus of the same wave-length whatever that wave-length may be.

The differences in the directional sensitivities of the light- and dark-adapted parafoveal retina, which are evident from a comparison of figs. 5 and 12 or 7 and 13, prove conclusively that we are in fact dealing with the directional properties of the retina and not with differences in light losses in the refractive system of the eye. Effects of the latter kind would be unaffected by the presence or absence of the central field.

By determining $\log_{10} U_\lambda$ for central and peripheral entry of the test stimulus at a series of brightnesses of the central field from zero upwards the change in directional sensitivity with brightness level could be followed. The subject remained in the dark for 1 hr. before each run, his pupil having been previously dilated with euphthalmine. The mean results of two runs at each of the wave-lengths 500, 580 and 690 mμ are plotted in figs. 14, 15 and 16. Each figure gives three curves:

I. $\log_{10} U_\lambda$ against $\log_{10} W_\mu$ for central entry of the test stimulus.

II. $\log_{10} U_\lambda$ against $\log_{10} W_\mu$ for peripheral entry of the test stimulus.

III. p_λ against $\log_{10} W_\mu$ derived from the previous curves by applying formula (1).

Consider first fig. 15 for which $\lambda = \mu = 580$ mμ. The curve of p_λ against $\log_{10} W_\mu$ falls into a *low brightness region* in which p_λ is approximately constant and small, a *transitional region* in which p_λ increases with $\log_{10} W_\mu$, and a *high brightness region* in which p_λ is again approximately constant but has a high value. Turning to the curves of $\log_{10} U_\lambda$ against $\log_{10} W_\mu$, we note that to begin with the gradient of curve I increases with $\log_{10} W_\mu$ and approaches a constant value. Then at about the beginning of the transitional region the gradient decreases with increase in $\log_{10} W_\mu$. Subsequently it increases again and finally approaches a constant value. Curve II behaves similarly except that the decrease in the gradient of the curve occurs at about the end of the transitional region. Graphs of the logarithm of the parafoveal l.b.i. against the logarithm of the conditioning brightness exhibiting a "change of law" of this kind were first observed using white light for both test stimulus and conditioning stimulation and their interpretation in terms of the duplicity theory has already been given (Stiles and Crawford 1932, 1934). It is assumed that if we could determine the l.b.i. $(U_\lambda)_s$ of the rod system acting alone we should obtain a curve of $\log_{10}(U_\lambda)_s$ against $\log_{10} W_\mu$ similar to curve A of fig. 17. The cone system acting alone would give, on the other hand, a curve of $\log_{10}(U_\lambda)_p$ against $\log_{10} W_\mu$ similar to curve B. In the practical case when both systems are in action, the measured $\log_{10} U_\lambda$ would coincide with $\log_{10}(U_\lambda)_s$ at low brightnesses where $\log_{10}(U_\lambda)_s$ is considerably smaller than $\log_{10}(U_\lambda)_p$, and with $\log_{10}(U_\lambda)_p$ at high brightnesses where the reverse is true. In the neighbourhood of the point of intersection of curves A and B, where $\log_{10}(U_\lambda)_s$ and $\log_{10}(U_\lambda)_p$ have comparable values the observed $\log_{10} U_\lambda$ would be smaller than either so that the experimental curve would follow some such course as that indicated by the dotted line C. Curve C is made up of three sections: a rod section at low brightnesses where C is coincident with A, a cone section at high brightnesses where C is coincident with B and a mixed section at intermediate brightnesses where C lies below both the curves A and B.

Accepting the view that the change of law in curves I and II of fig. 15 is produced in the way just described, we obtain a simple explanation of curve III. Suppose in fig. 17, curves A and B refer to central entry of the test stimulus. Assume now that the rods show no directional sensitivity at any brightness of the central field. Curve A will then apply equally for peripheral and central entry.* Suppose, on the other hand, that the cones show a *pronounced and constant* directional sensitivity at all brightness levels. Then the curve of $\log_{10}(U_\lambda)_p$ against $\log_{10} W_\mu$ for peripheral entry of the test stimulus (curve B') will have the same shape as curve B but will be

---

* Since p_λ has a small positive value in the low brightness region of curve III (fig. 15), the rods probably show a slight directional effect when stimulated with $\lambda = 580 \, \text{m}\mu$. For simplicity this effect has been ignored in constructing the curves of fig. 17 which are primarily intended to illustrate the principle of the suggested explanation.

F𝗂𝗀. 14

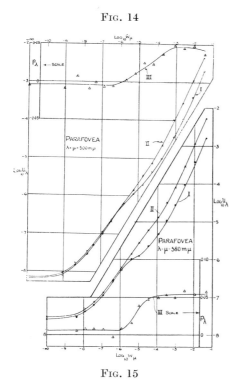

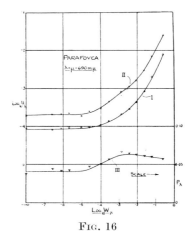

F𝗂𝗀. 15

F𝗂𝗀. 16

F𝗂𝗀𝗌. 14–16. For key see p. 81 of text.

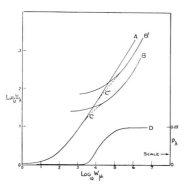

F𝗂𝗀. 17. Explanation of the results for parafoveal vision, in terms of the duplicity theory.

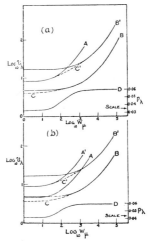

F𝗂𝗀. 18. Alternative explanations of the results for red light. In (*b*), *A* and *A′* refer to the rods and to central and peripheral entry respectively.

displaced parallel to the axis of $\log_{10}(U_\lambda)$ to higher values. The resultant curve of $\log_{10} U_\lambda$ against $\log_{10} W_\mu$ when both rod and cone systems are in operation will be represented for peripheral entry by curve C'. By taking the difference of curves C' and C and applying formula (1) we obtain the variation of p_λ with $\log_{10} W_\mu$ as curve D.

The main features of the experimental curves of fig. 15 are all reproduced in the corresponding curves C, C' and D of fig. 17. For this case the duplicity theory, together with the assumption of constant directional sensitivities for the rod and cone systems, provides a possible explanation of the change in directional sensitivity with brightness level.

The experimental curves for $\lambda = \mu = 500$ mμ (fig. 14) are generally similar to those for $\lambda = \mu = 580$ mμ and may be similarly explained. There are differences, however. The transitional region in curve III extends over a wider range, and the change of law in the curves of $\log_{10} U_\lambda$ against $\log_{10} W_\mu$ is observable only for curve I. These differences may be due to the rod and cone curves A and B (fig. 17) being so displaced that they intersect at a smaller angle.

For $\lambda = \mu = 690$ mμ (fig. 16), we may apply the above explanation in the way shown schematically in fig. 18a. There is an alternative possibility however; the rods when stimulated with red light may exhibit a well-developed directional sensitivity, although a smaller one than the cones. The scheme of fig. 18b would then apply. We are faced here with the uncertainty to which reference was made at the end of the previous section.

The more general case when test stimulus and central field have different wave-lengths will now be examined. Figs. 19 and 20 give respectively the results of two-point determinations for the combinations $\lambda = 580$, $\mu = 500$ and $\lambda = 450$, $\mu = 520$. With these combinations the transition from rod to cone vision in curves I and II and the corresponding change in the directional sensitivity measured by p_λ are very clearly shown. The results are in good accord with the explanation illustrated by the curves of fig. 17.

With the combination $\lambda = 500$, $\mu = 690$, the results are of a different character (fig. 21). Despite the large scatter in the experimental values we may admit that on the whole there is no systematic variation of p_λ with brightness level. The curve relating $\log_{10} U_\lambda$ and $\log_{10} W_\mu$ is nearly the same for central and peripheral entry and a "change of law" of the kind previously obtained is not in evidence. These facts suggest that at all values of $\log_{10} W_\mu$, the test stimulus is seen by rod vision. In our view this result is obtained because the rod curve (curve A, fig. 17) lies below and to the right of the two cone curves (B and B', fig. 17) and does not intersect them. The results for the combination $\lambda = 500$, $\mu = 660$ (fig. 22) allow of a similar

FIG. 19

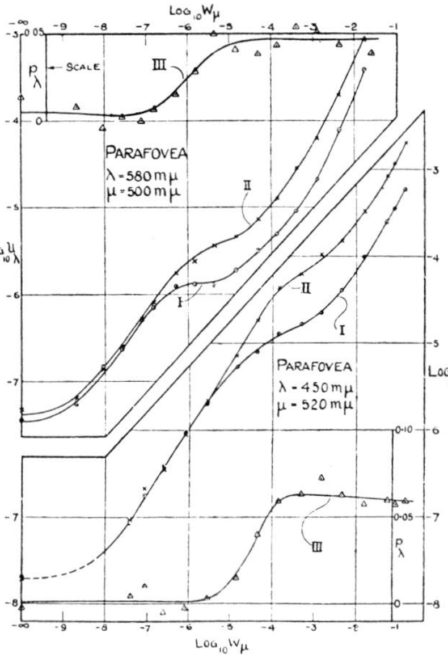

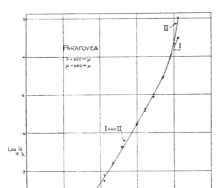

FIG. 20

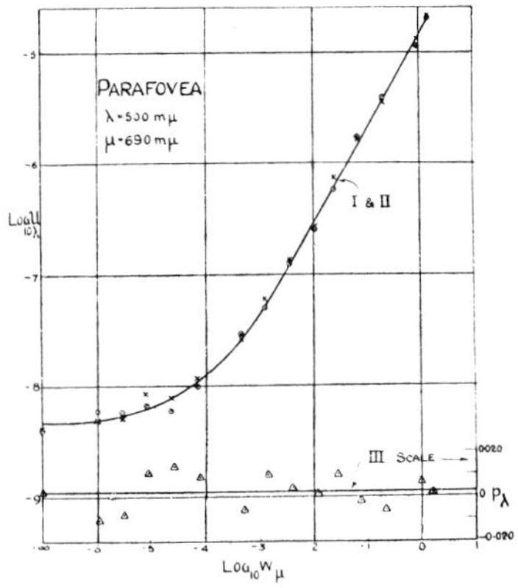

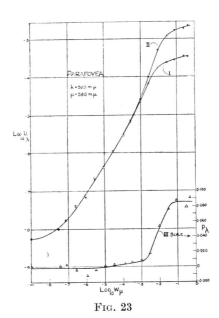

FIG. 21

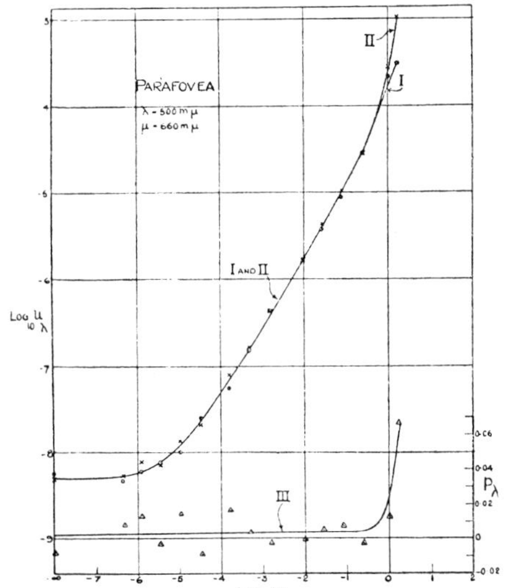

FIG. 22

FIG. 23

FIGS. 19–23. Key as for figs. 14–16.

interpretation, except that at the highest brightness level p_λ rises sharply. This rise is believed to be genuine but its explanation depends on a new factor to be dealt with later.

The interpretation of the results may now be carried a stage further. For each combination of λ and μ, we have envisaged a rod curve A and a cone curve B, but nothing has been said of the connection between the rod curves or the cone curves for different combinations. In the brightness range where curves I and II of fig. 22 are indistinguishable, the common curve according to our interpretation is purely a rod curve. A tracing of this curve can be fitted approximately over the rod sections of all the experimental curves of $\log_{10} U_\lambda$ against $\log_{10} W_\mu$* which possess an identifiable rod section. Thus to a first approximation the rod curve has the same shape for all combinations λ and μ for which it can be observed and is merely displaced (without rotation) to different positions with respect to the axes. Moreover, for two combinations with the same μ but different λ's the rod curves are found to have approximately the same positions with respect to the axis of $\log_{10} W_\mu$ but are relatively displaced in a direction parallel to the axis of $\log_{10} U_\lambda$. On the other hand, for two curves with the same λ but different μ's the rod curves have approximately the same positions with respect to the axis of $\log_{10} U_\lambda$ but are relatively displaced parallel to the axis of $\log_{10} W_\mu$.

It follows from these experimental conclusions that the relation between $\log_{10} (U_\lambda)_s$ {$(U_\lambda)_s$ stands for the l.b.i. of the rod system acting alone} and $\log_{10} W_\mu$ must be of the form

$$\log_{10} (U_\lambda)_s + \log_{10} s_\lambda = F\{\overline{\log_{10} W_\mu + \log_{10} S_\mu}\}, \tag{2}$$

where s_λ depends only on λ, S_μ depends only on μ and $F(x)$ is a fixed function of x determined by the shape of the rod curve. Relation (2) may be written

$$\log_{10} \overline{s_\lambda (U_\lambda)_s} = F\{\log_{10} \overline{W_\mu S_\mu}\}.$$

This implies that $s_\lambda (U_\lambda)_s$ is a fixed function of $S_\mu W_\mu$. It is equally true that $1/\overline{s_\lambda (U_\lambda)_s}$ is a fixed function of $S_\mu W_\mu$, which we may call $\xi_s\{\overline{W_\mu S_\mu}\}$.

Thus $$1/\overline{(U_\lambda)_s s_\lambda} = \xi_s\{\overline{W_\mu S_\mu}\},$$

or $$1/(U_\lambda)_s = s_\lambda \xi_s\{\overline{W_\mu S_\mu}\}. \tag{3}$$

The experimental data determine only the relative values of s_λ at different wave-lengths λ, and the relative values of S_μ at different wave-lengths μ.

---

* Including curves for a number of combinations for which the results cannot be given in full.

It is convenient to remove these ambiguities, (*a*) by giving the fixed function $\xi_s(x)$ the value unity when $x = 0$ so that s_λ is the reciprocal of the l.b.i. of the rods when W_μ, the intensity of the central field, is zero and (*b*) by giving the fixed function $\xi_s(x)$ the value 0·1 when $x = 1$. It follows from condition (*b*) that if $W_\mu S_\mu = 1$, $\xi_s(\overline{W_\mu S_\mu}) = 0·1$ and $1/(U_\lambda)_s$ has one-tenth its value for a central field of zero intensity. Thus S_μ equals the reciprocal of the intensity of the central field necessary to reduce $1/(U_\lambda)_s$ to one-tenth, or to increase $(U_\lambda)_s$ to ten times its value for zero field. In this sense S_μ measures the sensitivity of the rod system to the "conditioning" effect of central fields of different wave-lengths.

It is easily deduced from equation (3) that the curve of $(-\log_{10}\xi_s(x))$ against $\log_{10}x$ must have the same shape as the rod section of any experimental curve of $\log_{10}U_\lambda$ against $\log_{10}W_\mu$. The plot of $(-\log_{10}\xi_s(x))$ against $\log_{10}x$ shown as curve 1 in fig. 36 is simply the rod section of curves I and II of fig. 22 placed in such a position with respect to the axes that the two conditions $\xi_s(x) = 1$ when $x = 0$ and $\xi_s(x) = 0·1$ when $x = 1$ are satisfied. Thus curve 1 of fig. 36 completely defines the fixed function of the rods, $\xi_s(x)$.

The curve of $\log_{10}s_\lambda$ against λ will coincide approximately with the parafoveal curve of $\log_{10}(1/U_\lambda)$ against λ for zero field (fig. 11), except in the red end of the spectrum where $\log_{10}s_\lambda$ will have slightly lower values owing to the participation of the cones in determining U_λ. The mean values of $\log_{10}S_\mu$ obtained from the rod sections of the various experimental curves of $\log_{10}U_\lambda$ against $\log_{10}W_\mu$ are given in Table II. The variation of $\log_{10}S_\mu$ with μ is very similar to the variation of $\log_{10}s_\lambda$ with λ, as is shown by the approximate constancy of $\overline{\log_{10}s_\lambda - \log_{10}S_\mu}$, $(\lambda = \mu)$.

TABLE II

μ ...	440	500	520	580	660	690
$\log_{10}S_\mu$	6·6	7·3	7·1	6·4	4·1	3·1
$\overline{\log_{10}s_\lambda - \log_{10}S_\mu}$ at $\lambda = \mu$	1·0	0·9	1·1	0·9	1·0	1·1

This means that to a first approximation the relative values of lights of different wave-length in producing a threshold stimulation of the rods and in bringing the rods to a given level of stimulation are the same.

The above discussion applies in the first instance to the response of the rods to test stimuli entering centrally. To allow for entry at other points, the factor $10^{-p\lambda s(d-d_m)^2}$ may be introduced in the expression for $1/(U_\lambda)_s$ which now becomes

$$1/(U_\lambda)_s = 10^{-p\lambda s(d-d_m)^2} s_\lambda \xi_s(W_\mu S_\mu), \tag{4}$$

where $p_{\lambda s}$ determines the directional effect of the rods. For λ not greater than 600 mμ we may identify $p_{\lambda s}$ with the p_λ plotted in fig. 7. For longer wave-lengths $p_{\lambda s}$ may be less than p_λ.

Turning now to the cones, we consider the possibility that the l.b.i. of the cones $(U_\lambda)_p$ can be represented by an expression similar in form to that already obtained for the rods. For the combination $\lambda = 580$, $\mu = 500$ (fig. 19), the cone section of curve I extends from the highest brightness levels down to a brightness ($\log_{10} W_\mu = \bar{6}\cdot2$ approx.) where the curve becomes nearly horizontal and the l.b.i. of the cones has become constant. We may take a tracing of this pure cone curve and try to fit it over the cone sections of the curves for other combinations λ, μ, which have an identifiable cone section. The process is much less satisfactory than in the case of the rods, partly because for most of the available curves the mixed section of the curve where both rods and cones are operative intervenes before the flat part of the cone curve is reached.

A more radical difficulty is revealed by the measurements for the combination $\lambda = 500$, $\mu = 580$ (fig. 23). The curves of $\log_{10} U_\lambda$ against $\log_{10} W_\mu$ show a sharp "change of law" when $\log_{10} W_\mu$ is in the neighbourhood of $\bar{2}$ and at about the same brightness p_λ rises sharply. As before we attribute these features to a transition from rod to cone vision of the test stimulus. Comparing curves I and II of fig. 23 with the corresponding curves of fig. 15 for which μ has the same value (580 mμ), it is easy to see that the cone sections for the two cases cannot arise from a curve of fixed shape which is merely displaced parallel to the axis of $\log_{10} U_\lambda$ by varying amounts depending on the value of λ. If this were so the gradients of the cone sections in figs. 23 and 15 at a given value of $\log_{10} W_\mu$ would be the same, for these gradients are unaffected by displacements parallel to the axis of $\log_{10} U_\lambda$. Actually at $\log_{10} W_\mu = \bar{2}\cdot6$, the gradient (tangent) of curve I equals $0\cdot2$ in fig. 23 and $1\cdot0$ in fig. 15. Similarly, if we compare the cone sections of fig. 23 with those of fig. 14 for which λ has the same value, it is clear that the cone sections for the two cases cannot arise from a curve of fixed shape which is merely displaced parallel to the axis of $\log_{10} W_\mu$ by varying amounts depending on the value of μ.

It must be concluded from the above that the cone curves for different combinations λ, μ cannot be represented by an expression similar to (4). Other anomalies in the cone curves confirm this conclusion. Thus the simple idea of a curve of fixed shape which is displaced parallel to the axes of $\log_{10} U_\lambda$ and $\log_{10} W_\mu$ by amounts depending on the values of λ and μ respectively, breaks down for cone vision although it holds for rod vision. The more complex behaviour of the parafoveal cones is elucidated by the measurements for foveal vision of the stimulus which give the response of a cone system unobscured by the presence of a rod response. It appears that to explain the response of the cones the duplicity theory must be supplemented with the idea of three distinctive types of cone, an idea which is, of course, inherent in many forms of the trichromatic theory.

8. Central field illuminated: fovea

When the eye is adapted to a field of zero brightness, the fovea exhibits a pronounced directional sensitivity for all wave-lengths of the test stimulus. Measurements made with the central field illuminated show that this pronounced directional sensitivity is retained whatever the intensity and wave-length of the central field. These measurements consisted in the main of two-point determinations in which λ and μ were kept constant while the energy intensity of the central field W_μ was increased in steps from zero upwards. The determination of $\log_{10} U_\lambda$ for "central" entry of the test stimulus was made at $d_o = +\frac{3}{4}$ or $+1$ mm. (temporal) as it was known that for the fovea of this eye d_m equalled about 0·9 mm. The determination for peripheral entry was made, in most cases, at $d_p = -3$ mm. (nasal). Except where the contrary is indicated, the rays forming the central field entered the eye through the centre of the pupil, i.e. at $d = 0$. An adequate period of dark-adaptation preceded the run. A few minutes' adaptation to the higher brightness levels was necessary before steady values could be obtained.

The results obtained when the test stimulus and central field had the same wave-length are plotted in figs. 24–27. For $\lambda = \mu = 580$ mμ, p_λ remains practically constant at all brightness levels. For the other wave-lengths there is some variation in p_λ which can be followed despite the scatter of the experimental points. The curves relating $\log_{10} U_\lambda$ and $\log_{10} W_\mu$ for wave-lengths 500, 580 and 690 mμ are of nearly the same shape, that is to say, they can be obtained by moving a single curve without rotation to different positions with respect to the axes. The curves for the wave-length 430 mμ, however, show a significant difference in shape from the others. Thus even in the restricted case when test stimulus and central field have the same wave-length, the notion of a curve of fixed shape which is merely displaced to different positions with respect to the axes breaks down.

Figs. 28–35 give the results for eight combinations in which the wave-length of the test stimulus lies in the range 430 to 500 mμ while μ, the wave-length of the central field, is considerably greater than λ and lies in the range 500 to 590 mμ. For every combination except $\lambda = 430$, $\mu = 500$, the curves of $\log_{10} U_\lambda$ against $\log_{10} W_\mu$ show a "change of law" of the kind already met with for parafoveal vision, and p_λ shows a corresponding increase from an approximately constant value in a range of low brightnesses to an approximately constant but different value in a range of high brightnesses.

These features of the results can be explained by assuming that there are two types of cone in operation, each with distinctive properties. In fig. 31a* (p. 95), for example, we assume that the left-hand section of curve I, extrapolated as a broken line to higher values of $\log_{10} W_\mu$, is the curve connecting $\log_{10} U_\lambda$ with $\log_{10} W_\mu$ which would be obtained if cones of one type (type X) were acting alone. Similarly we assume that the right-hand section of curve I, extrapolated as a dotted line, is the curve which would be obtained if cones of the other type (type B) were acting alone. These component curves will lead to the observed curve when both types are in action if the observed l.b.i. coincides approximately with the smaller of the l.b.i.'s of the two types except where these have equal or nearly equal values.

Curve II is obtained by displacing the two component curves of curve I without rotation in a direction parallel to the axis of $\log_{10} U_\lambda$. The component curve of type B must be displaced by a greater amount than that of type X. This connexion between curves I and II is explained if the directional sensitivity of each type of cone is independent of brightness level and type B has a greater directional sensitivity than type X.

A similar explanation may be given of the results for the other combinations in this group if we admit that as λ decreases the vertical separation of the X and B component curves diminishes until for $\lambda = 430$ mμ (fig. 35) the X curve lies above the B curve at all values of $\log_{10} W_\mu$ and plays little if any part in determining the resultant curve. For $\lambda = 490$, $\mu = 590$ (fig. 29), curves I and II show a new feature. The B component curves become suddenly horizontal at $\log_{10} W_\mu = 1\cdot1$ approx. There is an indication of a similar effect for the combination $\lambda = 500$, $\mu = 580$ (fig. 28). This effect might be attributed to a third type of cone but as shown below such an explanation is unlikely. It appears instead that for certain wave-lengths μ, the conditioning effect of the central field on the B cones is limited, that is to say, however great the intensity of the central field it cannot increase the l.b.i. of the B cones above a certain value.

Setting aside the anomaly just noted, it is found that those sections of the experimental curves which are identified with the X or B component curves can all be fitted approximately with a curve of fixed shape (curve 2

* The experimental data in this figure are the same as in fig. 31.

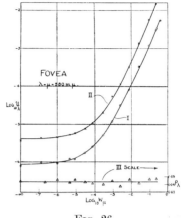

FIG. 24

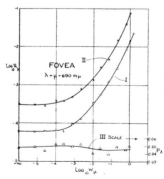

FIG. 26

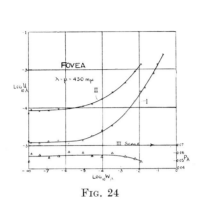

FIG. 25

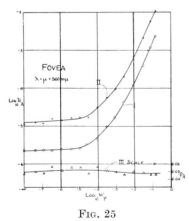

FIG. 27

FIGS. 24–27. Key as for figs. 14–16.

of fig. 36) which is moved (without rotation) to different positions with respect to the axes.

A series of twenty-one runs was then made with a test stimulus of wave-length 480 mμ and with central fields of wave-lengths ranging from 430 to 700 mμ. The l.b.i. was determined only for central entry of the test stimulus. The rays forming the central field entered the eye through the same point as the rays forming the test stimulus. Some of the results obtained are plotted in fig. 37. The vertical scale of fig. 37 is correct for all the data, but the horizontal scale is correct only for $\mu = 700$ mμ. For other values of μ the origin of the horizontal scale has been shifted by arbitrary amounts to give a convenient spacing of the curves. For all wave-lengths of the central field except 430 and 480 mμ, the experimental results can be represented approximately by the two curves shown, which are reproductions of curve 2 of fig. 36. Moreover, the upper of the two curves, which is associated with the B cones, flattens out at approximately the same value of $\log_{10}U_\lambda$ ($\bar{5}\cdot5$) for all values of μ. The lower curves, which are associated with the X cones, also flatten out at a common value, about $\bar{6}\cdot8$ in this case. This is to be expected, however, since with a central field of zero intensity ($\log_{10}W_\mu = -\infty$), $\log_{10}U_\lambda$ must be the same whatever the value of μ.* The horizontal separation of the B and X curves decreases as μ decreases below about 560 mμ until at $\mu = 480$ mμ the two curves no longer intersect and the results are represented by the X curve only. The limited conditioning of the B cones at high brightnesses is in evidence for $\mu = 580$ and 610 mμ, but not for $\mu = 560$ mμ or less. It is not observable for $\mu = 640$ or 700 mμ, but this may be because the brightness of the central field could not be made sufficiently high for these wave-lengths.

A selection from a similar set of nineteen runs with $\lambda = 430$ mμ and with μ varying from 640 to 410 mμ is shown in fig. 38. For μ greater than 460 mμ a single curve of the form of curve 2, fig. 36, can be drawn to represent the results apart from the limited conditioning effect which occurs for $\mu = 580$ and 620 mμ. For μ equal to 460 mμ or less two curves of the standard shape are required as shown. The two curves intersect before the upper curve has flattened out, but since the shape of the curves is fixed it can still be deduced that the upper curve would flatten out to about the same value of $\log_{10}\mu_\lambda$ ($\bar{5}\cdot5$) in each case.

In a third series of eleven runs, the wave-length of the central field was equal to 600 mμ in every case and the wave-length of the test stimulus was varied from 410 to 510 mμ (fig. 39). In the figure, the horizontal scale is correct for all combinations λ, μ. The vertical scale is correct only for

---

* Apart from day-to-day variations in the sensitivity of the eye.

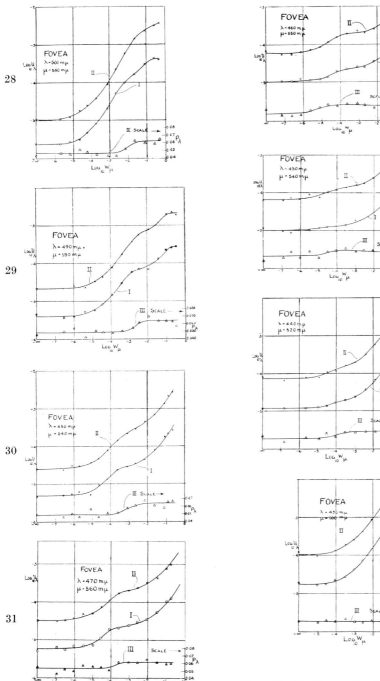

FIGS. 28–35. Key as for figs. 14–16.

$\lambda = 510$, $\mu = 600$ and is displaced by arbitrary amounts for the other cases. For $\lambda = 510$, $\mu = 600$, the upper and lower curves are associated with the B and X cones respectively. As λ decreases, the component curves maintain their positions with respect to the horizontal axis but they are displaced by different amounts parallel to the vertical axis. For $\lambda = 410$ and 430 mμ, the results are represented approximately by the B curve only. In every case the B curve becomes abruptly horizontal at $\log_{10} W_\mu = \bar{1}\cdot2$ approx. Thus, whatever the wave-length of the test stimulus, a central field of wave-length 600 mμ has a limited conditioning effect on the B cones and can raise the l.b.i. of the B cones to about $4\cdot3$ times the value for zero field but no more. Taking account of all the data obtained, it appears probable that the same thing is true for a central field of any wave-length exceeding 570 mμ although insufficient intensity of the central field prevents our observing the effect for $\mu = 640$ mμ or more.

The above results show that the l.b.i. of the B cones acting alone $(U_\lambda)_b$ can be represented approximately by the following expression, which is similar to that used for the rods,

$$1/(U_\lambda)_b = b_\lambda \, \xi\{\overline{W_\mu B_\mu}\} \, 10^{-p_{\lambda b}(d-d_m)^2}, \tag{5}$$

where b_λ is independent of μ and equals the reciprocal of the l.b.i. of the B
    cones when the central field has zero energy,

$\quad$ B_μ is independent of λ and equals the reciprocal of the energy of
    the central field necessary to raise the l.b.i. of the B cones to ten
    times the value for zero field,

$\quad$ $\xi(x)$ is a fixed function of x. Curve 2 of fig. 36 gives a plot of
    $\{-\log_{10}\xi(x)\}$ against $\log_{10}x$,

$\quad$ $p_{\lambda b}$ determines the directional sensitivity of the B cones for a test
    stimulus of wave-length λ.

For wave-lengths of the central field greater than 570 mμ, the modified form of $\xi(x)$ shown as curve 3 in fig. 36 must be used to allow for the limited conditioning effect obtained with these wave-lengths. In such cases B_μ is defined as "the reciprocal of the energy of the central field which would raise the l.b.i. of the B cones to ten times the value for zero field if the limited conditioning effect did not operate".

We may adopt an analogous expression for the l.b.i. of the X cones acting alone, $(U_\lambda)_x$. We put

$$1/(U_\lambda)_x = x_\lambda \, \xi\{\overline{W_\mu X_\mu}\} \, 10^{-p_{\lambda x}(d-d_m)^2}, \tag{6}$$

where x_λ, X_μ, $p_{\lambda x}$ are defined in precisely the same way as b_λ, B_μ and $p_{\lambda b}$

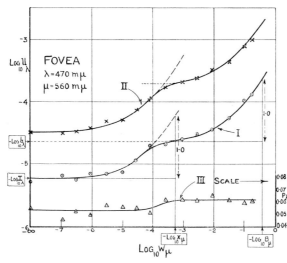

Fɪɢ. 31a

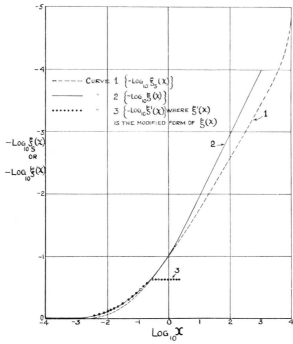

Fɪɢ. 36. The rod function $\xi_s(x)$, the cone function $\xi(x)$, and the modified cone function $\xi'(x)$ applicable to the blue cones when μ exceeds 570 mμ.

respectively. $\xi(x)$ is, to a sufficient approximation, the same function as for the B cones. No limited conditioning effect has been observed for the X cones.

From a curve such as curve I of fig. 31a where the X and B components are well defined the values of b_λ, B_μ, x_λ and X_μ are easily obtained in the way illustrated in the figure. For other cases the process is less certain. The mean results of all the determinations of b_λ, x_λ, B_μ and X_μ (for λ less than 520 mμ) are plotted in figs. 40 and 41. The curve of $\log_{10} b_\lambda$ against λ (curve 1, fig. 40) has a maximum at $\lambda = 440$ mμ approximately, which means that the B cones, or the blue cones as we may now call them, are most sensitive to test stimuli of wave-length 440 mμ. Owing to the limited conditioning effect the l.b.i. of the blue cones has a maximum value M_λ for central fields of wave-length μ greater than 570 mμ. Curve 2 of fig. 40 shows the observed variation of $\log_{10} 1/M_\lambda$ with λ. Curve 2 is obtainable from curve 1 by a simple vertical displacement. Thus, if what we have called the limited conditioning effect were due to a third type of cone, the relative spectral sensitivity to test stimuli of different wave-length would be the same as for the blue cones.

The curve of $\log_{10} B_\mu$ against μ (curve 1, fig. 41), shows that the conditioning effect of the central field on the blue cones is greatest for $\mu = 445$ mμ approx. The sensitivity curves of the blue cones to test stimuli of different wave-length (curve 1, fig. 40) and to central fields of different wave-length (curve 1, fig. 41) appear to be slightly different in shape in the region of the spectrum (410–510 mμ) where both can be followed although the difference may be experimental error. As μ increases beyond 510 mμ the curve of $\log_{10} B_\mu$ descends steadily until at $\mu = 570$ mμ it swings round and becomes horizontal to descend again steadily for μ greater than 600 mμ. This change of form at $\mu = 570$ mμ may be connected with the limited conditioning effect of central fields for which μ exceeds 570 mμ. If the limiting conditioning effect were due to a third type of cone, the appropriate sensitivity curve to central fields of different wave-length would have to exhibit something like a discontinuity in the neighbourhood of $\mu = 570$ mμ. The simpler view and the one adopted here is that we are dealing with a special property of the blue cones.

We are naturally led to consider whether two types of cone are sufficient to explain all measurements of the present type. Fig. 39 shows that as λ increases the vertical separation of the B and X component curves increases until at $\lambda = 510$ mμ the B component is responsible only for the upper extremity of the experimental curve. We may anticipate that for still greater values of λ (540 mμ or more) the process will be continued and the

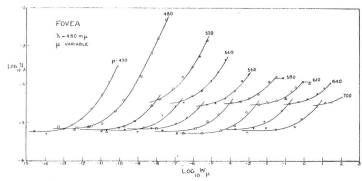

FIG. 37. Curves of $\log_{10} U_\lambda$ v. $\log_{10} W_\mu$ for $\lambda = 480$ mμ and different values of μ. (The curves are displaced by arbitrary amounts parallel to the axis of $\log_{10} W_\mu$ to give a convenient spacing.)

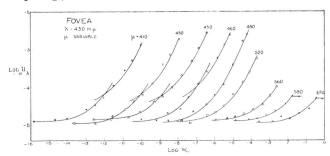

FIG. 38. Similar to fig. 37 but for $\lambda = 430$ mμ.

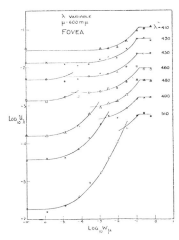

FIG. 39. Curves of $\log_{10} U_\lambda$ v. $\log_{10} W_\mu$ for $\mu = 650$ mμ and for different values of λ. (Curves displaced by arbitrary amounts parallel to the axis of $\log_{10} U_\lambda$ to give a convenient spacing.)

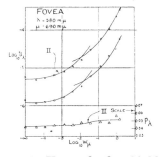

FIG. 42. Key as for figs. 14–16.

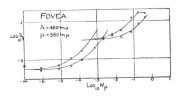

FIG. 43. For key see p. 100 of text.

experimental curve will consist simply of the X component.* Measurements show, however, that with test stimuli of wave-length greater than 540 mμ the relation between $\log_{10}U_\lambda$ and $\log_{10}W_\mu$ cannot be represented by the standard curve (curve 2, fig. 36) for all wave-lengths of the central field. In some cases, such as that shown in fig. 42, a change of law of the familiar kind is in evidence. Thus the X cone system is not a simple system. One possibility is that two cone systems, which we may call the green and red systems, are in operation, whose l.b.i.'s are represented by the expressions:

$$1/(U_\lambda)_g = g_\lambda\, \xi\{W_\mu G_\mu\}\, 10^{-p_{\lambda g}(d-d_m)^2}, \tag{7}$$

$$1/(U_\lambda)_r = r_\lambda\, \xi\{W_\mu R_\mu\}\, 10^{-p_{\lambda r}(d-d_m)^2}, \tag{8}$$

where $g_\lambda, G_\mu, p_{\lambda g}$ and r_λ, R_μ and $p_{\lambda r}$ have similar definitions to those given for b_λ, B_μ and $p_{\lambda b}$. The above expressions would then take the place of the single expression (6) for the X cones. Many more measurements will be required for the full working out of this view since it appears that the spectral sensitivities of the red and green systems do not differ so radically as do those of the blue and X systems. From the results so far obtained it is probable that for test stimuli of wave-length not greater than 510 mμ, the X component curve differs little from the curve of one of the two systems introduced above. Thus the values of $\log_{10}x_\lambda$ and $\log_{10}X_\mu$ plotted in figs. 40 and 41 may be identified with $\log_{10}g_\lambda$ and $\log_{10}G_\mu$ respectively. Using the data of fig. 42 and other similar data a first attempt can be made to construct the sensitivity curves of the green and red cones. The curves so obtained are shown as broken lines in figs. 40 and 41. In fig. 41, the three lower curves give the values obtained for $p_{\lambda b}$, $p_{\lambda g}$ and $p_{\lambda r}$ which measure the directional sensitivities of the blue, green and red cones. The difference between $p_{\lambda b}$ and $p_{\lambda g}$ for λ less than 500 mμ is well established. The crossing of the curves for $p_{\lambda g}$ and $p_{\lambda r}$ at $\lambda = 620$ mμ is less certain. In figs. 40 and 41 all curves or parts of curves shown by broken lines must be regarded as tentative only.

A striking difference in properties between the blue cones and the red or green cones is indicated if we compare the sensitivity to a test stimulus of given wave-length with the sensitivity to the conditioning effect of a central field of the same wave-length. This comparison may be made by taking the differences $\overline{\log_{10}b_\lambda - \log_{10}B_\mu}$, $\overline{\log_{10}g_\lambda - \log_{10}G_\mu}$ and $\overline{\log_{10}r_\lambda - \log_{10}R_\mu}$ for $\lambda = \mu$. $\overline{\log_{10}b_\lambda - \log_{10}B_\mu}$ is of the order of 2·0 whereas $\overline{\log_{10}g_\lambda - \log_{10}G_\mu}$

---

* This conclusion assumes that the sensitivity curves of the B and X components to test stimuli of different wave-length (curves 1 and 3 of fig. 40) will have approximately the same shape as the corresponding sensitivity curves to central fields of different wave-length (curves 1 and 2 of fig. 41) which can be followed throughout the spectrum.

and $\overline{\log_{10} r_\lambda - \log_{10} R_\mu}$ equal about 2·7 and 2·8 respectively. The meaning of this result is apparent if we note that the fixed function $\xi(x)$ approximates to $0\cdot11/x$ for sufficiently high values of x. Thus for central fields of sufficiently high brightness and for central entry of the test stimulus:

$$1/(U_\lambda)_b = b_\lambda \xi(\overline{W_\mu B_\mu}) = b_\lambda 0\cdot11/W_\mu B_\mu$$

or
$$\frac{(U_\lambda)_b}{W_\mu} = \frac{B_\mu}{0\cdot11 b_\lambda}. \tag{9}$$

Now when $\lambda = \mu$, $(U_\lambda)_b/W_\mu$ represents in a certain sense the Fechner fraction of the blue cones acting alone. Similarly, $(U_\lambda)_g/W_\mu = G_\mu/0\cdot11 g_\lambda$ and $(U_\lambda)_r/W_\mu = R_\mu/0\cdot11 r_\lambda$ represent respectively the Fechner fractions of the green and red systems acting alone. Thus the fact that $\overline{\log_{10} B_\mu - \log_{10} b_\lambda}$ or $\log_{10} B_\mu/b_\lambda$ exceeds $\overline{\log_{10} G_\mu - \log_{10} g_\lambda}$ or $\log_{10} G_\mu/g_\lambda$ by approximately $0\cdot7$ means that the *limiting Fechner fraction* of the blue cones at high brightnesses is about five times that of the green cones.

Reverting for a moment to the rods, Table II shows that for $\lambda = \mu$ $\overline{\log_{10} s_\lambda - \log_{10} S_\mu}$ equals about 1·0. Comparison with the cones is complicated by the difference in shape of the rod and cone functions (curves 1 and 2 of fig. 36). It can be deduced, however, that the Fechner fraction of the rods at high adapting brightnesses lies between 3 and 10 times the limiting Fechner fraction of the blue cones.

A brief reference must be made to the changes in the apparent colour of the test stimulus, when its intensity is just above the threshold, which are observed as the brightness of the central field is increased. In cases similar to that of fig. 31, there occurs a change in colour which corresponds broadly to the change in law of the experimental curve of $\log_{10} U_\lambda$ against $\log_{10} W_\mu$. In other cases where test stimulus and central field have the same wavelength, the test stimulus appears as a white flash.

9. CHANGE IN THE POINT OF ENTRY OF THE RAYS FORMING THE CENTRAL FIELD. FOVEAL VISION

When the rays forming the central field are sent into the eye near the periphery of the pupil instead of at or near the centre, measurements of the l.b.i. for different points of entry of the test stimulus give a curve of $\log_{10} U_\lambda$ against d of the same general shape as before. The main difference is that the absolute values of $\log_{10} U_\lambda$ are in general smaller for peripheral than for central entry of a central field of fixed energy. This means that the effectiveness of the central field in raising the l.b.i. above the value for zero field depends on the direction of incidence on the retina of the rays forming the central field. The magnitude of the directional effect for the central field is of the same order as that for the test stimulus. It is possible, however, that the curve of $\log_{10} U_\lambda$ against d may not be of quite the same shape for different points of entry of the central field. A difference was observed in one set of measurements, but has not yet been confirmed.

The two sets of data of fig. 43 show the variation of $\log_{10} U_\lambda$ with $\log_{10} W_\mu$ ($\lambda = 480$, $\mu = 580$) for a test stimulus entering at $d = +1$ (temp.) and for a central field entering at $+1$ (temp.) (circle points) or $-2\frac{3}{4}$ (nasal) (cross-points). To a first approximation each curve can be resolved into two component curves, corresponding to the blue and the green cones respectively, and the effect of changing the point of entry of the central field appears as a displacement of each component curve parallel to the axis of $\log_{10} W_\mu$. Similar results were obtained for the combination ($\lambda = 480$, $\mu = 600$). The horizontal displacement of each component curve determines the directional sensitivity of the corresponding type of cone to the conditioning effect of the central field just as the vertical separation of each component curve in fig. 31 determines the directional sensitivity to the test stimulus. It should be possible by this method to measure the directional sensitivity of the blue, green and red cones to the conditioning stimulation over the same range of values of μ for which B_μ, G_μ and R_μ can be determined (see fig. 41).

When the point of entry of the central field is allowed to vary the expressions given above for $1/(U_\lambda)_b$, $1/(U_\lambda)_g$ and $1/(U_\lambda)_r$ must be modified. As a tentative suggestion we may put

$$1/(U_\lambda)_b = b_\lambda \, 10^{-p\lambda b(d-d_m)^2} \xi\{W_\mu B_\mu 10^{-P_{\mu b}(d'-d_m)^2}\}, \tag{10}$$

and similar expressions for $1/(U_\lambda)_g$ and $1/(U_\lambda)_r$, where d' is the point of entry of the central field and $P_{\mu b}$ determines the directional sensitivity of the blue cones to a conditioning stimulation of wave-length μ. This form assumes that the curve of $\log_{10} U_\lambda$ against d has the same shape for all points of entry of the central field.

10. General discussion

Fig. 44 summarizes in a single diagram the connexion between the sensitivity and the condition of stimulation of the foveal retina to which we are led by the present work. We imagine that the eye views the $10°$ patch of

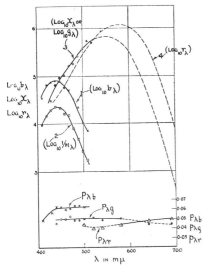

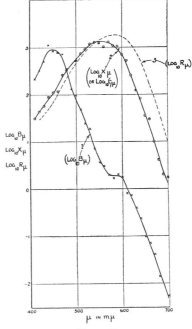

FIG. 40. Variation with λ of $\log_{10}b_\lambda$, $\log_{10}x_\lambda$ (or $\log_{10}g_\lambda$) $\log_{10}r_\lambda$, $\log_{10}(1/M_\lambda)$, $p_{\lambda b}$, $p_{\lambda g}$ and $p_{\lambda r}$.

FIG. 41

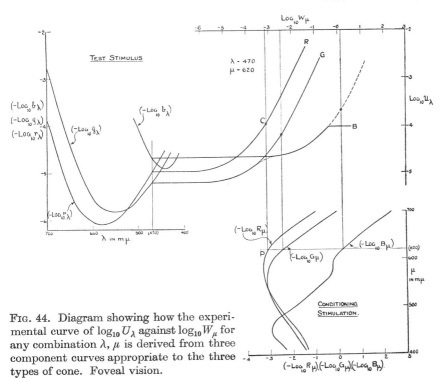

FIG. 44. Diagram showing how the experimental curve of $\log_{10}U_\lambda$ against $\log_{10}W_\mu$ for any combination λ, μ is derived from three component curves appropriate to the three types of cone. Foveal vision.

light of wave-length μ and energy W_μ and that we determine the l.b.i. U_λ, for a monochromatic test stimulus of wave-length λ at different energies W_μ from zero upwards. Our view is that there are three types of cone in operation, each one of which in the absence of the others would give a curve of $\log_{10} U_\lambda$ against $\log_{10} W_\mu$ similar in shape to curve 2 of fig. 36. In the top right-hand quadrant of fig. 44 the three curves R, G and B represent the variation of $\log_{10} U_\lambda$ with $\log_{10} W_\mu$ for the red, green and blue cones respectively, acting alone. The position of each curve with respect to the axes of $\log_{10} U_\lambda$ and $\log_{10} W_\mu$ is determined by the wave-lengths λ and μ. When W_μ becomes very small and $\log_{10} W_\mu$ tends to minus infinity, each of the three curves flattens out and $\log_{10} U_\lambda$ becomes constant. This constant value corresponds to the absolute threshold of the particular type of cone and depends only on the wave-length of the test stimulus. We have defined b_λ to be the reciprocal of the absolute threshold of the blue cones for a test stimulus of wave-length λ, so that curve B must flatten out to the value $\log_{10}(1/b_\lambda)$ or $\{-\log_{10} b_\lambda\}$. Similarly, curves R and G must flatten out to $\{-\log_{10} r_\lambda\}$ and $\{-\log_{10} g_\lambda\}$ respectively. In the top left-hand quadrant of fig. 44, $\{-\log_{10} b_\lambda\}$, $\{-\log_{10} g_\lambda\}$ and $\{-\log_{10}(r_\lambda)\}$ are plotted against λ, the vertical scale being precisely the same as the vertical scale of $\log_{10} U_\lambda$ on the other side of the diagram. The three curves are simply curves 1, 3 and 4 of fig. 40, turned upside down. Thus if we take a particular wave-length of the test stimulus, say $\lambda = 470$ mμ, then the vertical line through 470 on the axis of λ will intersect the curve of $\{-\log_{10} g_\lambda\}$ at the value to which curve G must flatten out when $\log_{10} W_\mu$ tends to minus infinity. The values at which curves R and B flatten out are similarly determined.

It remains to fix the position of curves R, G and B with respect to the axis of $\log_{10} W_\mu$. It will be recalled that R_μ, was defined as the reciprocal of the energy of the 10° patch necessary to raise the l.b.i. of the red cones to ten times their absolute threshold. That is to say, to cause such an increase the 10° patch must have energy W_μ such that

$$\log_{10} W_\mu = \log_{10}(1/R_\mu) = \{-\log_{10} R_\mu\}.$$

In the lower right-hand quadrant of fig. 44 $\{-\log_{10} R_\mu\}$ is plotted against μ, the horizontal scale being precisely the same as the horizontal scale of $\log_{10} W_\mu$ at the top of the figure. Thus if we take a particular wave-length of the 10° patch, say $\mu = 620$ mμ, the horizontal line through 620 on the axis of μ must intersect the curve of $\{-\log_{10} R_\mu\}$ at a point P whose coordinate on the scale of $\log_{10} W_\mu$ will be the value of $\log_{10} W_\mu$ necessary to raise the l.b.i. of the red cones to ten times their absolute threshold. The point on the curve R at which the l.b.i. is ten times the absolute threshold is marked with a dot C and the position of curve R is fixed by bringing this dot to lie on the vertical line through P.

A similar procedure fixes the position of curves G and B except that for B if μ exceeds 570 mμ the curve must be modified to the form of curve 3 of fig. 36 after its position has been determined by the above method. This modification of curve B is necessary in the example illustrated in fig. 44.

It is clear that with the aid of the diagram of fig. 44 the three curves R, G and B can be drawn in for any wave-lengths of test stimulus and central field.

It has been tacitly assumed that both test stimulus and the conditioning stimulation enter at $d = d_m$. For other points of entry of the test stimulus the curves R, G and B must be shifted upwards parallel to the axis of $\log_{10} U_\lambda$ by amounts $p_{\lambda b}(d - d_m)^2$, $p_{\lambda g}(d - d_m)^2$ and $p_{\lambda r}(d - d_m)^2$ respectively. For other points of entry of the central field the component curves must be shifted to the right parallel to the axis of $\log_{10} W_\mu$ by amounts $P_{\mu b}(d' - d_m)^2$, $P_{\mu g}(d' - d_m)^2$ and $P_{\mu r}(d' - d_m)^2$.

The derivation of the resultant curve of $\log_{10} U_\lambda$ against $\log_{10} W_\mu$ for foveal vision now depends on a method for determining $\log_{10} U_\lambda$ at each value of $\log_{10} W_\mu$ from the values of $\log_{10}(U_\lambda)_b$, $\log_{10}(U_\lambda)_g$ and $\log_{10}(U_\lambda)_r$ given by curves B, G and R. We have been able to proceed without defining precisely how this is to be done by assuming that $\log_{10} U_\lambda$ will not exceed the smallest of $\log_{10}(U_\lambda)_b$, $\log_{10}(U_\lambda)_g$ and $\log_{10}(U_\lambda)_r$ and will be actually equal to it except when the smallest and the next smallest have about the same value. Further work on this point is necessary.

For parafoveal vision it has been shown that the rods give rise to a curve of $\log_{10} U_\lambda$ against $\log_{10} W_\mu$ which has the shape of curve 1 of fig. 36 and whose position with respect to the axes is fixed, in any given case, by the values of $\log_{10} s_\lambda$ and $\log_{10} S_\mu$. The relation between $\log_{10} U_\lambda$ and $\log_{10} W_\mu$ given by the parafoveal cones cannot be represented in this simple way. By assuming that the parafoveal cones, like the foveal cones, consist of three species, each with its own spectral sensitivities to test stimulus and conditioning stimulation, we can explain the parafoveal measurements. If the parafoveal and foveal cones had identical properties it would only be necessary to add the rod curve as a fourth component curve in fig. 44 and determine the resultant of the four component curves so obtained. When this is done the resultant curves for different combinations λ and μ reproduce the main features of the experimental curves for parafoveal vision, and show anomalies of the kind noted at the end of § 7. However, the agreement in the cone regions of the curves is not quantitative, and we must conclude that there are significant differences in the spectral sensitivities of the parafoveal and foveal cones of corresponding type. On the other hand, the shape of the individual cone component curves is probably the same for both parafovea and fovea. Thus, a tracing of curve 2 of fig. 36 can be fitted over the cone sections of curves I and II in fig. 19.

Evidence for the existence of three types of cone and a first crude determination of the unique set of spectral sensitivity curves for these types have been obtained in this investigation by a method completely independent of colour-matching measurements. The precise connexion between the three mechanisms demanded by colour-matching experiments and the three types of cone assumed here must be close but it remains to be elucidated.

The writer has much pleasure in acknowledging the assistance rendered by Mr Gordon-Smith and Mr Dew in carrying out the measurements described. His thanks are also due to Professor Hartridge for helpful criticism of the paper.

The work was carried out under the auspices of the Illumination Research Committee of the Department of Scientific and Industrial Research.

Summary

A light ray terminating on a given point of the retina has different visual effects depending on its direction of incidence on the retina. The direction of incidence can be varied by sending the ray into the eye through different points of the pupil opening. The primary object of this work was to determine the effect of direction of incidence on threshold sensitivity but the results obtained cover the wider problem of the dependence of threshold sensitivity on the condition of stimulation of the retina. The test stimulus was a patch of light of diameter $1°$ and of wave-length λ, exposed for a fraction of a second every few seconds. U_λ, the smallest perceptible intensity of the test stimulus, was measured in energy units, the sensitivity then being defined as $1/U_\lambda$. With parafoveal vision of the test stimulus by the dark-adapted eye it was found that direction of incidence had little effect on sensitivity when λ was less than $580 \, m\mu$ but a pronounced effect for longer wave-lengths. The dark-adapted fovea gave a pronounced directional effect at all wave-lengths.

The condition of the retina was modified by making the subject view a patch of light of diameter $10°$ (wave-length μ, and intensity W_μ) at whose centre the test stimulus was applied as an *additional* stimulus. For parafoveal vision, the directional effect showed a marked increase in passing from low to high intensities, and the curve connecting the threshold value U_λ and the intensity of the conditioning field W_μ showed a corresponding change of law. These two connected effects are attributed to a change from rod vision at low intensities to cone vision at high intensities, the rods and cones being assumed to have different directional properties. For foveal vision, which involves the cones only, somewhat similar effects were observed and are explained by assuming three types of cones for which the relative spectral sensitivities are roughly determined. Normally the threshold value increases proportionally with the intensity of the conditioning field at high intensities (Weber's Law) but a striking deviation from this rule was observed for a blue test stimulus on a red conditioning field. Increase in the intensity of the conditioning field beyond a certain value produced no corresponding increase in the threshold value. This result is ascribed to a special property of the "blue" cones. In the present investigation the hypothesis of three types of cone whose properties have been approximately determined has been developed from measurements which are completely independent of colour-matching data.

References

Abney and Watson 1916 *Philos. Trans.* A, **216**, 81.
Crawford 1937 *Proc. Roy. Soc.* B, **124**, 81.
Dziobek 1934 *Licht*, **4**, 150.
Goodeve 1936 *Proc. Roy. Soc.* A, **155**, 664.
Stiles 1937 *Proc. Roy. Soc.* B, **123**, 90.
Stiles and Crawford 1932 *Phys. Soc. Discussion on Vision*, p. 194.
— — 1933 *Proc. Roy. Soc.* B, **112**, 428.
— — 1934 *Proc. Roy. Soc.* B, **116**, 55.
Wright and Nelson 1934 *Proc. Phys. Soc.* **48**, 401.

Paper IV: Reprinted from the Proceedings of the Royal Society, Series B, Vol. 133, 1946.

Separation of the 'blue' and 'green' mechanisms of foveal vision by measurements of increment thresholds

By W. S. STILES, *The National Physical Laboratory*

(*Communicated by Sir John Parsons, F.R.S.—Received* 19 *July* 1945— *Read* 15 *November* 1945)

The curve relating the smallest perceptible intensity of a blue test stimulus with the intensity of an orange conditioning field against which it is viewed shows a characteristic division into low- and high-intensity components, indicating the operation of two mechanisms of cone vision at the fovea. The justification for calling these 'blue' and 'green' mechanisms is taken from an earlier investigation (Stiles 1939). While most subjects show this division clearly, for some the low-intensity component is masked by the intrusion of rod vision. The correctness of this view is established by measurements made while the eye is recovering from an intense light adaptation. The individual variations of the sensitivies of the 'green' and 'blue' mechanisms in twenty subjects are assessed. Further evidence is obtained of an anomalously low threshold for the 'blue' mechanisms at very high conditioning fields of orange light.

INTRODUCTION

The operation of three receptor mechanisms in rod-free foveal vision can be demonstrated, and some of their properties, e.g. their spectral sensitivity curves, can be determined to a first approximation by measurements of the liminal brightness increment (l.b.i.) under suitable conditions (Stiles 1939).* This conclusion rests mainly on measurements for one eye. A key feature of the results was the form of the curve relating the l.b.i. to the intensity of the conditioning stimulation for a test stimulus of short wave-length (below about 510 mμ) and a conditioning stimulation of long wave-length (above about 530 mμ). All such curves were found to show a 'change of law' enabling them to be represented as the resultant of two component curves, associated respectively with the 'green' and 'blue' cone

* This paper is referred to as I throughout.

mechanisms, the former coinciding with the experimental curve at low-conditioning intensities, the latter at high. This association is justified by the way the component curves are displaced with respect to the co-ordinate axes when the wavelengths of test stimulus and conditioning stimulation are independently changed. From the observed displacements it appeared that the low intensity component curve was attributable to a mechanism having maximum sensitivity at a wavelength of 540 mμ approx., and the high intensity component curve to one having maximum sensitivity at 445 mμ approx.

In the present work the variation of the l.b.i. with conditioning intensity has been determined with a blue test stimulus and an orange conditioning stimulation for a group of twenty subjects. The results show a high-intensity 'blue' component in every case and in about half the cases the low-intensity 'green' component appears much as in investigation I. For some subjects, however, abnormally low values of the l.b.i. are obtained at low-conditioning intensities, suggesting that rod vision is playing a part. To test this point, the recovery of the eye after adaptation to an intense white light was determined by measurements of the l.b.i. for the blue test stimulus on a dark background. The recovery curves for the subjects in question show the characteristic two stages which Hecht (1937) and others have found to be associated with retinal areas where both rod and cone mechanisms are operative. With the aid of these recovery curves, the 'green' component curves can be determined approximately for all subjects, with one doubtful case. While confirming strongly the conclusion that the 'green' and 'blue' cone mechanisms can be separated by measurements of the l.b.i., the results reveal considerable variations among individuals both in the absolute and the relative sensitivities of the two mechanisms. In I it was observed that at a sufficiently high intensity of an orange or red conditioning stimulation further increase produced no corresponding increase in the l.b.i. of the 'blue' cone mechanism. From the present results it appears that this limited conditioning effect of orange or red light on the 'blue' mechanism occurs for most subjects.

By measurements of the l.b.i. with a different choice of colours for the test and conditioning stimuli, the 'green' and 'red' mechanisms can also be separated, although with more difficulty (I). Under the conditions of the present work, the 'red' mechanism is not in evidence and need not be referred to again.

2. Experimental details

The subject applied his eye to an artificial pupil and saw a circular patch of orange light of diameter 18° (the conditioning stimulation), containing at its centre four black fixation dots defining a square of 2° side (figure 1 a). The test stimulus, a square patch of blue light of 1° side, was superposed on the orange background at the centre of the fixation square in flashes of 0·2 sec. once in every 1·4 sec. Its intensity was variable by the subject. The latter fixated carefully at the centre of the four black dots, and *after several minutes' adaptation to the orange field* adjusted the test stimulus to be on the limit of visibility. Four or more settings were made. The intensity of the conditioning stimulation was then raised and the process repeated. For the special case of zero conditioning intensity, the dark fixation dots could not be seen and were replaced by four feeble points of orange light. A complete set of observations at 12 intensities from zero upwards occupied about 2 hr., including a preliminary period of about 20 min. dark adaptation.

The lay-out of the apparatus and its mode of operation are made clear by figure 1*b* and the following key:

E Artificial pupil of diameter 2·7 mm.

S_1 500 W opal lamp run at a colour temperature of approximately 2700° K.

X Sheet of plain glass carrying four opaque spots of white paint which appeared as black dots when silhouetted against S_1. When S_1 was extinguished, the spots were faintly illuminated by a small lamp placed above the filters F_O, F_N (not shown).

F_O, F_N Chance's light orange glass and gelatine neutral filters (as required).

C Composite glass cube of 3 cm. side with half-reflecting diagonal surface.

L_1 Lens imaging the fixation points and diaphragm D at infinity: power to suit subject's refractive error, 4 D for emmetropic eye.

S_2 Ribbon filament lamp run at colour temperature of approximately 2450° K.

L_2, L_3 Lenses of power 6·5 and 4 D respectively giving a real image of S_2 on diaphragm D.

F_B, F_N Ilford's spectrum blue and gelatine neutral filter (if required).

H Rotating sector passing the light from S_2 for 0·2 sec. in every 1·4 sec.

W_x, W_y Opposed neutral wedges for varying continuously the intensity of the test stimulus.

D Diaphragm containing a square aperture covered by the image of S_2.

(The screening of the apparatus is not shown.)

The approximate relative energy distributions E_λ of the lights used for test and conditioning stimuli are plotted in figure 1*c*. Their colours approximate to those of monochromatic lights of wave-lengths 470 and 615 mμ respectively.

For tests on the recovery of the eye, a rectangular panel (5 × 12·5 cm.) of diffusing glass illuminated to a brightness of 770 candles/ft.² (white light) was mounted by the side of the main apparatus. The subject stared at this panel with both eyes from a distance of about 8 cm. for 10 min. At a given moment the panel illumination was extinguished and the subject quickly transferred his eye to the aperture E and signalled as soon as the test stimulus, set at a suitable intensity, became visible. The test stimulus intensity was then considerably reduced, by the experimenter, and again the subject signalled when he could just see it, and so on. In the later stage of the recovery process the subject himself made settings to the liminal intensity. Throughout, lamp S_1 was kept extinguished so that the test stimulus appeared on a field of zero intensity.

The simpler apparatus and technique, compared with those used in I, were adopted mainly to make the tests less tiresome for the subject and to reduce the

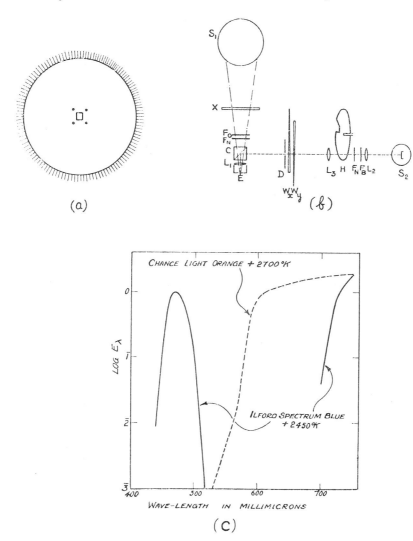

FIGURE 1

call on his time. The use of colour filters and non-Maxwellian view gives a 'cleaner' conditioning field than before, but, setting by the subject, the use of a material artificial pupil and the abandonment of the dental impression method for fixing the subject's head make for less satisfactory measurements. Details of the subjects are given in table 1.

TABLE 1

subject	sex	age	eye used in measurements	colour vision (normal unless otherwise indicated)
A	M.	43	left	—
B	F.	24	right	—
C	M.	53	right	—
D	M.	38	right	—
E	M.	37	left	—
F	M.	53	right	—
G	M.	38	right	—
H	M.	43	left	—
I	M.	33	left	—
J	F.	39	right	—
K	M.	34	right	deuteranomalous
L	M.	38	left	—
M	F.	18	right	—
N	M.	35	left	—
O	M.	50	right	—
P	M.	38	right	protanope
Q	F.	17	left	—
R	M.	46	right	—
S	F.	17	left	—
T	M.	23	right	—

3. Curves showing the variation of the liminal brightness increment with the conditioning intensity

The circle points of figure 2 show the observed variation of the l.b.i. with conditioning intensity for the writer's left eye. The cross-points are observations for this eye obtained in I* and refer to monochromatic test and conditioning stimuli of nearly the same colours as the present filtered lights. The two-component form is clearly shown by both sets of points, and the positions of the component curves along the axis of abscissae are in satisfactory agreement. Their positions along the ordinate axis would not be expected to agree precisely for three reasons:

(i) the exposure time of the test stimulus has been increased (0·063–0·2 sec.);

(ii) the effective wave-length of the test stimulus is slightly shorter (480–470 mμ approx.);

(iii) the 'subject-setting' method gives slightly higher values for the l.b.i. than the 50 % probability method used in I (difference estimated at about 0·1 or 0·15 log unit).

The quantitative effects of (i) and (ii) can be estimated approximately, (i) from the Blondel-Rey law (1911), (ii) from the shapes of the spectral sensitivity curves of

---

* The l.b.i. U_λ and conditioning stimulation W_μ were then expressed in energy units but have been converted to photons by multiplying by $2\cdot18 \times 10^5 V_{480}$ and $2\cdot18 \times 10^5 V_{610}$ respectively, where V_λ is the C.I.E. relative visibility function. The photon is a unit of retinal stimulation: 1 photon is equivalent to 1 candle/m.² or 0·093 candle/ft.² seen through an artificial pupil of area 1 sq.mm.

the 'blue' and 'green' mechanisms. Including the effect of (iii), the circle points would be expected to fall below the cross-points by about 0·2 log unit ('green' component) and 0·3 log unit ('blue' component). Thus the agreement here is also very satisfactory.

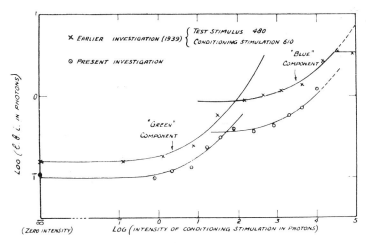

FIGURE 2. Observations for left eye of subject A (W.S.S.).

The (l.b.i./conditioning intensity) curves for the remaining nineteen subjects fall into three groups:

(*a*) those which can be represented as *the resultant* of two component curves (circle points of figure 3);*

(*b*) those like (*a*), except that at zero intensity the l.b.i. is abnormally low (circle points of figure 4);*

(*c*) those with abnormally low l.b.i. values at several of the low intensities (circle points of figure 5).*

By *the resultant* is to be understood a curve whose value at each intensity is equal, at least to a first approximation, to the lesser of the values of the two component curves.

For several subjects in each group the l.b.i. is anomalously low at one or two of the highest conditioning intensities. The discussion of this feature of the results is postponed to § 5.

The low values of the l.b.i. obtained at low intensities in groups (*b*) and (*c*) are almost certainly caused by the intrusion of rod vision. From the measurements of the recovery curve of the eye given below an approximate estimate of the l.b.i. of true cone vision at zero intensity can be made, and the values obtained are plotted as the square points in figures 4 and 5. Observations of the l.b.i. falling materially below the square-point value are to be attributed to rod response, and

* In figures 3–5 the scale of ordinates is correct for the top curve but must be shifted down 1 log unit for the second curve, 2 for the third, and so on.

if such observations are excluded the results for the subjects in groups (*b*) and (*c*) can be represented by two component curves as shown. In figure 5 the excluded points may be regarded as forming a third, *rod component* curve.

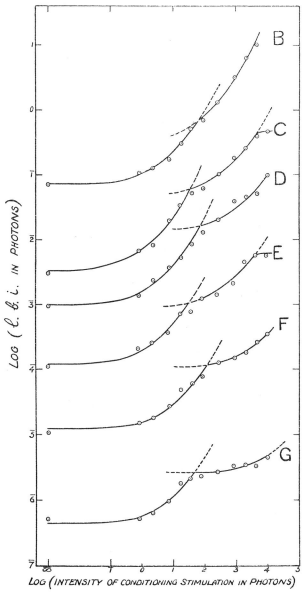

FIGURE 3. Observations for subjects in group (*a*).

All the cone component curves drawn in figures 2–5 are obtained from a curve of fixed shape which is displaced (without rotation) to different positions in the diagram to give for each subject the best fit with the experimental points in the high- or the low-intensity range. The basic curve of fixed shape is the one derived in I for the writer's left eye ($-\log \xi(x)$ v. $\log x$, shown as curve 2 in figure 36 of I). On the whole this shape, when applied to the present measurements, is satisfactory for all subjects, but because of the comparatively short range of points on each

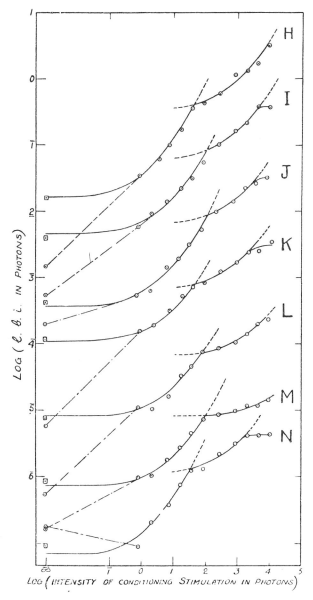

FIGURE 4. Observations for subjects in group (*b*).

component the test is not a critical one. However, the results are consistent with the view that the curve relating the l.b.i. of cone vision to the conditioning intensity is the resultant of two component curves of similar shape, the same for all subjects, whose positions relative to the co-ordinate axes vary considerably from one subject to another. It is apparent from figures 3–5 that the changes of position are in general different for the two components, i.e. the *resultant curve* is not displaced bodily without change of shape.

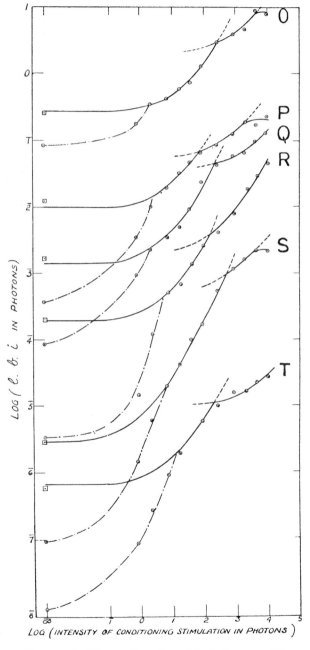

FIGURE 5. Observations for subjects in group (*c*).

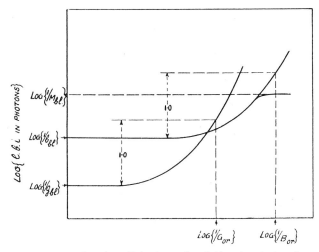

log {conditioning stimulation in photons}

FIGURE 6. Derivation of the sensitivities of the mechanisms.

TABLE 2. SENSITIVITIES OF THE 'BLUE' AND 'GREEN'
MECHANISMS FOR TWENTY SUBJECTS

(Expressed in reciprocal photons)

subject	log g_{bl}	log G_{or}	log (G_{or}/g_{bl})	log b_{bl}	log B_{or}	log (B_{or}/b_{bl})	log M_{bl}	log (b_{bl}/M_{bl})
A	1·06	$\bar{3}$·73	$\bar{4}$·67	0·41	$\bar{5}$·08	$\bar{6}$·67	—	—
B	1·12	$\bar{2}$·16	$\bar{3}$·04	0·44	$\bar{4}$·95	$\bar{4}$·51	—	—
C	1·36	$\bar{2}$·59	$\bar{3}$·23	0·29	$\bar{4}$·30	$\bar{4}$·01	$\bar{1}$·32	0·97
D	1·03	$\bar{2}$·45	$\bar{3}$·42	$\bar{1}$·84	$\bar{5}$·84	$\bar{4}$·00	—	—
E	0·88	$\bar{2}$·40	$\bar{3}$·52	0·08	$\bar{4}$·30	$\bar{4}$·22	$\bar{1}$·25	0·83
F	0·92	$\bar{2}$·00	$\bar{3}$·08	$\bar{1}$·92	$\bar{5}$·16	$\bar{5}$·24	—	—
G	1·34	$\bar{2}$·00	$\bar{4}$·66	0·61	$\bar{6}$·67	$\bar{6}$·06	—	—
H	1·78	$\bar{2}$·86	$\bar{3}$·08	0·45	$\bar{4}$·08	$\bar{5}$·63	—	—
I	1·36	$\bar{2}$·37	$\bar{3}$·01	0·16	$\bar{5}$·97	$\bar{5}$·81	$\bar{1}$·40	0·76
J	1·45	$\bar{2}$·42	$\bar{4}$·97	0·15	$\bar{5}$·86	$\bar{5}$·71	$\bar{1}$·50	0·65
K	0·93	$\bar{2}$·18	$\bar{3}$·25	0·13	$\bar{5}$·93	$\bar{5}$·80	$\bar{1}$·50	0·63
L	1·11	$\bar{2}$·15	$\bar{3}$·04	0·13	$\bar{5}$·41	$\bar{5}$·28	—	—
M	1·20	$\bar{2}$·14	$\bar{4}$·94	0·06	$\bar{6}$·70	$\bar{6}$·64	—	—
N	1·09	$\bar{2}$·74	$\bar{3}$·65	$\bar{1}$·99	$\bar{4}$·40	$\bar{4}$·41	$\bar{1}$·36	0·63
O	0·56	$\bar{3}$·82	$\bar{3}$·26	$\bar{1}$·64	$\bar{5}$·65	$\bar{4}$·01	$\bar{1}$·05	0·59
P	1·04	$\bar{2}$·01	$\bar{4}$·97	0·21	$\bar{5}$·93	$\bar{5}$·72	$\bar{1}$·68	0·53
Q	0·87	$\bar{2}$·28	$\bar{3}$·41	$\bar{1}$·40	$\bar{5}$·26	$\bar{5}$·86	—	—
R	0·72	$\bar{2}$·25	$\bar{3}$·53	$\bar{1}$·67	$\bar{4}$·50	$\bar{5}$·83	—	—
S	1·53	$\bar{2}$·92	$\bar{3}$·39	$\bar{1}$·29	$\bar{5}$·95	$\bar{4}$·66	$\bar{2}$·63	0·66
T	1·22	$\bar{2}$·08	$\bar{4}$·86	$\bar{1}$·97	$\bar{5}$·13	$\bar{5}$·16	—	—

g_{bl} = sensitivity of the 'green' mechanism to the blue test stimulus.
b_{bl} = sensitivity of the 'blue' mechanism to the blue test stimulus.
G_{or} = sensitivity of the 'green' mechanism to the orange conditioning stimulation.
B_{or} = sensitivity of the 'blue' mechanism to the orange conditioning stimulation.
M_{bl} = sensitivity of the 'blue' mechanism to the blue test stimulus when the conditioning
    stimulation has produced its maximum effect.

According to I, the high- and low-intensity components are respectively the l.b.i. curves which would be obtained if the 'blue' and 'green' cone mechanisms acted alone. Thus differences in position of the component curves are to be interpreted as differences in the sensitivities of these mechanisms. Sensitivity of a mechanism to the test stimulus is defined as the reciprocal of the l.b.i. at zero conditioning stimulation, and sensitivity to the conditioning stimulation as the reciprocal of the intensity of the latter required to raise the l.b.i. to ten times its value at zero intensity. The derivation of these sensitivities for the green and blue mechanisms from the positions of the corresponding component curves is made clear by figure 6 and the values obtained for the twenty subjects are set out in table 2.

4. RESULTS: RECOVERY CURVES

If the intrusion of rod vision is responsible for very low values of the l.b.i. at low intensities, we should not expect these low values to be reached rapidly after the eye has been exposed to a high brightness because of the known slow recovery (dark-adaptation) of the rod mechanism. The recovery curves for subjects Q and I belonging to groups (c) and (b) respectively, are reproduced on the left in figures 7 and 8, and indicate that a time of the order of 20 min. is required before the l.b.i. value previously observed at zero intensity is reached. Moreover, the curves show an initial cone phase and a later rod phase and the final l.b.i. of true cone vision is clearly defined. These final cone values are transferred as the square points in the (l.b.i./conditioning intensity) curves shown on the right in the same figures. The recovery curves for the extreme types in group (a) (subjects B and G) show the more rapid single phase recovery curve appropriate to pure cone vision (figure 9).

The recovery curves for the remaining subjects were in general similar to those just discussed although in one or two cases (particularly for subject S), the cone to rod transition is less marked and the uncertainty in fixing the true cone l.b.i. at zero intensity is greater.

There are three reasons which could account for the intrusion of rod vision for some subjects:

(i) their foveas may contain rods or, at the least, the rod-free area may be smaller than the 1° square test stimulus;

(ii) they may have failed to maintain strict foveal fixation;

(iii) foveal fixation as normally understood may have been maintained but their rod-free areas may be displaced.

As regards (i), Abney & Watson (1916) found that three out of eight subjects showed characteristic rod properties at the fovea (test light, diam. 34 min.) and were emphatic that fixation errors were not responsible. In the present measurements, cause (ii) was certainly operating for some subjects. With the blue test stimulus used the ratio of rod to cone sensitivities reaches its highest value and every one had difficulty in fixating at zero conditioning stimulation. Subjects K

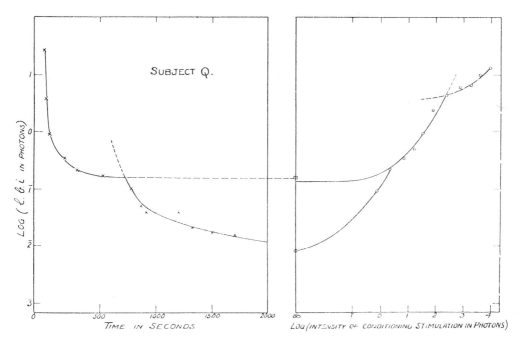

FIGURE 7. Recovery curve and (l.b.i./intensity level) curve.

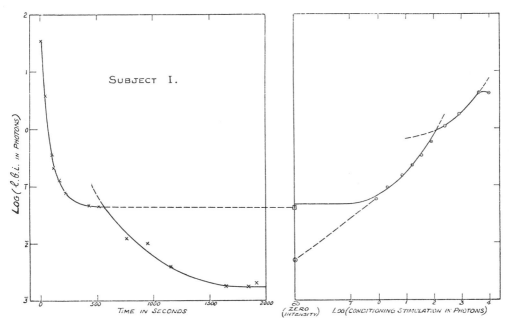

FIGURE 8. Recovery curve and (l.b.i./intensity level) curve.

and O gave single phase recovery curves and did not repeat the abnormally low values of the l.b.i. at low intensities, obtained in the original (l.b.i./conditioning intensity) runs. On the other hand, one subject (N) gave a well-defined two-phase recovery curve, reaching lower values of the l.b.i. in the rod phase than had been obtained previously under steady conditions at zero intensity. These differences are attributable to varying success in maintaining fixation on different occasions.

Cause (iii) is certainly operative for one subject T for whose retina, it is known from other work, a rod-free response at low intensities can be obtained if the direction of fixation is about $\frac{1}{2}°$ to the left of the test stimulus.

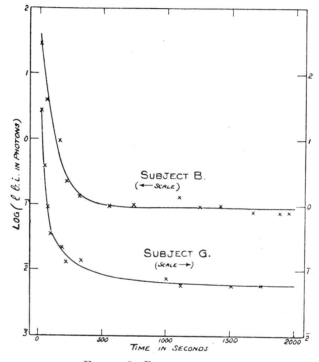

FIGURE 9. Recovery curves.

5. LIMITED CONDITIONING EFFECT OF RED LIGHT ON THE 'BLUE' CONE MECHANISM

In figure 2, upper curve, the l.b.i. for the highest conditioning intensity is about 0·3 log unit below the value expected from the 'blue' component curve. This is not just a bad observation but an example of an effect consistently observed in I, that as the intensity of an orange or red conditioning stimulation was increased it raised the l.b.i. of the 'blue' mechanism in the normal way to a certain value and thereafter produced no further increase. For green or blue conditioning stimulations this did not occur. The intensity available in the present apparatus was insufficient to reach the range of constant l.b.i. for the writer's eye (see lower curve of figure 2), but for several other subjects it appears to have been reached. Most of the observed l.b.i. values belonging to the high-intensity range in figures 2–5 differ from the 'blue' component curve as drawn by less than 0·1 log unit. Suppose the results of a particular subject are accepted as showing a limited conditioning effect if the observed l.b.i. at the highest intensity lies below the 'blue' component curve as drawn by 0·2 log unit or more. On this basis nine subjects show it, the effect being most marked for subject N. From the results for these cases, estimates have been made of M_{bl}, the reciprocal of the upper limiting value of the l.b.i. of the 'blue' mechanism (see figure 6). The log of this quantity and of the ratio b_{bl}/M_{bl} are given in table 2. Log (b_{bl}/M_{bl}) takes values ranging from 0·53 to 0·97 with an average of 0·69 compared with the value 0·63 obtained in I as the mean from many curves for the writer's left eye.

It appears therefore that limited conditioning sets in when the conditioning stimulation is sufficient to raise the log (l.b.i.) of the 'blue' mechanism by about 0·7 log unit. From the shape of the standard component curve it is readily determined that if L and N are the conditioning intensities required to raise the l.b.i. of the 'blue' mechanism by 1·0 and 0·7 respectively, then $\log N = \log L - 0.45$. We should not expect to observe limited conditioning if $\log N$ exceeds 4·00, the log of the maximum conditioning intensity used in the measurements. But by definition $\log B_{or} = \log (1/L) = -\log L$, so that $\log N > 4.00$ is equivalent to $\log B_{or} < \bar{5}\cdot55$. From the values of $\log B_{or}$ given in table 2, it is seen that none of the subjects for whom $\log B_{or} < \bar{5}\cdot55$ shows limited conditioning in the present tests, although two (A and K) are known from other work to show it at higher intensities. Of the thirteen subjects for whom $\log B_{or} > \bar{5}\cdot55$, nine show the effect. In sum, therefore, $9+2 = 11$ subjects out of $13+2 = 15$ are known to show limited conditioning (about 3 in 4), while the remaining five subjects would not be expected to show it in the present measurements.

The anomalously low l.b.i. values at high intensities are regarded as a special property of the 'blue' mechanism and not as the initial part of the component curve of an additional mechanism. The reasons for this view are given in I.

6. INDIVIDUAL VARIATIONS IN THE SENSITIVITIES OF THE 'BLUE' AND 'GREEN' MECHANISMS

In figure 10 the sensitivity to the test stimulus is plotted against the sensitivity to the conditioning stimulation for each subject and for the two mechanisms. The total range of variation and the standard deviations of the log sensitivities have the following values:

	total range	standard deviation
$\log g_{bl}$	1·2	0·28
$\log G_{or}$	1·2	0·31
$\log b_{bl}$	1·3	0·34
$\log B_{or}$	2·3	0·60

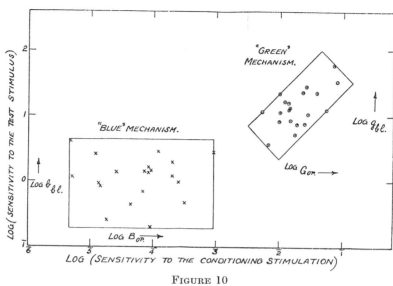

FIGURE 10

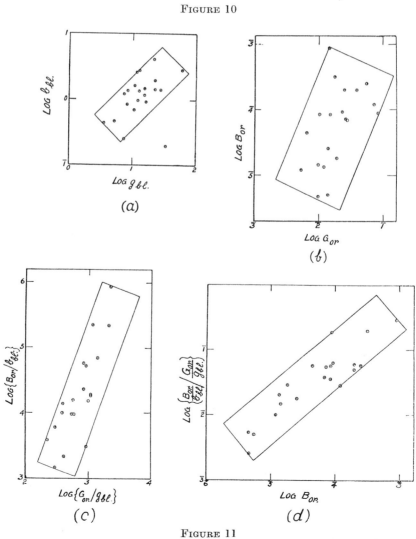

FIGURE 11

The spread arises in part from uncertainty in fitting the component curves to the observations, in part from a true individual variation which appears to be greatest for B_{or}. For the 'green' mechanism there is a weak correlation of the two sensitivities $\log g_{bl}$ and $\log G_{or}$ but for the 'blue' mechanism there is no correlation.

The following points are illustrated in figure 11:

(i) $\log b_{bl}$ v. $\log g_{bl}$. The sensitivities to the test stimulus tend to increase together and proportionally for the two mechanisms but subject S appears to be exceptional in this respect (figure 11a).

(ii) $\log B_{or}$ v. $\log G_{or}$. The sensitivities to the conditioning stimulation show a slight tendency to increase together but not proportionally (figure 11b).

(iii) $\log g_{bl}$ v. $\log B_{or}$ and $\log b_{bl}$ v. $\log G_{or}$. No correlation (not reproduced).

(iv) $\log (B_{or}/b_{bl})$ v. $\log (G_{or}/g_{bl})$. These log ratios tend to increase together but not proportionally (figure 11c).

(v) $\log \left\{ \dfrac{B_{or}}{b_{bl}} \Big/ \dfrac{G_{or}}{g_{bl}} \right\}$ tends to increase proportionally with $\log B_{or}$ (figure 11d) but shows no correlation with $\log b_{bl}$, $\log G_{or}$ or $\log g_{bl}$.

The quantity $\log \left\{ \dfrac{B_{or}}{b_{bl}} \Big/ \dfrac{G_{or}}{g_{bl}} \right\}$ is of some interest as for monochromatic test and conditioning stimuli it would remain unchanged if the subject made all his observations through a colour filter of arbitrary spectral transmission and this fact was ignored in working out the results so that the filter was treated as part of the eye. If such a colour filter had transmissions t_{or} and t_{bl} for the orange and blue lights, it is clear that the observed sensitivities would become $B_{or}t_{or}$, $G_{or}t_{or}$, $b_{bl}t_{bl}$, $g_{bl}t_{bl}$, respectively, but we should have

$$\log \left\{ \frac{B_{or}t_{or}}{b_{bl}t_{bl}} \Big/ \frac{G_{or}t_{or}}{g_{bl}t_{bl}} \right\} = \log \left\{ \frac{B_{or}}{b_{bl}} \Big/ \frac{G_{or}}{g_{bl}} \right\}.$$

The effective widths of the spectrum bands corresponding to the present non-monochromatic stimuli are small and it may fairly be concluded from the wide variation of

$$\log \left\{ \frac{B_{or}}{b_{bl}} \Big/ \frac{G_{or}}{g_{bl}} \right\}$$

that individuals differ in a way which cannot be assimilated to selective absorption by a pigment layer.

The outstanding feature in the above correlations, which are not of course all independent, is the large and dominating variation of $\log B_{or}$, the sensitivity of the 'blue' mechanism to orange light.

7. Conclusions

1. Measurements of the liminal brightness increment show for all subjects the operation of two cone mechanisms ('green' and 'blue') in foveal vision.

2. For some subjects, rod vision intrudes at low intensities, but this difficulty can be dealt with by determining the cone l.b.i. before the rods have had time to recover from intense light adaptation.

3. Individual variations are most marked in the sensitivity of the 'blue' cone mechanism to orange light.

4. Most subjects give evidence of a limited conditioning effect of orange light on the 'blue' cone mechanism.

The work described above has been carried out as part of the research programme of the National Physical Laboratory and this paper is published by permission of the Director.

REFERENCES

Abney & Watson 1916 *Phil. Trans.* A, **216**, 91.
Blondel & Rey 1911 *J. Phys. Théor. Appl.* **1**, 530.
Hecht 1937 *Physiol. Rev.* **17**, 239.
Stiles 1939 *Proc. Roy. Soc.* B, **127**, 64.

Paper V: Reprinted from The Proceedings of the Physical Society, Vol. 58, 1946.

A MODIFIED HELMHOLTZ LINE-ELEMENT IN BRIGHTNESS-COLOUR SPACE

By W. S. STILES,

Teddington

MS. received 6 *July* 1945

ABSTRACT. Helmholtz, Schrödinger and others have considered the relation between the trichromatic coordinates, x, y, z and $x+\delta x$ $y+\delta y$, $z+\delta z$, of two juxtaposed light patches which can just be discriminated by the eye. The Helmholtz expression,

$$\left(\frac{\delta x}{a+x}\right)^2 + \left(\frac{\delta y}{b+y}\right)^2 + \left(\frac{\delta z}{c+z}\right)^2 = \text{const.} = \delta s^2,$$

is the most readily interpretable in terms of the trichromatic theory, but to explain the observed variation of the hue limen through the spectrum it demands double-peak fundamental response curves which are at variance with other evidence. It also leads to a step-by-step visibility curve of wrong shape. The difficulties mentioned are removed by introducing different constant factors in the three terms. Such a modification is indicated independently by recent measurements of the liminal brightness increment, from which appropriate values of the factors have been derived. The factor in each term is simply related to the limiting Fechner fraction of the corresponding trichromatic mechanism, i.e., the Fechner fraction $\Delta B/B$ which would be observed at sufficiently high brightnesses B if visual discrimination depended on that mechanism only. The modified expression for δs^2 is applied to the calculation of hue limens, the step-by-step visibility curve, the Fechner fraction curves, and the general colour limen at different points of the colour triangle. Certain main features of the experimental results are correctly reproduced, but discrepancies with Wright and MacAdam's measurements of general colour limens may indicate that the modified element ignores some factor which is operative in their experiments.

----

§1. INTRODUCTION

THE examination of the properties of the proposed line-element will be preceded by a brief comment on earlier work. It was Helmholtz (1891) who first attempted to express in mathematical form the condition for two juxtaposed light patches to be on the limit of discrimination by the eye. He suggested that any two just-distinguishable patches would have trichromatic co-ordinates x, y, z and $x+\delta x$, $y+\delta y$, $z+\delta z$ respectively, satisfying a relation of the form,

$$3\delta s^2 \equiv \left(\frac{\delta x}{a+x}\right)^2 + \left(\frac{\delta y}{b+y}\right)^2 + \left(\frac{\delta z}{c+z}\right)^2 = 3F^2, \qquad \ldots\ldots (1)^*$$

where a, b, c and F are constants. The trichromatic co-ordinates here are the actual quantities of a particular set of primaries required to match the light patch—not the actual quantities divided by their sum (the unit co-ordinates). It is customary to regard the quantity δs defined in (1) as the length of the line-element in a non-Euclidean space of co-ordinates x, y, z. In this so-called brightness-colour space, the points corresponding to any pair of just-distinguishable light patches are the same elementary distance F apart. If a change is made to a different set of primaries and the relation (1) is expressed in terms of the new co-ordinates of the light patches, the simple form of the relation is lost and it is no longer the case that each term depends on one co-ordinate only. Thus, if the original form is valid at all, it is valid for only one set of the infinitely many sets of primaries which would serve equally well for the statement of the results of colour-matching measurements. The Helmholtz line-element implies, in fact, a particular set of primaries which, on the usual physiological interpretation of the trichromatic theory, we should expect to be the fundamental set such that each primary stimulates one, and only one, of the cone mechanisms. The quantities of the fundamental primaries required to match a monochromatic patch of unit energy intensity define three functions of wave-length—the spectral *sensitivity curves* or *fundamental response curves* of the three mechanisms.

Helmholtz took König's measurements of the trichromatic co-ordinates of the spectrum colours and sought to express them in terms of a set of primaries for which the relation (1) would be valid. The test was that the values of the hue limen through the spectrum as derived from (1) should agree with the measurements of this quantity made by König and Dieterici (1884). Helmholtz actually used the simpler form,

$$3\delta s^2 \equiv \left(\frac{\delta x}{x}\right)^2 + \left(\frac{\delta y}{y}\right)^2 + \left(\frac{\delta z}{z}\right)^2 = 3F^2, \qquad \ldots\ldots (2)$$

which (1) reduces at sufficiently high intensities when a, b, c can be neglected compared with x, y, z respectively. He was able to find a set of primaries which

----

* The factor 3 is introduced so that F has a simple physical meaning, as explained below Relation (1) is sometimes referred to as *the threshold condition*.

satisfied this test fairly well. But the corresponding fundamental response curves (reproduced as figure 8 in Peddie's *Colour Vision*) each have two pronounced maxima and are quite unlike the *Grundempfindungen* proposed by König from a consideration of the properties of colour-blinds. Moreover, as Schrödinger (1920) pointed out, they lead to an impossible double-peak form for the step-by-step visibility curve (the curve showing the relative energies of neighbouring spectrum colours which appear equally bright).

Schrödinger raised a further objection to the Helmholtz line-element. Although the step-by-step visibility curve can be derived from the line-element and its associated fundamental response curves, some additional assumption is necessary to determine when the eye will judge as equally bright two juxtaposed patches which differ widely in colour. Schrödinger assumed that two patches would appear equally bright if any change in the intensity of one of them would increase the minimum number of just-perceptible steps needed to pass from one to the other. The minumum number for any two light patches A and B is proportional to the integral

$$\int_A^B ds$$

taken along the geodesic in b.c. space. Thus the assumption is that A will match B when the intensity of B is adjusted to make this integral a minimum. While mathematically attractive, this definition of equality of brightness is not very plausible from a physiological standpoint. Applied to the Helmholtz element, it makes brightness a non-additive property of lights, in conflict with Abney's law. Schrödinger proposed an alternative line-element,

$$\delta s^2 \equiv \frac{1}{\alpha x + \beta y + \gamma z}\left[\frac{\alpha \delta x^2}{x} + \frac{\beta \delta y^2}{y} + \frac{\gamma \delta z^2}{z}\right] = F^2, \qquad \ldots\ldots(3)$$

which, on his assumption, makes brightness proportional to $\alpha x + \beta y + \gamma z$ and, therefore, strictly additive. An adequate criticism of this line-element will not be attempted, but it appears to the writer inconsistent with the threshold measurements considered below.

Since Schrödinger's theoretical work, several investigators have determined by experiment sets of pairs of just-distinguishable patches on various lines and surfaces in b.c. space. Most of these measurements were made at fairly high intensities and were confined to a particular class of just-distinguishable pairs, namely, those in which the members of each pair appeared equally bright (colour-limen type *). The observations on which the modified line-element of this paper is based were of a rather different nature, and are best introduced by considering the application of the Helmholtz element to another ·special class of just-distinguishable pairs of patches (liminal-increment type).

§2. APPLICATION OF THE HELMHOLTZ LINE-ELEMENT TO PAIRS OF JUST-DISTINGUISHABLE PATCHES OF LIMINAL INCREMENT TYPE

A pair is of this type if the physical stimulus in one patch is obtained from that of the other by the *addition* of a further stimulus. Consider the special

* Measurements of the hue limen amd the minimum perceptible colorimetric purity (Priest and Brickwedde, 1926) are of this type, as well as the more general colour limens recently determined by Wright (1941).

case when one patch is monochromatic, of wave-length μ and energy intensity W_μ, while the other is a mixture of wave-lengths μ and λ (λ in general different from μ), of energy intensities W_μ and U_λ respectively. The threshold condition (1) takes the form,

$$\left[\frac{U_\lambda r_\lambda'}{a+W_\mu r_\mu'}\right]^2 + \left[\frac{U_\lambda g'}{b+W_\mu g_\mu'}\right]^2 + \left[\frac{U_\lambda b_\lambda'}{c+W b_\mu'}\right]^2 = 3F^2, \quad \ldots\ldots(4)$$

where r_λ', g_λ', b_λ' are the fundamental response functions of the x, y, z or "red", "green", "blue" mechanisms respectively. Equation (4) may be written

$$\left(\frac{1}{U_\lambda}\right)^2 = [r_\lambda \eta (R_\mu W_\mu)]^2 + [g_\lambda \eta (G_\mu W_\mu)]^2 + [b_\lambda \eta (B_\mu W_\mu)]^2 \quad \ldots\ldots(5)$$

or

$$\left(\frac{1}{U_\lambda}\right)^2 = \left(\frac{1}{U_{\lambda r}}\right)^2 + \left(\frac{1}{U_{\lambda g}}\right)^2 + \left(\frac{1}{U_{\lambda b}}\right)^2, \quad \ldots\ldots(6)$$

where

$$\eta(p) = \left(\frac{1}{1+9p}\right)$$

and

$$r_\lambda = r_\lambda'/aF\sqrt{3}, \qquad R_\lambda = r_\lambda'/9a, \qquad \frac{1}{U_{\lambda r}} = r_\lambda \eta (R_\mu W_\mu),$$

$$g_\lambda = g_\lambda'/bF\sqrt{3}, \qquad G_\lambda = g_\lambda'/9b, \qquad \frac{1}{U_{\lambda g}} = g_\lambda \eta (G_\mu W_\mu), \quad \left.\right\} \ldots\ldots(7)$$

$$b_\lambda = b_\lambda'/cF\sqrt{3}, \qquad B_\lambda = b_\lambda'/9c, \qquad \frac{1}{U_{\lambda b}} = b_\lambda \eta (B_\mu W_\mu).$$

$U_{\lambda r}$, $U_{\lambda g}$ amd $U_{\lambda b}$ may be regarded as the values which U_λ would assume if, in turn, each of the three mechanisms were acting alone. Since $\eta(0) = 1$, then, since $\frac{1}{U_{\lambda r}} = r_\lambda$ when $W_\mu = 0$, and r_λ is the reciprocal of the absolute threshold (in energy units) of the red mechanism for light of wave-length λ. Also, since $\eta(1) = 0 \cdot 1$, R_μ is the reciprocal of the energy intensity W_μ of light of wave-length μ required to raise $U_{\mu r}$, the difference threshold of the red mechanism, to ten times the absolute threshold $(1/r_\lambda)$. Similar interpretations apply to g_λ, G_μ, b_λ, B_μ. For $\lambda = \mu$, we have

$$\frac{R_\lambda}{r_\lambda} = \frac{G_\lambda}{g_\lambda} = \frac{B_\lambda}{b_\lambda} = \frac{F\sqrt{3}}{9}. \quad \ldots\ldots(8)$$

For fixed λ and μ it is convenient to illustrate relation (5) by a plot of $\log(1/U_\lambda)$ against $\log W_\mu$, and to show plots of $\log(1/U_{\lambda r})$, $\log(1/U_{\lambda g})$ and $\log(1/U_{\lambda b})$ in the same diagram (figure 1). The latter curves (component curves) all have the same shape, but their respective positions in the diagram are determined by the values of r_λ, g_λ, b_λ (position on the ordinate axis) and R_μ, G_μ, B (position on the abscissa axis). If $\mu = \lambda$, the component curves all tend asymptotically at high values of W_μ to the line : *ordinate* $= \log(1/F\sqrt{3}) - abscissa$, while the resultant curve $(\log 1/U_\lambda)$ tends to the line : *ordinate* $= \log(1/F) - abscissa$. If $\mu \neq \lambda$, the component curves may intersect so that the resultant curve exhibits a more or less pronounced "change of law" as illustrated.

§3. BASIC MEASUREMENTS

Given the seven functions $\eta(p)$, r_λ . . . . B_μ the resultant curve for any combination (λ, μ) can be drawn at once. An attempt at the converse problem of determining the seven functions from a number of experimental curves of $\log (1/U_\lambda)$ against $\log W_\mu$ has recently been made. The main points of this work (Stiles, 1939) will be briefly indicated. The present application was not in mind and the conditions of observation differed considerably from those implied in the foregoing discussion.

(*a*) The subject viewed, not two small juxtaposed patches but a large (10° diam.) patch of wave-length μ and energy intensity W_μ, at whose centre a small (1° square)

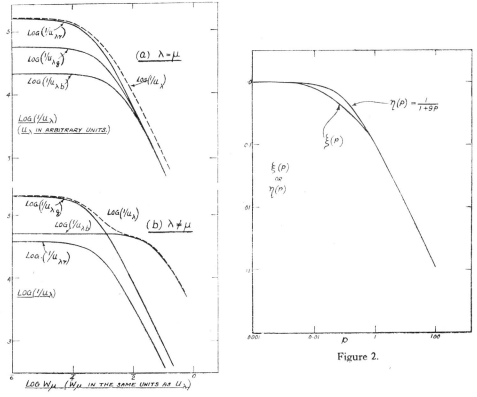

Figure 1.

Figure 2.

patch of wave-length λ and energy intensity U_λ' was applied in flashes (0·063 sec.) as an additional stimulus. Thus within the 1° square during the flash the energy intensity equalled $W_\mu + U_\lambda'$, while that of the surrounding field remained at W_μ throughout. The subject fixated the centre of the 10° patch, and great care was taken to ensure that the observations corresponded to foveal and cone (rod-free) vision of the additional stimulus. By repeated exposures of the latter at different energies U_λ', W_μ being kept constant, the critical intensity U_λ was determined at which the subject had a 50% chance of seeing the 1° patch.

(*b*) By measuring U_λ in this way for a series of values of W_μ from zero upwards, a curve of $\log (1/U_\lambda)$ against $\log W_\mu$ was obtained for various pairs of wave-lengths λ and μ. These experimental curves corresponded to the broken-line curves in figure 1. For example, with $\lambda = 480$ mμ, $\mu = 540$ mμ, the experimental curve closely resembled the broken-line curve of figure 1 (*b*). It was the characteristic form of such experimental curves which first suggested that they were really resultant curves derivable from component curves of fixed shape. This view was supported by the fact that when λ was kept constant at 480 mμ and μ was varied, the experimental curve was modified as though (referring to figure 1 (*b*)) the component curves $\log(1/U_{\lambda g})$ and $\log(1/U_{\lambda b})$ were displaced parallel to the axis of $\log W_\mu$, while remaining in the same position along the axis of $\log(1/U_\lambda)$. On the other hand, when μ was kept constant and λ varied, the experimental curve was modified as though the component curves were displaced parallel to the axis of $\log(1/U_\lambda)$. These regularities in the results may be called the "displacement rules".

From nearly 100 curves of $\log(1/U_\lambda)$ against $\log W_\mu$ for the writer's left eye, it was concluded that all such curves for this eye could be regarded as resultants of three component curves of a common fixed shape whose positions in the diagram depended on λ and μ. The most satisfactory fixed shape to suit all the results was chosen by trial, and the positions in the diagram at which component curves of this shape had to be placed to yield a resultant curve agreeing with the experimental curve were determined for the various combinations of λ and μ studied. Actually no more than two component curves contributed to the experimental curve for any particular combination, but to cover all combinations in accordance with the displacement rules three components were necessary.

(*c*) The common shape of the component curves was represented as a function $\xi(p)$ (figure 2) defined so that $\xi(p) = 1$ for $p = 0$, $\xi(p) = 0\cdot1$ for $p = 1$. Thus $\xi(p)$ played the rôle of the function $\eta(p)$ above. It is apparent from figure 2 that the difference between the two functions is small and confined to values of p below 1. The expression for a particular component, say the "red" component, then took the form,

$$\log(1/U_{\lambda r}) = \log[r_\lambda \xi(R_\mu W_\mu)],$$

where for given λ and μ the constants r_λ and R_μ fix the position of the curve in the diagram. Conversely, when the position had been determined as explained above, the values of r_λ and R_μ were obtained. Although this method yielded values for each of the functions r_λ, R_μ, g_λ, etc., in a part only of the visible spectrum, the ranges were extended by assuming the ratios $\dfrac{R_\lambda}{r_\lambda}$, $\dfrac{G_\lambda}{g_\lambda}$, $\dfrac{B_\lambda}{b_\lambda}$ to be approximately independent of λ. This appeared to be nearly true in regions where both numerator and denominator functions could be followed. The tentative determinations of the six functions r_λ to B_μ are plotted as the continuous-line curves of figures 3 to 5. The absolute values depend on the unit in which energy intensity is expressed. Here and elsewhere in this paper, by *energy intensity* is to be understood the flux of radiation entering the eye, expressed in ergs per sec. per square degree of the light patch. The values given refer to the case when the pupil of entry at the eye is small and concentric with the natural pupil. Rather different values apply when the pupil is large or eccentric, on account of the directional properties of retinal sensitivity.

(*d*) On the assumption that $\dfrac{R_\lambda}{r_\lambda}$, $\dfrac{G_\lambda}{g_\lambda}$ and $\dfrac{B_\lambda}{b_\lambda}$ are constants independent of λ,

the values of these ratios were found to be (very approximately) in the proportion

$$\frac{R}{r_\lambda} : \frac{G_\lambda}{g_\lambda} : \frac{B_\lambda}{b_\lambda} = 0.78 : 1 : 4.46.$$

(*e*) The resultant curve was related to the component curves by the following rough rule : for a given $\log W_\mu$, $\log 1/U_\lambda$ ... equals the greatest of $\log(1/U_{\lambda r})$ $\log(1/U_{\lambda g})$ and $\log(1/U_{\lambda b})$, except when the greatest and next greatest have nearly the same value. In the latter case $\log(1/U_\lambda)$ exceeds the greatest by a small amount, of the order of 0.1.

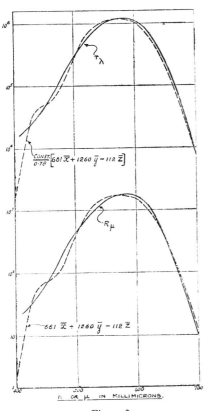

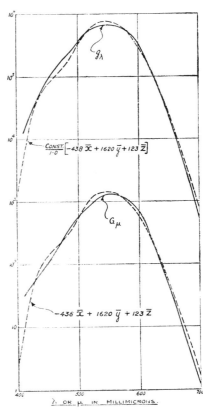

Figure 3.   Figure 4.

(*f*) A breakdown in the analysis of the results on the above lines occurred when the 10° patch was orange or red and of very high intensity (about 30,000 photons) and when the additional stimulus was blue (*limited conditioning effect of red light on the blue mechanism*). Colour-match equations also break down after adaptation to intensities of this order (Wright, 1936).

Setting aside the effect noted in (*f*), the experimental results differ from the predictions of the line-element and associated primaries of Helmholtz in the following respects:—

(i) The function $\eta(p)$ is replaced by a slightly different function $\xi(q)$.

(ii) The spectral sensitivity functions have the same general form as König's *Grundempfindungen.*

(iii) The ratios $\dfrac{R_\lambda}{r_\lambda}$, $\dfrac{G_\lambda}{g_\lambda}$, $\dfrac{B_\lambda}{b_\lambda}$ are not equal: $\dfrac{B}{b_\lambda}$ is materially greater than the other two. It follows that for $\lambda = \mu$, the three component curves in diagrams such as figure 1 no longer tend to a common line at high intensities.

(iv) The effects of the three mechanisms add up, if anything, to a smaller extent than required by the sum of squares relation (6).

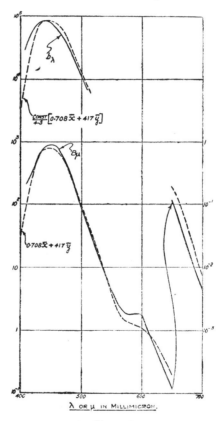

Figure 5.

For $\lambda = \mu$, the ratios $\dfrac{U_{\lambda r}}{W_\lambda}$, $\dfrac{U_{\lambda g}}{W_\lambda}$, $\dfrac{U_{\lambda b}}{W_\lambda}$ are the Fechner fractions* of the respective mechanisms. Since $\xi(p)$ tends to $\dfrac{1}{9p}$ as p becomes large, it is clear that

$$\frac{U_{\lambda r}}{W} = \frac{1}{W_\lambda r_r \xi(R_\lambda W_\lambda)}$$ approaches $9\dfrac{R_\lambda}{r_\lambda}$ at high intensities W_λ. Thus the ratios

$\dfrac{R_\lambda}{r_\lambda}$, $\dfrac{G_\lambda}{g_\lambda}$, $\dfrac{B_\lambda}{b_\lambda}$ are proportional respectively to the *limiting Fechner* fractions of the

---

* Historically it would be more accurate to call these ratios " Weber fractions ", but it has seemed preferable to follow the more usual practice.

three mechanisms, and (iii) implies that, contrary to the assumption of Helmholtz, the different mechanisms have different limiting Fechner fractions.

The precision of threshold measurements is low, and during a long investigation the properties of the eye may undergo systematic changes. There can be no question of a precise determination of the unknown functions by the methods used. All that can be claimed is that the derived functions reproduce the main features of the experimental curves.

§ 4. MODIFIED LINE-ELEMENT

Following the hints given by the basic measurements, we may construct a tentative line-element for application to any pair of just-distinguishable light patches, not necessarily of liminal increment type. Suppose the patches P' and P have absolute energy distributions $W_\lambda' d\lambda$ and $W_\lambda d\lambda$ respectively. Put

$$\zeta(p) = 9\xi(p), \qquad R = \int W_\lambda R_\lambda d\lambda, \qquad \delta R = \int (W_\lambda' - W_\lambda) R_\lambda d\lambda \quad \ldots\ldots(10)$$

and define G, δG, B, δB similarly, where $\xi(p)$, R_λ, G_λ, B_λ are the *experimental functions** plotted in figures 2 to 5. Introduce the quantities ρ, γ, β proportional to the limiting Fechner fractions of the three mechanisms,

$$\rho : \gamma : \beta = \frac{R_\lambda}{r_\lambda} : \frac{G_\lambda}{g_\lambda} : \frac{B_\lambda}{b_\lambda} = 0.78 : 1 : 4.46, \qquad \ldots\ldots(11)$$

and satisfying

$$\frac{1}{\rho^2} + \frac{1}{\gamma^2} + \frac{1}{\beta^2} = 1, \qquad \ldots\ldots(12)$$

so that $\dfrac{1}{\rho^2} = 0.612$, $\dfrac{1}{\gamma^2} = 0.369$, $\dfrac{1}{\beta^2} = 0.0185$. The proposed line-element is then

$$\delta s^2 \equiv \left[\frac{\delta R}{\rho} \zeta(R)\right]^2 + \left[\frac{\delta G}{\gamma} \zeta(G)\right]^2 + \left[\frac{\delta B}{\beta} \zeta(B)\right]^2 = F^2, \quad \ldots\ldots(13)$$

which reduces at high intensities to

$$\delta s^2 \equiv \left[\frac{1}{\rho}\frac{\delta R}{R}\right]^2 + \left[\frac{1}{\gamma}\frac{\delta G}{G}\right]^2 + \left[\frac{1}{\beta}\frac{\delta B}{B}\right]^2 = F^2, \qquad \ldots\ldots(14)$$

where F is a constant.

If the two patches have the same *relative* energy distributions, their intensities may be specified by their total energies T' and T (or by their total energies weighted according to any function of wave-length, such as the visibility curve). Their Fechner fraction is then given by

$$\frac{\delta T}{T} \equiv \frac{T' - T}{T} = \frac{\delta R}{R} = \frac{\delta G}{G} = \frac{\delta B}{B}.$$

Thus, by (14) and (12), $\dfrac{\delta T}{T} = F$ at high intensities, or F is the limiting Fechner fraction for any pair of patches of the same relative energy distribution whatever form that may take. The factor 3 introduced into (1) gives F a similar meaning for the Helmholtz line-element. Experimentally, the value of F depends on the

* The definitions of R_λ, G_λ, B_λ are modified later.

precise conditions of observation. It is round about 0·01 for the conditions normally used in determining colour limens, and this value will be used in the calculations which follow.

For just distinguishable patches of liminal increment type, δR, δG and δB are all positive or all negative. In applying the line-element generally, it is assumed that the signs of δR, δG, δB are immaterial, so that, for example, slight excess stimulations of the red and green mechanisms make the same contribution to the limen whether the excesses occur both in the same or one in each patch.

§5. COLOUR MATCHING

Light patches whose representative points P′ in b.c. space lie within the small ellipsoid centred on P and defined by (13) are indistinguishable from, and therefore in colour match with, P. In colour-matching measurements the objective is to bring the variable colour to the centre of this ellipsoid, and the condition for an ideal match may be taken to be $\delta R = \delta G = \delta B = 0$, or $\int W_{\lambda}' R_{\lambda}\, d\lambda = \int W_{\lambda} R_{\lambda}\, d\lambda$, and two similar equations.* R_{λ}, G_{λ}, B_{λ} were, in fact, obtained by a method completely independent of colour-matching, but their introduction into the line-element relates them at once to the distribution coefficients $\bar{x}$, $\bar{y}$, $\bar{z}$ derivable from colour-matching measurements. In terms of these coefficients, the conditions for a colour match are

$$\int W_{\lambda}' \bar{x}\, d\lambda = \int W_{\lambda} \bar{x}\, d\lambda$$

and two similar equations. Thus R_{λ}, G_{λ}, B_{λ} should be linear forms in $\bar{x}$, $\bar{y}$, $\bar{z}$. The distribution coefficients for the writer's eye (a normal trichromat) have not been determined, but using the coefficients of the C.I.E. Standard Observer in the Standard Reference System (C.I.E. 1931) an approximate linear representation of R_{λ}, G_{λ}, B_{λ} is obtained as follows :—

$$
\left.
\begin{aligned}
(R_{\lambda}) & \quad 6{\cdot}61 \,.\, 10^{2}\,\bar{x} + 1{\cdot}26 \,.\, 10^{3}\bar{y} - 1{\cdot}12 \,.\, 10^{2}\bar{z}. \\
(G_{\lambda}) & \quad -4{\cdot}38 \,.\, 10^{2}\,\bar{x} + 1{\cdot}62 \,.\, 10^{3}\bar{y} + 1{\cdot}23 \,.\, 10^{2}\bar{z}, \\
(B_{\lambda}) & \quad 7{\cdot}08 \,.\, 10^{-1}\bar{x} + 0 \,.\, \bar{y} \quad\quad + 4{\cdot}17 \,.\, 10^{2}\bar{z}.
\end{aligned}
\right\} \quad \ldots\ldots (15)
$$

These linear forms are plotted as the broken lines in figures 3 to 5. The agreement between the broken and continuous curves is fairly satisfactory when it is recalled (*a*) that the experimental uncertainties in determining R_{λ}, G_{λ}, B_{λ} are considerable—much greater than for $\bar{x}$, $\bar{y}$, $\bar{z}$; (*b*) that results for a single eye and for an average eye are being compared. The basic measurements (§ 3) could be represented almost as well by using the expressions (15) in place of R_{λ}, G_{λ}, B_{λ}, and by making the same substitutions in the definitions of R, δR, etc., the line element would lead automatically to the correct colour-matching equations for the C.I.E. standard observer. From now on, therefore, R_{λ}, G_{λ}, B_{λ} are supposed defined by the expressions (15). We are, of course, still dependent on the basic measurements for the coefficients in (15) and for the relative values of ρ, γ, β.

---

* Even if an ideal colour match is not achieved, (13) ensures that these equations shall be approximately true, i.e. δR will be small compared with R, and so on.

§6. STEP-BY-STEP VISIBILITY CURVE

In the experimental determination of the visibility curve by the step-by-step method, the two juxtaposed patches have slightly different colours and the intensity of one is varied until the "difference" between the two patches is a minimum. If the colour difference is appropriately chosen, the two patches are just indistinguishable at this minimum setting of the intensity. The visibility curve is derived from the line-element (14) by a corresponding procedure. The unit co-ordinates (in the fundamental system) of the two patches, i', j', k' and i, j, k, are required, where

$$i' = \frac{R'}{R' + G' + B'} = \frac{R'}{\Sigma'}, \qquad i = \frac{R}{R + G + B} = \frac{R}{\Sigma}, \qquad \ldots\ldots(16)$$

and j', k' ; j, k are similarly defined.

In terms of these, the line-element (13) takes the form

$$\delta s^2 \equiv \left[\frac{\Sigma' i' - \Sigma i}{\rho} \zeta(i)\right]^2 + \text{ two similar terms.} \qquad \ldots\ldots(17)$$

By varying Σ', keeping i', j', k' constant, the intensity of patch P' is varied without altering its colour. The minimum value of δs^2 under such a variation is reached when

$$0 = \frac{1}{\rho^2}\left[2i'(\Sigma' i' - \Sigma i)\zeta(\Sigma i)\right]^2 + \text{ two similar terms,}$$

or, reverting to the earlier notation and retaining only first-order quantities, when

$$0 = \frac{\delta R}{R}\left[\frac{R}{\rho} \zeta(R)\right]^2 + \frac{\delta G}{G}\left[\frac{G}{\gamma} \zeta(G)\right]^2 + \frac{\delta B}{B}\left[\frac{B}{\beta} \zeta(B)\right]^2. \qquad \ldots\ldots(18)$$

Strictly, the colour difference of the two patches should be chosen so that at the minimum setting $\delta s = F$, but it suffices both in the theory and in the experimental method for this condition merely to be approached.

The equality-of-brightness condition (18) applies to any pair of patches of nearly the same colour. In the special case of monochromatic patches of wave-lengths $\lambda, \lambda + \delta\lambda$ and energy intensities $W_\lambda, W_\lambda + \delta W_\lambda$, (18) becomes

$$-\frac{\delta W_\lambda}{W_\lambda} = \delta\lambda\left[\frac{C_r^2}{R_\lambda} \frac{dR_\lambda}{d\lambda} + \frac{C_g^2}{G_\lambda} \frac{dG_\lambda}{d\lambda} + \frac{C_b^2}{B_\lambda} \frac{dB_\lambda}{d\lambda}\right], \qquad \ldots\ldots(19)$$

where

$$C_r^2 = \frac{\left[\frac{R}{\rho} \zeta(R)\right]^2}{\left[\frac{R}{\rho} \zeta(R)\right]^2 + \left[\frac{G}{\gamma} \zeta(G)\right]^2 + \left[\frac{B}{\beta} \zeta(B)\right]^2} \qquad \ldots\ldots(20)$$

and C_g^2, C_b^2 are similarly defined. By successive applications of (19) we can determine the energy intensities of a series of monochromatic patches whose wave-lengths increase in small steps from the blue to the red, and each of which matches in brightness its next neighbours in the series. The reciprocal of the patch energy plotted against wave-length represents a step-by-step visibility curve whose shape will depend in general on the intensity level, specified, say, by the value of W_λ at $\lambda = 555$ mμ.   At sufficiently high intensity levels C_r^2, C_g^2, C_b^2 tend to $1/\rho^2$, $1/\gamma^2$, $1/\beta^2$ respectively, and the visibility curve approaches the limiting form

$$V_\lambda = \frac{\text{const.}}{W_\lambda} = \text{const. } R_\lambda^{1/\rho^2} \, G_\lambda^{1/\gamma^2} \, B_\lambda^{1/\beta^2}. \qquad \dots \dots (21)$$

As usual, the constant is adjusted so that V_λ has the maximum value unity.

The circle points in figure 6 represent relative visibilities calculated from the expression (21).   Except in the blue, these points lie very close to the full-line curve, which is a plot of the C.I.E. visibility function.   The discrepancy in the blue is greatly reduced if the comparison is made with the mean visibility curve obtained by Gibson and Tyndall (1923) for 52 observers (38 on ends) using the step-by-step method.*   In the several investigations of the visibility curve in which large groups of observers have been used, the variations between

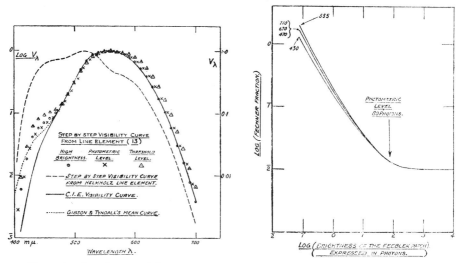

Figure 6.   Step-by-step visibility curves.   Figure 7.   Fechner fraction curves.

observers are markedly greater in the blue (say 455 mμ) than in the red (say 655 mμ).   On this general ground any theoretical derivation of the visibility curve may be expected to meet greater difficulties in the blue than in the red.

The broken curve in figure 6 is the visibility function for the Helmholtz line-element, but assuming the response functions (15).   It is derived from (21) by putting

$$\frac{1}{\rho^2} = \frac{1}{\gamma^2} = \frac{1}{\beta^2} = \frac{1}{3}.$$

Equally unacceptable curves are obtained by applying to the Helmholtz element König's *Grundemfindungen* or the double-peak response curves of Helmholtz. The Hecht response curves (Hecht, 1932), each of which is a fair approximation to the visibility curve, would make the Helmholtz or the modified line-element consistent with the visibility curve, but would render it incapable of explaining the basic measurements (§ 4).

* I am indebted to Prof. Hecht for drawing my attention to this point.   He also points out that the mean curve of Coblenz and Emerson (1917) shows a hump in the blue, and that a protanope studied by Hecht and Shlaer gave a curve similar in this respect to a normal observer.

The standard photometric brightness level at which the C.I.E. visibility curve applies may be taken as 25 equivalent metre candles seen through an eye pupil of 10 sq. mm. area, or 79·5 photons.   A monochromatic patch of wavelength 555 mμ has this brightness when its energy intensity W_λ equals $3·66 \times 10^{-4}$ erg per sec. per square degree.   The limiting form (21) of the derived visibility curve is barely reached at this value of W_{555}, and the curve must be derived from (19) by a method of successive approximation.   The results of the calculation are shown as the cross-points in figure 6.   The agreement with the C.I.E. curve is substantial, although in the red it is rather less close than for the high-intensity curve.   As the intensity is reduced below the photometric level, the derived curve undergoes some further modification, to assume finally the form shown by the triangle-points of figure 6, when the absolute threshold is reached. The second limiting form (22) can be obtained from (19) or directly from the line-element (13) by using the principle that at the absolute threshold all light patches are equally bright :

$$V_\lambda = \text{const.} \sqrt{\left(\frac{R_\lambda}{\rho}\right)^2 + \left(\frac{G_\lambda}{\gamma}\right)^2 + \left(\frac{B_\lambda}{\beta}\right)^2}. \qquad \ldots\ldots (22)$$

The main effects of lowering the intensity level are to increase slightly the visibilities in the orange and red and in the blue.   It must be emphasized that the line-element (13) is intended to represent foveal and strictly cone vision.   The small changes in the visibility curve just considered are quite distinct from the very much larger changes (Purkinje effect) which occur when, by the use of a large or eccentrically fixated matching field, the rods participate in the matching process.

No determinations of the foveal cone visibility curve by the step-by-step method have been made at low intensities.   Walters and Wright (1943) used a fixed red comparison patch and worked with the full-colour difference.   They found that at low intensities the visibility curve showed a slight shift of the maximum towards the blue, which they think may have resulted from some admixture of rod vision, and a " lump " in the curve at about 600 mμ, which they attribute to a tendency of the red mechanism to retain its sensitivity over a greater intensity range than the green or blue mechanisms.

Relation (18) is the differential of the function

$$P(R, G, B) = P_r(R) + P_g(G) + P_h(B),$$

where

$$P_r(R) = \int^R \frac{dR}{R} \left[\frac{R\zeta(R)}{\rho}\right]^2,$$

and P_g, P_b are similarly defined.   All lights (not necessarily monochromatic) for which $P(R, G, B)$ has the same value can be linked in small steps by series of intermediate lights, adjacent lights in any series having the same brightness. We may say that all such lights have the same " small-step " brightness.   But P_r, P_g and P_b are not linear functions of their arguments, so that " small-step " brightness is not additive.   To estimate the magnitude of the breakdown in the additive law, we will use for $P(R, G, B)$ the form to which it reduces at high intensities, namely,

$$\log_e \left[R^{1/\rho^2} G^{1/\gamma^2} B^{1/\beta^2}\right].$$

If lights 1 and 2 have the same small-step brightness,

$$R_1^{1/\varrho^2} G_1^{1/\gamma^2} B_1^{1/\beta^2} = R_2^{1/\varrho^2} G_2^{1/\gamma^2} B_2^{1/\beta^2},$$

and the equality of brightness still holds if their intensities are changed by the same factor, α say, since

$$(R_1\alpha)^{1/\varrho^2} (G_1\alpha)^{1/\gamma^2} (B_1\alpha)^{1/\beta^2} = (R_2\alpha)^{1/\varrho^2} (G_2\alpha)^{1/\gamma^2} (B_2\alpha)^{1/\beta^2}.$$

But if lights 1 and 2 each match light 3 in brightness, the mixture of 1 and 2 will not in general match light 3 increased to double its original intensity, since

$$(R_1 + R_2)^{1/\varrho^2}(G_1 + G_2)^{1/\gamma^2}(B_1 + B_2)^{1/\beta^2} = (2R_3)^{1/\varrho^2} (2G_3)^{1/\gamma^2}(2B_3)^{1/\beta^2}$$

is not in general true. The discrepancy may be expected to be greatest when the colours of 1 and 2 are most widely different, and it is estimated that about the worst case arises with monochromatic lights in the blue (470 mμ) and red (680 mμ). The colour of light 3 is immaterial. Calculation for this case shows that

$$(R_1 + R_2)^{1/\varrho^2}(G_1 + G_2)^{1/\gamma^2}(B_1 + B_2)^{1/\beta^2} = (2\cdot63R_3)^{1/\varrho^2} (2\cdot63G_3)^{1/\gamma^2}(2\cdot63G_3)^{1/\beta^2}.$$

The breakdown in additivity corresponds to the difference between 2 and 2·63, or about 27%. As a second example, take a white of energy distribution $W_\lambda d\lambda$ appropriate to a black body of temperature 2060°K. and compare its small-step brightness with the sum of the small-step brightnesses of its component wavelengths. Additivity would require

$$\int R_\lambda^{1/\varrho^2} G_\lambda^{1/\gamma^2} B_\lambda^{1/\beta^2} W_\lambda d\lambda = \left\{\int W_\lambda R_\lambda d\lambda\right\}^{1/\varrho^2} \left\{\int W_\lambda G_\lambda d\lambda\right\}^{1/\gamma^2} \left\{\int W_\lambda B_\lambda d\lambda\right\}^{1/\beta^2},$$

but calculation shows that the equation is in error by about 8%. This second case is the one used by Ives to test the additivity of brightness as assessed in the flicker photometer. He found additivity held good within the experimental error (1 or 2%). No similar check of additivity for small-step brightness has been made, and it cannot be said with certainty that discrepancies of the kind indicated by the line-element would not be observed, although there is no positive evidence for them. The results of brightness matching by flicker photometry, like those obtained by direct-comparison photometry with full colour difference, cannot be derived from the line-element without additional assumptions and will not be discussed.

§ 7. FECHNER FRACTION CURVES

Although the modified line-element assumes that the red, green and blue mechanisms have different limiting Fechner fractions at high intensities, it still leads to a common value F for the limiting Fechner fraction of a pair of just-distinguishable and similarly-coloured light patches, whatever that colour may be. This is in accordance with König and Brodhun's classic measurements of the Fechner fractions of white and monochromatic light. These measurements were made with large patches, each $3° \times 4\frac{1}{2}°$, and it is only at the higher intensities studied that the results can be accepted as referring to cone vision. The wide divergence in the observed values of the Fechner fraction at lower intensities is caused by the intrusion of the rods. The change with intensity in the Fechner fraction of monochromatic patches as predicted by the modified line-element (13) is shown in figure 7. The Fechner fraction, plotted as ordinate, is the just-distinguishable difference in patch intensity divided by the intensity of the *feebler* patch, and the intensity level, plotted as abscissa, is the intensity of the feebler patch. For $\lambda = 555\,m\mu$, this intensity is expressed in photons and for other wave-lengths in units such that all colours have the same brightness when compared on the basis of the calculated step-by-step visibility curve for the photometric level (figure 6). The Fechner fraction curves for different wave-lengths are not very different, but for the extreme blue the Fechner fraction has a rather smaller value at low intensities than for other colours.

§8. HUE LIMEN

The hue limen, or the difference of wave-length of two just-distinguishable monochromatic patches of equal brightness, is obtained from relations (13) and (18) by the substitutions.

$$R = W_\lambda R_\lambda, \quad \delta R = R_\lambda \delta W_\lambda + W_\lambda \frac{dR_\lambda}{d\lambda} \delta\lambda, \text{ etc.}$$

On eliminating W_λ, the equation for the hue limen $\delta\lambda$ takes the form :

$$F^2 = \delta\lambda^2 \left[\left\{ \frac{C_r^2 - 1}{R_\lambda} \frac{dR_\lambda}{d\lambda} + \frac{C_g^2}{G_\lambda} \frac{dG_\lambda}{d\lambda} + \frac{C_b^2}{B_\lambda} \frac{dB_\lambda}{d\lambda} \right\}^2 \left\{ \frac{R}{\rho} \zeta(R) \right\}^2 + \text{two similar terms} \right] \quad \dots\dots(23)$$

At high intensities this reduces to

$$F^2 = \delta\lambda^2 \left[\left\{ \frac{1/\rho^2 - 1}{R_\lambda} \frac{dR_\lambda}{a\lambda} + \frac{1/\gamma^2}{G_\lambda} \frac{dG_\lambda}{d\lambda} + \frac{1/\beta^2}{B_\lambda} \frac{dB}{d\lambda} \right\}^2 1/\rho^2 + \text{two similar terms} \right]. \quad \dots\dots(24)$$

The equation used by Helmholtz is the special case of (24), when ρ, γ, β are made equal.

The values of the hue limen through the spectrum have been calculated from (23), assuming a common brightness for all colours on the basis of the calculated step-by-step visibility curve for the photometric level (figure 6) and an actual brightness of 80 photons for $\lambda = 550\ m\mu$.

Table 1. Values of hue limen at the photometric level derived from the modified line element

λ (mμ)	$\delta\lambda$ (mμ)	λ (mμ)	$\delta\lambda$ (mμ)	λ (mμ)	$\delta\lambda$ (mμ)
410	5·7	510	2·06	610	1·43
420	3·9	520	2·74	620	1·88
430	2·22	530	2·88	630	2·42
440	1·75	540	2·87	640	3·2
450	1·41	550	2·62	650	4·7
460	1·63	560	2·03	660	6·8
470	1·14	570	1·72	670	11
480	0·82	580	1·44	680	18
490	0·97	590	1·27	690	29
500	1·45	600	1·26		

The calculated values are plotted in figure 8 together with five experimental curves obtained by Wright and Pitt (1934) at an average intensity level (480 to

650 mμ) of 70 photons.   An outstanding difference between the theoretical and experimental curves is that in the former the limens in the blue are relatively low.

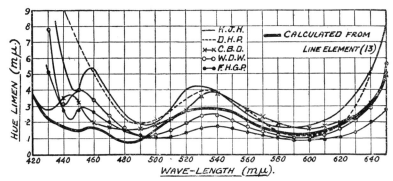

Figure 8.   Observed (Wright and Pitt, 1934) and calculated values of the hue limen.

In the determination of the experimental curves it was necessary to use lower intensities in the extreme blue, the total range being about 20 to 1.   This may account for some of the difference.

§9.   GENERAL COLOUR LIMEN

If two patches P and P′, not necessarily monochromatic, have the same brightness and are just distinguishable, they define a general colour limen.   The general colour limens for a given common brightness level are conveniently displayed in a C.I.E. (x, y) chart (a) by marking pairs of just-distinguishable colours on various lines joining spectrum colours to other spectrum colours or to purples (Wright, 1941), or (b) by drawing small closed curves (ellipses) about various points in the chart, the colours corresponding to all points on each such curve being just distinguishable from the central colour.   The modified line-element will now be applied to calculate the g.c.l. (general colour limen) ellipses for the 25 colours used in the recent investigation by MacAdam (1942).   Using an ingenious optical system, MacAdam arranged that, by turning a single control knob, the colour of a light patch was varied along a line in the C.I.E. chart while its brightness (C.I.E.) was automatically held constant.   Repeated colour matches were made with a second juxtaposed patch of the same brightness and of a fixed colour on the given line.   The standard deviations of the settings were determined, a setting being specified by the distance in the chart between the variable and fixed points.   The standard deviation is closely related to, and may be taken as proportional to, the diameter of the g.c.l. ellipse at the fixed colour in the direction of the given line.   MacAdam determined for one subject the complete ellipses for 25 fixed colours distributed fairly evenly over the domain between the spectrum locus and the line of purples.

Denoting by $t_{mn}(m, n=1, 2, 3)$ the coefficients in the forms (15), the R co-ordinate of a patch of absolute energy distribution $W_\lambda d\lambda$ is given by

$$R = t_{11}x' + t_{12}y' + t_{13}z', \qquad \ldots \ldots (25)$$

where $x' = \int W_\lambda \bar{x}\, d\lambda, \qquad y' = \int W_\lambda \bar{y}\, d\lambda, \qquad z' = \int W_\lambda \bar{z}\, d\lambda,$

and similar equations hold for G and B. The C.I.E. unit co-ordinates x, y, z are then $x = x'/w'$, $y = y'/w'$, $z = z'/w'$, where $w' = x' + y' + z'$. The quantity y' is proportional to the C.I.E. brightness of the patch and, in fact, recalling the units in which $W_\lambda d\lambda$ is expressed, we have :

$$\text{patch brightness in photons} = 2 \cdot 19 \, . \, 10^5 \int W_\lambda \bar{y} \, d\lambda, \quad \cdot$$

where the mechanical equivalent of light has been taken as $0 \cdot 0015$ watts per lumen. MacAdam worked with a C.I.E. brightness of 15 millilamberts seen through a pupil of $2 \cdot 6$ mm. diameter, that is, with a brightness of 271 photons. The calculation will be applied, therefore, to the case,

$$\int W_\lambda \bar{y} \, d\lambda = y' = w'y = \frac{271}{2 \cdot 19 \, . \, 10^5} = 1 \cdot 24 \, . \, 10^{-3}.$$

The R co-ordinate of the just-distinguishable patch is $R + \delta R$, where

$$\delta R = t_{11} \delta x' + t_{12} \delta y' + t_{13} \delta z',$$

and similar equations hold for δG and δB. In MacAdam's observations $\delta y' = 0$. The differentials $\delta x'$, $\delta z'$, expressed in terms of dx, δy, are then :

$$\delta x' = \frac{y'}{y} \left\{ \delta x - \frac{x}{y} \delta y \right\},$$

$$\delta z' = \frac{y'}{y} \left\{ \overline{\frac{x-1}{y}} \delta y - \delta x \right\}.$$

Thus,

$$\delta R = \delta x \, . \, \frac{y'}{y} \, (t_{11} - t_{13}) + \delta y \, . \, \frac{y'}{y^2} (x \overline{t_{13} - t_{11}} - t_{13}),$$

$$R = x \, . \, \frac{y' t_{11}}{y} + y' t_{12} + z \, . \, \frac{y'}{y} \, t_{13}, \qquad \qquad \ldots \ldots (26)$$

and, inserting these expressions, the line-element (13) takes the form

$$F^2 = \delta x^2 \left[\left\{ \frac{p_{11}}{\rho} \zeta(R) \right\}^2 + \left\{ \frac{p_{21}}{\gamma} \zeta(G) \right\}^2 + \left\{ \frac{p_{31}}{\beta} \zeta(B) \right\}^2 \right.$$

$$+ 2\delta x \, \delta y \left[p_{11} p_{12} \left\{ \frac{\zeta(R)}{\rho} \right\}^2 + p_{21} p_{22} \left\{ \frac{\zeta(G)}{\gamma} \right\}^2 + p_{31} p_{32} \left\{ \frac{\zeta(B)}{\beta} \right\}^2 \right]$$

$$+ \delta y^2 \left[\left\{ \frac{p_{12}}{\rho} \zeta(R) \right\}^2 + \left\{ \frac{p_{22}}{\gamma} \zeta(G) \right\}^2 + \left\{ \frac{p_{32}}{\beta} \zeta(B) \right\}^2 \right], \qquad \ldots \ldots (27)$$

where

$$p_{11} = \frac{y'}{y} (t_{11} - t_{13}), \qquad p_{12} = \frac{y'}{y^2} (x \overline{t_{13} - t_{11}} - t_{13})$$

$$p_{21} = \frac{y'}{y} (t_{21} - t_{23}), \qquad p_{22} = \frac{y'}{y^2} (x \overline{t_{23} - t_{21}} - t_{23}),$$

$$p_{31} = \frac{y'}{y} (t_{31} - t_{32}), \qquad p_{32} = \frac{y'}{y^2} (x \overline{t_{33} - t_{31}} - t_{33}),$$

For a given colour x, y, the g.c.l. ellipse is completely determined by the equation

(27). The semi-axes and orientation of the ellipse have been calculated for MacAdam's 25 colours and are as follows:—

Table 2

Colour MacAdam's figure number	C.I.E. co-ordinates			Semi-axes		Angle between major axis and axis of x (degrees)
	x	y	z	Major	Minor	
23	0·160	0·057	0·783	$0·235 \cdot 10^{-2}$	$0·139 \cdot 10^{-2}$	85
24	0·187	0·118	0·695	0·62	0·285	75
25	0·253	0·125	0·622	0·71	0·272	53
26	0·150	0·680	0·170	2·84	1·26	106
27	0·131	0·521	0·348	2·60	1·04	101
28	0·212	0·550	0·238	2·37	1·13	97
29	0·258	0·450	0·292	1·90	0·97	86
30	0·152	0·365	0·483	1·86	0·76	96·
31	0·280	0·385	0·335	1·67	0·85	78
32	0·380	0·498	0·122	1·53	1·04	83
33	0·160	0·200	0·640	1·10	0·44	92
34	0·228	0·250	0·522	1·24	0·57	76
35	0·305	0·323	0·372	1·43	0·72	68
36	0·385	0·393	0·222	1·47	0·83	63
37	0·472	0·399	0·129	1·23	0·78	54
38	0·517	0·350	0·123	1·14	0·61	44
39	0·475	0·300	0·225	1·27	0·52	43
40	0·510	0·236	0·254	1·17	0·31	35
41	0·596	0·283	0·121	1·02	0·35	33
42	0·344	0·284	0·372	1·30	0·60	57
43	0·390	0·237	0·373	1·18	0·44	45
44	0·441	0·198	0·361	1·13	0·284	36
45	0·278	0·223	0·499	1·14	0·49	62
46	0·300	0·163	0·537	0·91	0·33	50
47	0·365	0·153	0·482	0·99	0·24	39

In figures 9 and 10 the calculated and MacAdam's ellipses are plotted in the C.I.E. chart. There is some similarity. The orientations of the ellipses correspond rather well (figure 11), and their areas show a correlation (figure 12). The computed areas exceed MacAdam's on the average by a factor of 20·7 ($4·5^2$), but MacAdam's refer to standard deviations, which he estimates to be about one-third the corresponding limens. The axis ratios of the ellipses cover a range of about 2·5 to 1 and have average values 2·3 (calculated) and 2·9 (MacAdam's), but they show no correlation (figure 13).

MacAdam reports a limited number of observations for a second subject. The ratio of the g.c.l.s of the two subjects varies, for different points and directions in the chart, over a range of about 0·8 to 2·5. For colour No. 35 sufficient results are given to construct the ellipse for the second subject (figure 14*), and in table 3 the characteristics of the ellipses of the two subjects are compared.

* The plotted points in this figure were read off the smooth curves of MacAdam's figures 8 to 19, and there will be some reading error.

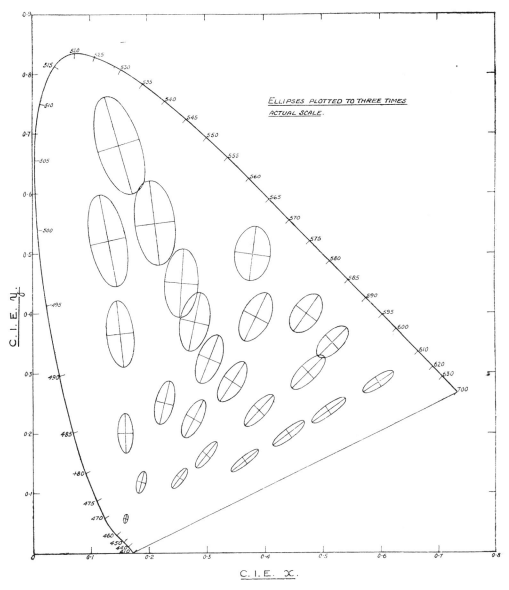

Figure 9. G.C.I. ellipses calculated from the line-element (13).

Table 3

	Major semi-axis	Minor semi-axis	Ratio of axes	Area of ellipse	Inclination of major axis to axis of x (degrees)
Principal subject (P.G.N.)	$0 \cdot 25 \cdot 10^{-2}$	$0 \cdot 086 \cdot 10^{-2}$	$2 \cdot 9$	$6 \cdot 7 \cdot 10^{-6}$	70
Second subject (D.L.M.)	$0 \cdot 31$	$0 \cdot 165$	$1 \cdot 88$	$16 \cdot 1$	44

In Wright's investigation (1941), the subjects determined equal colour steps on various lines in the C.I.E. chart, and in figure 15 the logarithm of the observed colour step is plotted against distance from one end of the line for four of the principal lines studied. Wright's colour steps were not actual limens but

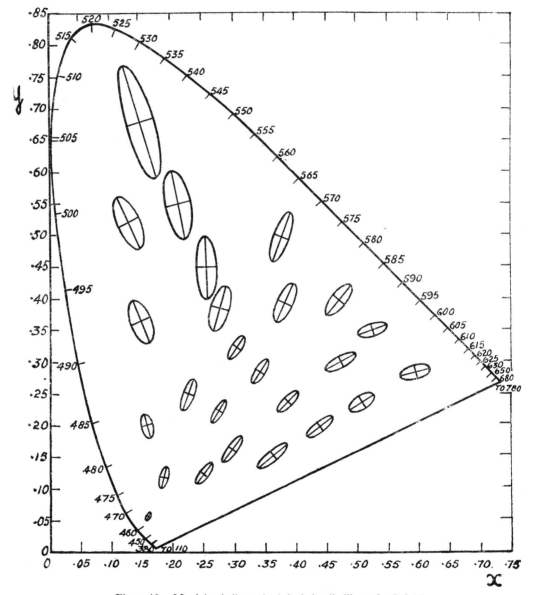

Figure 10.   MacAdam's " standard deviation " ellipses for P.G.N.

" equal small colour differences " ; he found that after practice a subject could maintain a reasonably steady criterion.   On the average, the colour step was about three times the limen.   In reporting his results, Wright reduced the steps for the four subjects to about the same average values by applying suitable constant factors : figure 15 shows the results before the application of these factors.

No direct calculations from the line-element were made for comparison with Wright's results, but a fair idea of the variations along the several lines was obtained by interpolation from the 25 computed ellipses of figure 9. A similar derivation was made from MacAdam's ellipses for P.G.N (figure 10). In figure 15

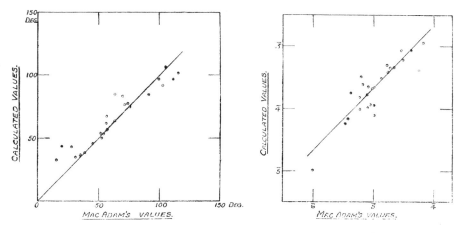

Figure 11. Inclination of the major axis of ellipse to the axis of *x*.

Figure 12. Log (area of ellipse).

the computed colour limens times 3 are shown as the thick-line graphs and MacAdam's standard deviations times 9 as the broken-line graphs. These factors allow for the average systematic differences between small colour step and limen, limen and standard deviation, as estimated by Wright and MacAdam

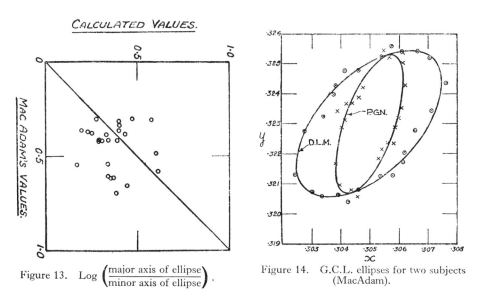

Figure 13. $\text{Log}\left(\dfrac{\text{major axis of ellipse}}{\text{minor axis of ellipse}}\right)$.

Figure 14. G.C.L. ellipses for two subjects (MacAdam).

respectively. Admitting that these factors may differ for different subjects, and that *F* may also differ, it is fair to suppose the four line-element curves in figure 15 all shifted up or down by the same amount when comparing with the experimental curves of each subject. Even then there is no close agreement with

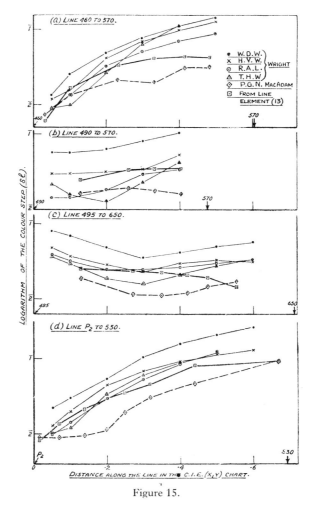

Figure 15.

the curves of any of the five subjects. It may be noted that the experimental curves of different subjects, compared in the same way, show differences which are hardly less marked.

§ 10. DISCUSSION

The line-element may be regarded as a mathematical model of the mechanism underlying a particular group of visual properties (increment threshold, colour-matching relations, visibility curve, etc.). In the Helmholtz and modified elements, the respective terms correspond to three component mechanisms, with each of which is associated a unique spectral sensitivity curve. A difference between adjacent light patches will be perceived by the action of one of these component mechanisms, say the red, if the product,

$$|\delta x| \left(\frac{\sqrt{3}}{a+x}\right) (\text{Helmholtz element}) \quad \text{or} \quad |\delta R| \left(\frac{\zeta(R)}{\rho}\right) (\text{modified element}),$$

exceeds F. The first factor in these products is the difference of stimulation of the red mechanism in the two patches, evaluated on the basis of the red spectral-sensitivity curve. The second factor defines the sensitivity of the red mechanism in the state to which it is brought by the total stimulation, x or R, which may be taken here as approximately the same in the two patches. The product, on this view, is a measure of the response of the red mechanism to the difference of stimulation. The only interaction between the red, green and blue component mechanisms contemplated by these line-elements is a certain degree of summation of their

responses, $\dfrac{\delta x \sqrt{3}}{a+x}$, etc., according to the sums of squares relation.

The Schrödinger element (3) is an example of the wider class represented by

$$\delta s^2 \equiv [\delta x \cdot g_x(x, y, z)]^2 + [\delta y \cdot g_y(x, y, z)]^2 + [\delta z \cdot g_z(x, y, z)]^2 = F^2.$$

$$\dots \dots (28)$$

For line-elements in this class, the component mechanisms preserve their individuality—with each is associated a unique spectral sensitivity curve *—but they are so linked that the state of each as indicated by the sensitivity factors g_x, g_y, g_z depends on the stimulations of all three mechanisms. This linkage is additional to the summation of responses according to the sum of squares relation.

For the above elements, the axes of the small ellipsoid defined by the line-element at each point of f.c. space are parallel to the co-ordinated axes. In the more general element,

$$\delta s^2 \equiv \underset{m,\,n}{\Sigma}\, g_{mn}\delta x_m \delta x_n = F(m, n = 1, 2, 3), \qquad \dots \dots (29)$$

the axes of the elementary ellipsoids at different points are not necessarily parallel to the axes of the ellipsoid at any one point in the space, but different rotations are in general required for different points. A rotation of the axes corresponds to a change of the primaries so that on this model the spectral-sensitivity curves of the three mechanisms are progressively modified as the stimulation (defined by the position in b.c. space) is varied.

To what extent does the simple model defined by the modified line-element (13) fit the facts? The matter is complicated by the very considerable differences in the experimental results of different subjects. To be satisfactory, the line-element (13) with a particular numerical determination of R_λ, G_λ, B_λ, ρ, γ, β, F and $\zeta(p)$ should reproduce the colour-matching values, the step-by-step visibility curve, the increment and colour limens and possibly some other visual properties of a particular eye, or, more precisely, of a particular rod-free area of a given retina. Changes in the visual properties in passing from one rod-free area to another in the same or a different eye should all be accounted for at a stroke by a change in the numerical determination of the line-element. For the comparisons made in this paper, a single numerical determination has been used : for the distribution coefficients $\bar{x}$, $\bar{y}$, $\bar{z}$ the C.I.E. values, for the fundamental response curves the function defined in (15) for the limiting Fechner fractions numbers in the proportion $0{\cdot}78 : 1 : 4{\cdot}46$, and for F the value $0{\cdot}01$. While certain main features of the experimental results are reproduced, satisfactory quantitative agreement with the measurements of all the visual properties for some particular subject has not been demonstrated. In fact no such complete set of measurements is available. For the restricted group of

* Except in the degenerate case when any two of g_x, g_y, g_z stand in a constant ratio.

colour-limen measurements, the comparisons made (figures 8 to 15) show differences which could no doubt be reduced by a different numerical determination of the line-element for each subject. But in the case of MacAdam's subject P.G.N. it can be shown that complete agreement could not be reached by any change in which the fundamental response functions R_λ, G_λ, B_λ remained always positive, linear forms in the C.I.E. distribution coefficients. (See Appendix.) Our conclusion must be that the modified line-element, constructed to suit measurements of increment limens, leads to the right kind of step-by-step visibility curve, but is in difficulties when applied to measurements of colour limens.

§ 11. ACKNOWLEDGMENT

This paper is published by permission of the Director of the National Physical Laboratory.

APPENDIX

The Gaussian curvature of the surface of constant C.I.E. brightness according to the modified line-element

Following Silberstein (1943), the unit C.I.E. co-ordinates x, y for colours of a given constant C.I.E. brightness can be regarded as curvilinear co-ordinates on a surface embedded in a three-dimensional Euclidean space, the distance apart of neighbouring points on this surface being defined by the expression for the line-element δs. This expression, for the modified line-element, is the square root of the right-hand side of equation (27). Silberstein uses an empirical expression for δs derived from MacAdam's measurements for the subject P.G.N. (figure 10), and shows that the Gaussian curvature K of the surface is not only not constant, but that it is positive in some areas, negative in others.

The Gaussian curvature is invariant to transformations, linear or non-linear, of the co-ordinates x, y, and it is permissible to employ R, G in place of x, y. For the modified line-element, an expression for K is obtained quite easily if we accept for $\zeta(p)$ the approximation $\dfrac{9}{1+9p}$, to which it reduces when p exceeds 1. This corresponds to using curve $\eta(p)$ instead of curve $\xi(p)$ (figure 2). K is then given by

$$K = \frac{\rho^2\gamma^2\beta^2(1+9R)(1+9G)(1+9B)v_r v_g v_b(9y' + v_r + v_g + v_b)}{[\rho^2 v_r^2(1+9R)^2 + \gamma^2 v_g^2(1+9G)^2 + \beta^2 v_b^2(1+9B)^2]^2}, \quad \ldots\ldots(30)$$

where $y' = v_r R + v_g G + v_b B = \text{const.}$ This condition is obtained by solving the equation (25) for x', y', z' ; it expresses the fact that the colours considered all have a constant C.I.E. brightness (equal to $2\cdot19 \cdot 10^5 \, y'$ photons).

Since for real colours R, G and B are all positive, it is clear that the Gaussian curvature will have the same sign at all points of the surface of constant C.I.E. brightness.

Computation gives

$$v_r = 2\cdot70 \times 10^{-4}$$
$$v_g = 4\cdot07 \times 10^{-4}$$
$$v_b = -4\cdot76 \times 10^{-5}$$
$$v_r + v_g + v_b = 6\cdot29 \times 10^{-4}.$$

Thus $v_r v_g v_b (9y' + v_r + v_g + v_b)$, and hence K, is negative for any value of y', i.e. for any C.I.E. brightness.

It follows that the modified line-element is inconsistent with MacAdam's results for P.G.N., which for different colours yield K values of opposite sign. This inconsistency persists however ρ, γ, β be chosen and whatever change be made in the fundamental response curves R_λ, G_λ, B_λ provided these remain linear forms in the C.I.E. distribution coefficients, and lead to all positive co-ordinates R, G, B for real colours.

REFERENCES

COBLENZ, W. W. and EMERSON, W. B., 1917. *Sci. Pap. U.S. Bur. Stand.* No. 303.
GIBSON, K. S. and TYNDALL, E. P. T., 1923. *Sci. Pap. U.S. Bur. Stand.* No. 475.
HECHT, S., 1932. *Discussion on Vision*, Phys. and Opt. Societies, 126.
HELMHOLTZ, H. VON, 1891. *Z. Sinnesphysiol.* **3**, 517.
KÖNIG, A. and DIETERICI, C., 1884. *Ann. Phys., Lpz.*, **22**, 579.
MACADAM, D. L., 1942. *J. Opt. Soc. Amer.* **32**, 247.
PRIEST, I. G. and BRICKWEDDE, F. G., 1926. *J. Opt. Soc. Amer.* **13**, 306.
SCHRÖDINGER, E., 1920. *Ann. Phys., Lpz.*, 63.
SILBERSTEIN, L., 1943. *J. Opt. Soc. Amer.* **33**, 1.
STILES, W. S., 1939. *Proc. Roy. Soc.* B, **127**, 64.
WALTERS, H. V. and WRIGHT, W. D., 1943. *Proc. Roy. Soc.* B, **131**, 340.
WRIGHT, W. D., 1936. *J. Physiol.* **87**, 23.
WRIGHT, W. D., 1941. *Proc. Phys. Soc.* **53**, 93.
WRIGHT, W. D. and PITT, F. H. G., 1934. *Phys. Proc. Soc.* **46**, 459.

Errata

Page 51. Formula (17): replace $\zeta(i)$ by $\zeta(\Sigma i)$.
Equation between (17) and (18): replace $\zeta(\Sigma i)$ by $\zeta(\Sigma i)^2$ and delete the upper suffix 2 outside the bracket.

Page 57. Line 8: replace 271 by 253.
Final equation (p_{31}): replace t_{32} by t_{33}.

Paper VI: Reprinted in part from Rev. d'Opt., 1949.

* INVESTIGATIONS OF THE SCOTOPIC AND TRICHROMATIC MECHANISMS OF VISION BY THE TWO-COLOUR THRESHOLD TECHNIQUE

by W. S. STILES

(The National Physical Laboratory, Teddington, England)

SOMMAIRE. — Etude des mécanismes scotopiques et trichromatiques par la technique du seuil bicolore : *Les possibilités de la technique du seuil bicolore, utilisées par Roaf, Stiles, Crawford, et plus récemment par de Vries, sont discutées et quelques-uns des résultats déjà obtenus sont résumés. Dans cette technique la rétine est exposée à une lumière unicolore et sa sensibilité de seuil à une lumière d'épreuve, en général d'une autre couleur, est déterminée. Cette lumière d'épreuve est appliquée comme une excitation additionnelle et est, généralement, de petites dimensions pour que les propriétés d'une région particulière de la rétine puissent être étudiées. Entre autres, les résultats suivants ont été obtenus : avec les observations parafovéales de la lumière d'épreuve et avec un choix approprié de couleurs, la transition bâtonnet-cône dans la courbe reliant la valeur du seuil et l'intensité d'adaptation est déplacée vers de très hautes intensités et la composante bâtonnet de la courbe peut être suivie dans un domaine de 10^5 à 1 en valeur de seuil.*

Avec l'observation fovéale sans bâtonnet la participation ue trois mécanismes rétiniens a été établie et des déterminations approchées de leurs courbes de sensibilité spectrale par des méthodes indépendantes d'égalisation de couleurs ont été faites. Des variations accusées dans la sensibilité de ces mécanismes dans le champ fovéal ont été observées, le mécanisme « bleu » montrant au centre un minimum de sensibilité. Pendant le processus d'adaptation de l'obscurité à un champ de haute intensité, le délai pour atteindre l'équilibre final de la sensibilité de seuil est beaucoup plus long pour le « bleu » que pour les autres mécanismes.

Excerpt A

How increment thresholds came to be introduced.

This paper will be concerned only with investigations in which the quantity measured is the threshold (the two-colour *threshold* technique), and it will deal in the main with the case when the conditioning stimulus is continuously exposed, so that the retina is in equilibrium with it, and the test stimulus is superposed as an additional stimulus. If, in this case, test and conditionning stimuli have the same colour, the observed threshold may be regarded as a measure of the ability of the eye to discriminate small differences of brightness, a visual property whose systematic study began with the classic investigation by König and Brodhun in

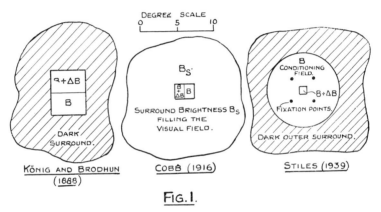

FIG. 1.

Field appearance in measurements of intensity discrimination.

1888. The use of different colours for the two stimuli — a comparatively recent development — appears as a logical extension of changed methods of measuring brightness discrimination. König and Brodhun worked with a rather large bipartite photometric matching field (fig. 1) and required the subject to vary the intensity of one half until he judged it to be just perceptibly brighter than the other. Later, a more uniform condition of stimulation of the retina was achieved by surrounding the bipartite field with an illuminated zone — a kind of guard-ring — and Cobb [1] showed that for a given brightness of the matching field, the threshold was minimal when the surround had about the same brightness as the bipartite field. By exactly matching the brightness of the surround with the darker half of the bipartite field and by eliminating all dividing lines, the presentation to the subject became a large uniformly bright conditioning stimulus on which was superposed a small test stimulus corresponding to the *excess* brightness of the brighter half of the original field. Workers with this type of presentation were interested in practical questions of visibility, and the notion of comparing the brightnesses of juxtaposed patches was replaced by the simpler one of merely detecting the presence of an object — the test stimulus — on an otherwise featureless background. The latter criterion is equally applicable when the test stimulus differs in colour from the conditioning stimulus on which it is superposed and it was a small step to extend the investigations in this direction.

Meanwhile the need for distinguishing carefully between direct (foveal) and indirect (extrafoveal) vision of the test stimulus had led to the use of smaller test stimuli and to the introduction of fixation points into the field. These were usually weak points of red light adjusted by the subject to be just comfortably visible. A practical difficulty was that, on prolonged steady fixation, feebly visible objects seen extrafoveally tend to fade from view. While this phenomenon is of considerable interest on its own account, its study presents special difficulties and much can be learnt by confining attention to the initial sensitivity of the retina, say, within one second of the application of the test stimulus. For these reasons a flashing instead of a continuously exposed test stimulus has usually been adopted for extrafoveal observations. The flashing test stimulus lends itself readily to the determination of the so-called S-shaped curves which show how the probability of seeing the test stimulus increases as its intensity is raised. The threshold is then defined as the intensity at which this probability equals 0.5. Convenience in this respect and the desirability of adhering to a single method of observation sufficiently account for the use of a flashing test stimulus for both foveal and extrafoveal observation in most of the work discussed below. But, in addition, the flashing test stimulus has the advantage of providing another experimental variable — duration of stimulus — which can be of use in probing the visual mechanism.

Excerpt B
6. Differences in light adaptation time of the cone mechanisms.

The work of Kohlrausch, Hecht, Wald and others has shown that as the retina becomes adapted to darkness after exposure to a high brightness, the parafoveal threshold falls in two stages, an initial stage attributable to the cones and a final stage, to the rods. It might be expected that by suitable choice of the colours of the test stimulus and of the preliminary high intensity conditioning stimulus, the foveal threshold would fall in stages corresponding to different cone mechanisms. Foveal recovery curves of this kind have not been reported (see Mandelbaum and Mintz) [4]. The reason may be that the transition from one mechanism to another occurs very early in the recovery process where the threshold is steeply descending and where the practical difficulties of detecting a change of law are severe. However, in the complementary situation, when the retina is adapted initially to darkness and the foveal threshold is measured during several minutes

after the exposure of an intense conditioning field, the time to reach an equilibrium value shows variations which can be related to the different cone mechanisms. Immediately on exposure of the conditioning stimulus, the threshold is
raised to a high value and the main characteristic of the subsequent change is
conveniently specified by the time taken for the threshold to drop to twice the
final equilibrium value (light adaptation time). For a conditioning stimulus of
wave-length 600 mμ and intensity about 5,000 photons, a number of determinations of light adaptation time for test stimuli of different wave-lengths are reproduced in Fig. 15. These were obtained with a test stimulus of 15′ diam., 0.2 sec.
duration, imaged on the foveal retina 0.5° to the temporal side of the centre. From
the previous work it is known that when equilibrium is reached with the conditioning stimulus in question, the observed threshold is the threshold of the « blue »
mechanism for wave-lengths of the test stimulus below about 500 mμ. The salient
feature of Fig. 15 is the protracted light adaptation time for wave-lengths below
500 mμ, and it may be inferred that compared with the « green » mechanism, the
« blue » mechanism is slow in adapting to high intensities of orange light. This
conclusion is borne out by observations on other subjects and with a larger test
stimulus viewed foveally. A possible, smaller difference in the light adaptation
times of the « green » and « red » mechanisms is also indicated but this is less certain. It should be observed that in the equilibrium state the conditioning stimulus
used raises the threshold of the « blue » mechanism above the value appropriate

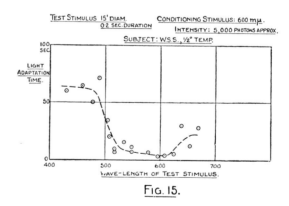

FIG. 15.

Variation of the light-adaptation time with wave-length of the test
stimulus at a high intensity orange conditioning stimulus.

to zero brightness only by about 0.3 log units whereas it raises the thresholds of
the « green » and « red » mechanisms by about 2.2 and 2.6 log units respectively.
The longer delay with the « blue » mechanism is not therefore to be attributed to a
greater difference between the initial and final states as « measured » by the equilibrium threshold values. Suppose now the wave-length of the test stimulus is
kept fixed at 430 mμ and conditioning stimuli of different wave-lengths through

the spectrum are considered, the intensity for each wave-length being adjusted
to raise the equilibrium threshold for the « blue » mechanism by a fixed amount.
Provided this amount is not too large (say below 0.5 log units) the initial and
final equilibrium thresholds can safely be attributed to the « blue » mechanism,
for all wave-lengths of the conditioning stimulus except possibly in the extreme
blue. It might be expected then if the « blue » mechanism is reacting as an independent mechanism that the light adaptation time would have the same high value
for all wavelengths μ of the conditioning stimulus (excepting the extreme blue,
$\mu < 450$ mμ). Experiments on these lines, which however are only in the preliminary stage, indicate that this is not the case and that the light adaptation time increases systematically from a low value of the order of 15 sec. or less when $\mu < 500$ mμ,
to a high value of the order of 60 sec. when $\mu > 600$ mμ. It appears in fact that
the process responsible for the delay in the light adaptation of the « blue » mechanism has associated with it a relative spectral sensitivity curve which is not that
of the « blue » mechanism itself and which may agree more closely with the curves
of the « red » or « green » mechanisms. Further work should show whether we have
here another example of a coupling between the cone mechanisms which is
apparent only when the retina is in a state of change, that is to say, a coupling
of the kind made probable by Wright's investigations of the apparent colour of
test stimuli seen by an eye recovering from selective fatigue [11].

REFERENCES

[1] Cobb, P. W. « The effect on foveal vision of bright surroundings III and IV ». *Journ. Exp. Psych.*, 1, p. 419 and p. 540, 1916.

[2] Roaf, H. E. « The influence of coloured light on the sensitivity of the eye through various regions of the spectrum. » *Quarterly J. Exper. Physiol.*, 18, p. 243, 1928.

[3] Roaf, H. E. « The influence of coloured surrounds and coloured backgrounds on visual thresholds ». *Proc. Roy. Soc.*, 110 B, p. 448, 1932.

[4] Stiles, W. S. « The directional sensitivity of the retina and the spectral sensitivities of the rods and cones ». *Proc. Roy. Soc.*, 127 B, p. 64, 1939.

[5] Hecht, S., Peskin, J. C., and Patt, M. « Intensity discrimination in the human eye ». *I. Gen. Phys.*, 22, p. 7, 1938.

[6] Stiles, W. S. « The separation of the « blue » and « green » mechanisms of foveal vision by threshold measurements ». *Proc. Roy. Soc.* 133 B, p. 418, 1946.

[7] de Vries, H. L. « The basic sensation curves of the three-color theory ». *J. O. S. A.*, 36, p. 121, 1946.

[8] Stiles, W. S. « The basic sensation curves of the three-color theory ». *J. O. S. A.*, 36, p. 491, 1946.

[9] Willmer, E. N. and Wright, W. D. « Colour sensitivity of the fovea centralis ». *Nature*, 156, pp. 119-121, 1945.

[10] Thomson, L. C. and Wright, W. D. « The colour sensitivity of the retina within the central fovea of man ». *J. of Physiolog.* 105, p. 316, 1947.

[11] Wright, W. D. « The foveal light adaptation process ». *Roy. Soc. Proc.*, 122 B, p. 220, 1937.

[12] Holladay, L. L. « The fundamentals of glare and visibility ». *J. O. S. A.*, 12, p. 171, 1926.

[13] Le Grand, Y. « Recherches sur la diffusion de la lumière dans l'œil humain ». *Rev. d'Optique*, 16, p. 201 and p. 241, 1937.

[14] Mandelbaum, J. and Mintz, E. U. « The sensitivities of the colorer receptors as measured by dask adaptation ». *Amer. J. of ophthalm*, 24, p. 1241, 1941.

Paper VII: Reprinted from Documenta Ophthalmologica, Vol. 3, 1949.

INCREMENT THRESHOLDS & THE MECHANISMS
OF COLOUR VISION
By W. S. Stiles

The National. Physical Laboratory, Teddington, Middlesex

Determinations of the smallest quantity of light and the smallest difference of brightness which the eye can detect under various conditions have played an important part in the development of the duplicity theory of vision. But until comparatively recently such measurements have not been related very closely with the other main co-ordinating hypothesis of visual research — the trichromatic theory. In this paper I propose to discuss some of the later work on intensity thresholds, in which the operation of more than one mechanism of cone vision is indicated by experimental methods very similar to those used in consolidating the duplicity theory. The general picture of the threshold sensitivity of the retina to which this work leads will first be sketched in, and some tentative elaborations and modifications will then be briefly considered.

The simple experimental situation to which the discussion will be mainly confined may be described as follows. The retina is exposed and adapted to a field uniform in intensity and colour. Ideally, this field should cover the whole retina but in most of the relevant measurements substantially the same results are obtained with a patch of some 10° diameter, * centred on the region of the retina whose properties are under investigation, the rest of the field being dark. At the centre of this adapting field a small uniform patch of light — the test stimulus — is superimposed, that is to say, it is added to the adapting stimulus. The basic measurement consists in determining the least perceptible intensity of the test stimulus. The quantity so obtained is a function of the variables determining the test stimulus — angular size, exposure time, spectral composition etc. — and of those determining the adapting field — intensity, spectral composition, etc. When the test stimulus and adapting field have the same spectral composition the quantity measured would normally be called an intensity threshold, absolute if the adapting field has zero intensity, differential if that is not the case. But some of the most significant results are obtained when test stimulus and

---

* This and other angular sizes quoted later all refer to the external field.

adapting field have different spectral compositions and it is preferable to use the general term *increment threshold* to cover all cases. It will be supposed (a) that pupil variations are eliminated by the use of an artificial pupil or by the correction of the results to refer to a pupil of fixed size, (b) that stimulus intensities are expressed in energy units (ergs per sec. entering the eye per square degree of external field) for monochromatic stimuli, and in luxons ($=$ photons) for mixed light stimuli.

Consider first a hypothetical retina possessing a unique relative spectral sensitivity function σ_λ. By this is meant that if, in any observation, the stimuli incident on the retina include an energy intensity W' of wave-length λ', the substitution of an energy intensity W'' of wave-length λ'' will be undetectable visually, where the ratio $(W'/W'') = (\sigma_{\lambda''}/\sigma_{\lambda'})$ depends on λ' and λ'' but on nothing else. If the increment threshold U_λ on a field of zero intensity is determined for a particular region of this retina, using a monochromatic test stimulus of prescribed size, exposure time etc., the values obtained will depend on the wavelength λ, let us say, in accordance with curve 1 in the left-hand panel of Fig. 1. Taking a particular test stimulus wave-length λ', and applying an adapting field of wave-length μ', the increase in the threshold as the intensity W_μ of the field is raised will be represented by a curve such as 2 in Fig. 1. From the assumption of a unique relative spectral sensitivity function σ_λ it follows that any change in the wave-lengths of the test stimulus will merely displace curve 2 bodily parallel to the axis of log U_λ by an amount determined by curve 1. Similarly a change in the wave-length μ of the adapting field will displace curve 2 parallel to the axis of log W_μ and the amount of the shift will be determined by a curve — curve 3 of Fig. 1 — which has the same shape as curve 1. (Note: it is convenient to plot log W_μ to half the scale of log U_λ, and the shape of curves 1 and 3 is then kept the same by plotting μ to half the scale of λ.) Thus the threshold properties of the hypothetical retinal area for the prescribed test stimulus are completely defined by the three curves 1, 2 and 3, of which 1 and 3 have the same shape.

It is useful to put this specification into symbols. Let the reciprocal threshold for a test stimulus of wave-length λ on a field of zero intensity be represented by S_λ, and let S_μ be the reciprocal of the

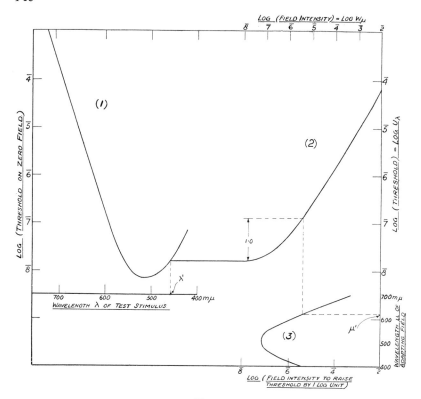

Fig. 1.

The curve of log (threshold) against log (field intensity) for a
single retinal mechanism, and its relation to the
spectral sensitivity curves of the mechanism

intensity of an adapting field of wave-length μ which raises the
threshold to 10 times its value on zero field. Then the threshold
U_λ for any values of λ, μ and W_μ is given by:

$$(I/U_\lambda) = S_\lambda \, \xi_s \, (W_\mu \, S_\mu),$$

where the empirical function ξ_s (x), is determined by the shape
of curve 2 and by the conditions:

$$\xi_s \, (o) = 1, \; \xi_s \, (1) = (1/10).$$

Adopting the usual convention that the relative spectral sensitivity
function σ_λ has the value 1 at the wave-length of maximum sensitivity, we put

$$S_\lambda = I_s \, \sigma_\lambda \quad S_\lambda = J_s \, \sigma_\lambda$$

where I_S and J_S will be called the test and field constants. They are independent of the wave-lengths but will in general depend on the other characteristics of test stimulus and adapting field.

Suppose that two individuals have retinae of the type in question but with different sensitivity functions, test constants, etc., and suppose they pool the information they receive from their eyes. If their retinae are similarly adapted and stimulated, the increment threshold of the 'team' will equal the smaller of the thresholds appropriate to each member observing separately. We ignore here the reduction in the resultant threshold by probability summation associated with the fact that there is always a considerable range of test stimulus intensity within which there is some probability, in between 0 and 1, of seeing the test stimulus. (See Stiles, 1944). The threshold response of the team will be represented by a diagram like that of Fig. 2, it being understood that for any value of log W_μ the lower of the two values of log U_λ given by the individual t.v.i. * curves must be taken. In general we may expect that for certain values of λ and μ, for example in the case illustrated, the individual t.v.i. curves will intersect and the resultant curve will be divided into low and high intensity ranges. Moreover the two parts of the resultant curve will move independently as λ and μ are varied. A diagram of precisely the same kind is to be expected if the two retinae belong to one individual and, while otherwise retaining their independence, have their end-organs intermingled to form one composite retina. They are then automatically subjected to the same conditions of stimulation. This, in its essentials, is the conception of the threshold sensitivity of the extrafoveal retina offered by the simple duplicity theory, and in many respects it corresponds with the facts. Experiment yields extrafoveal t.v.i. curves which show a clear division into low and high brightness ranges attributable respectively to rod and cone mechanisms with maximal sensitivities in the blue-green and yellow-green or yellow. This is well illustrated by the measurements of Hecht, Peskin & Patt (1938) for the case $\lambda = \mu$ (Fig. 3). When different wave-lengths are used for the test and adapting stimuli, curves with a still more marked transition can be obtained (Fig. 4). Experiment shows that the t.v.i. curve of the rod mechanism is

---

* t.v.i. curve (= threshold versus intensity curve) will be used as an abbreviation for any curve relating log (increment threshold) and log (field intensity).

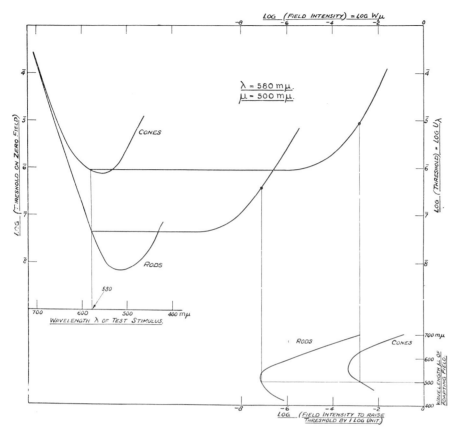

Fig. 2.

The curve of log (threshold) against log (field intensity) when
two retinal mechanisms are involved, for example, the rod
and cone mechanisms of parafoveal vision

displaced by changes in λ and μ in just the way described above
for a simple mechanism with a unique spectral sensitivity curve. This
is also substantially true for the t.v.i. curve of the cone mechanism
if the test stimulus is sufficiently large (1° or more in diameter)
and if attention is confined to the case $\lambda = \mu$. But when test
stimulus and adapting field have different wave-lengths, the theory
breaks down. It is found that the t.v.i. curve of the extrafoveal cone
mechanism cannot be regarded as a curve of fixed shape which is
merely displaced parallel to the axes of log U_λ and log W_μ
respectively by changes in λ and μ.

So far only extrafoveal vision has been considered but a similar complexity is observed in the t.v.i. curves of the cone mechanism obtained with foveal vision of a test stimulus which is small enough

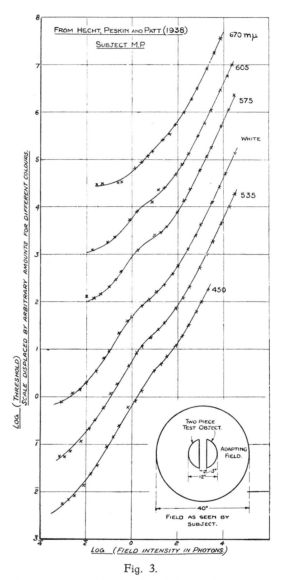

Fig. 3.

Variation of log (threshold) with log (field intensity) obtained with a flashing test stimulus (exposure time 0.04 sec.) and with test and adapting stimuli of the same colour (Hecht, Peskin & Patt, 1938)).

to lie wholly in the rod-free area of the retina. As the rod section is absent from such curves they provide much more satisfactory material on which to base a discussion of the threshold properties of cone vision.

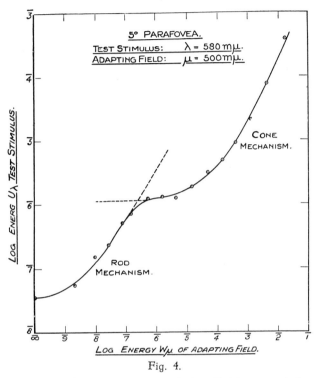

Fig. 4.

Variation of log (threshold) with log (field intensity) for a 1° flashing test stimulus of yellow light (exposure time 0.063 sec.) on a blue-green field: 5°- parafoveal vision. (Stiles, 1939)

Bearing in mind that the cone mechanism is responsible for colour vision, it is not surprising that the tentative theory of the sensitivity of the foveal (rod-free) retina to which we are led by measurements of the t.v.i. curves, postulates three component mechanisms. Each of these is assumed to respond in the same way as the hypothetical retina first considered, the spectral sensitivity functions, test and field constants being different for the different mechanisms. On the other hand the shapes of their t.v.i. curves are taken to be the same. Just as in the simple duplicity theory of extrafoveal vision. the resultant threshold of the combination is put equal, to a first approximation, to the smallest of the thresholds ot the component mechanisms.

TABLE 1.

Specification of the threshold sensitivity of the foveal retina.

Mechanism	Relative spectral sensitivity	Field Constant	Test Constant	Reciprocal threshold on zero field	Reciprocal of the intensity of an adapting field which raises the threshold by the factor 10
'red'	ϱ_λ	I_r	J_r	$r_\lambda = \varrho_\lambda \, I_r$	$R_\lambda = \varrho_\lambda \, J_r$
'green	γ_λ	I_g	J_g	$g_\lambda = \gamma_\lambda \, I_g$	$G_\lambda = \gamma_\lambda \, J_g$
'blue'	β_λ	I_b	J_b	$b_\lambda = \beta_\lambda \, I_b$	$B_\lambda = \beta_\lambda \, J_b$

Shape of the component t.v.i. curve defined by ξ (x) where ξ (o) = 1, ξ (1) = 1/10.

The diagram of Fig. 5 summarizes this theory and the necessary scheme of symbols is given in Table 1. Before proceeding it must be emphasized that Fig. 5 is based on observations made with a

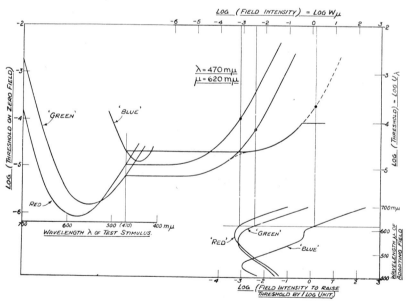

Fig. 5.

Relation of the curve of log (threshold) against log (field intensity) for foveal vision to the spectral sensitivity curves of the three cone mechanisms. (Stiles, 1939)

146

square test stimulus of about 1° side, i.e. with a test stimulus which covered a considerable proportion of the rod-free area and which therefore could give only some kind of average or resultant response. The recent work of Willmer & Wright (1945) and Thomson & Wright (1945) by colour-matching methods has shown clearly that the properties of the retina are by no means uniform over the rod-free area. Something will be said later about intrafoveal variations in threshold sensitivity but for the present we shall be concerned only with the response to the comparatively large, 1° test stimulus.

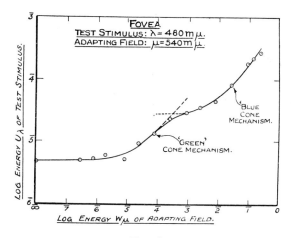

Fig. 6.

Variation of log (threshold) with log (field intensity) for foveal vision of a 1° flashing test stimulus, showing high and low brightness ranges attributable respectively to 'blue' and 'green' cone-machanismus. (Stiles, 1939)

The experimental basis for the diagram of Fig. 5 may be considered under two heads: (a) evidence that foveal t.v.i. curves can be resolved into components which are displaced parallel to the axes of $\log U\lambda$ and $\log W_{\mu}$ by changes in λ and μ respectively, (b) observations necessary to determine the spectral sensitivity functions and test and field constants of the mechanisms associated with the different components. The strongest evidence under (a) is obtained by taking a test stimulus with a wave-length λ in the range 460 to 490 mμ. and an adapting field of wavelength μ greater than 520 mμ. Fig. 6 shows a typical t.v.i. curve in this

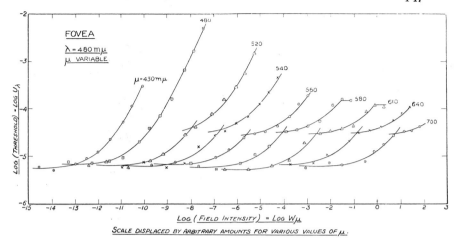

Fig. 7.

Effect on the curve of log (threshold) against log (field intensity) of changing the wave-length of the field keeping the test stimulus wave-length the same. Foveal vision of a 1° flashing test stimulus. (Stiles, 1939)

range with clearly defined low and high intensity components attributable respectively to the 'green' and 'blue' mechanisms. The relative lateral shift of the 'green' and 'blue' components as μ is changed, keeping λ constant, and the relative vertical shift as λ is changed, keeping μ constant, are illustrated in Figs. 7 and 8.

In the latter figure, it will be noted that for all values of λ the 'blue' component deviates from the t.v.i. curve of standard shape by flattening out when the 'blue' threshold has been raised by about 0.6 log units. This special feature of the 'blue' component curve (limited conditioning effect of long-wave light on the 'blue' mechanism) is observed when the adapting field has a wave-length above about 570mμ, and is probably associated with the secondary peak or hump which appears in the curve of log B_μ just above this wave-length. The intensity of the adapting field when the deviation from the standard shape begins is of the order of 30,000 luxons (= photons). The latest measurements show that the flattening of the 'blue' component curve is only temporary and that at still higher adapting intensities the increase in the threshold is resumed. Some evidence has recently been obtained of anomalies in the threshold response of the other mechanisms at very high adapting

148

intensities and an elaboration of the tentative theory to cover such cases will be necessary.

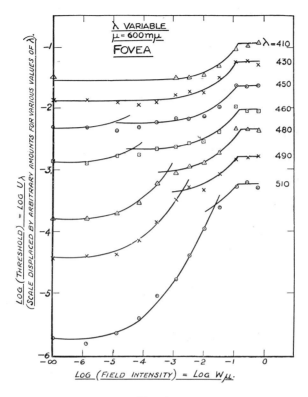

Fig. 8.

Effect on the curve of log (threshold) against log (field intensity) of changing the wave-length of the test stimulus keeping the field wave-length the same. Foveal vision of a 1° flashing test stimulus (Stiles, 1939)

Turning to heading (b) the methods used will be illustrated by one example. Admitting that for a deep red test stimulus the increment threshold on zero field is materially lower (say by 0.5 log units or more) for the 'red' mechanism than for the other two mechanisms, the low intensity section (corresponding to an increase in threshold of not more than 0.5 log units) of the observed t.v.i. curve for an adapting field of any wave-length μ. must coincide with the t.v.i. curve of the 'red' mechanism. From the position of the curve along the axis of log W_μ the quantity $J_r \, _{\rho\mu} = R_\mu$ defining the sensitivity of the 'red' mechanism to the adapting effect of the field can be determined for the whole spectrum. The curve of log $R\mu$ in Fig. 5 was derived in this way.

The question of the uniqueness of the spectral sensitivity functions and other constants of the three mechanisms determined from threshold measurements is a difficult one. We know that the spectral response curves yielded by colour-matching measurements are indeterminate to the extent of any linear transformation. While the derivation from threshold measurements is not subject to a similar formal indeterminacy, the accuracy of such measurements is low and the derived quantities are correspondingly indefinite. The difficulty of the analysis depends to a great extent on the distance apart in the spectrum of the respective spectral sensitivity curves. Thus the threshold properties of the mechanism with maximum sensitivity at about 440 mμ. can be determined with greater certainty than can the separate properties of the 'green' and 'red' mechanisms with maxima in the ranges 540—550 and 580—590 mμ. respectively.

With these cautionary remarks in mind, it may be noted that as regards position in the spectrum, the spectral sensitivity functions of Fig. 5 are in general agreement with the curves of Wright (1934) and Walters (1942) obtained by the method of binocular colour-matching, and with those of König & Dieterici (1892) and, more recently, those of Pitt (1947) which were based on a comparison of the colour-matching properties of normal and colour-defective subjects. Another important property of each mechanism is the ratio of the field and test constants, e.g. J_r / I_r For the 'green' and 'red' mechanisms this ratio has about the same value but for the 'blue' it is greater by a factor of about 5. The significance of the ratio is made clear by noting that when test and field stimuli have the same wave-length ($\lambda = \mu$), the ratio U_λ / W_λ corresponds to what is commonly called the Fechner fraction. Suppose that only one of the mechanisms — say the 'red' — is in action then

$$(U_\lambda/W_\lambda) = 1 \ (W_\lambda \ I_r \ _{\rho\lambda}) \ \xi \ (W_\lambda \ J_r \ _{\rho\lambda})$$

is the Fechner fraction of the 'red' mechanism. The empirical function $\xi \, (x)$ for $x > 2$ is represented approximately by the expression A/x where A is a constant. Thus the Fechner fraction of the 'red' mechanism approximates at high intensities to the value $\frac{J_r}{I_r} \cdot \frac{1}{A}$. It appears then that for the 'blue' mechanism the limiting Fechner fraction is some 5 times as large as for the 'green' or 'red'. This difference is closely related to the difference in luminosity factors associated with the blue, green and red unitary stimuli in the usual colorimetric theory (Stiles, 1946 b).

The diagram of Fig. 5 refers specifically to one eye, an eye which by the usual tests of colour vision was classed as normal. The most characteristic feature — the splitting of the t.v.i. curve for a blue test stimulus on an orange (or red) adapting field into low and high intensity components corresponding to the 'green' and 'blue' mechanisms — has been confirmed for 20 subjects (18 normal, 1 deuteranomalous, 1 protanopic) (Stiles, 1946 a). There are however large variations in the positions of the two components in the diagram, including variations in their relative positions. From the last observation, it follows that in passing from one individual to another the modifications in the sensitivities — test and field — are not generally the same for the green' and 'blue' mechanisms. As regards the 'green' and 'red' mechanisms it is probable that the subject of Fig. 5 is exceptional in having a sensitivity curve log r_λ for the 'red' mechanism which reaches a higher maximum value than that of the corresponding 'green' curve, log g_λ. Experimentally this corresponds to the fact that for this subject the sensitivity (reciprocal threshold) on zero field has its greatest value at about 590 mμ. as compared with about 560 mμ. for most subjects (Wald, 1945). Confirmation of the approximate positions *along the spectrum* of the relative spectral sensitivity functions is provided by the results of de Vries (1946) who used methods rather similar to that described above for the determination of R_μ.

It would be of considerable interest if in t.v.i. curves such as that of Fig. 6, the low brightness or green' component could be followed to intensities above the point of intersection with the high brightness or 'blue' component. There seems to be some possibility of doing this. Consider, for example, an experiment in which two monochromatic test stimuli, one in the violet and one in the blue-green, are exposed side by side on an orange adapting field. From the scheme of Fig. 5 we should expect the positions of the component

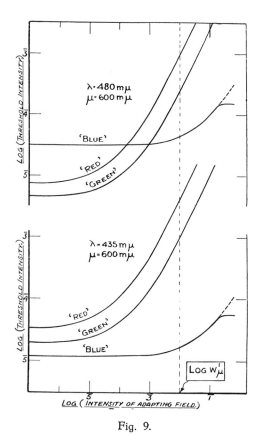

Fig. 9.

Derivation of the curves of log (threshold) against log (field
intensity) from the component curves of the three cone
mechanisms.

t.v.i. curves for these stimuli to be as shown in Fig. 9. At a high
adapting intensity W^1 above the intersection of the 'blue' and
green curves for $\lambda = 480$ mμ., suppose the intensities of the two
stimuli to be adjusted to their respective threshold values. As both
test stimuli are seen by means of the 'blue' mechanism they should
be indistinguishable in all respects including apparent colour, and
this should continue to be true if their intensities are increased
together in the same proportion until, for $\lambda = 480$ mμ., the threshold
of the green' mechanism is reached. At that intensity or perhaps
a little above it, we may expect the two stimuli to be distinguishable.
Preliminary experiments on these lines indicate that the two stimuli

do in fact appear similar over a certain range above the threshold, and begin to differ in apparent colour at about the expected intensity.

In passing from the low to the high intensity range of t.v.i. curves showing the transition from the 'green' to the 'blue' mechanism (e.g. Fig. 6), the appearance of the test stimulus at just above the threshold changes. The apparent colour becomes purplish instead of blue or blue-green and there is a loss in sharpness of outline. The latter effect suggests that the 'blue' mechanism has an intrinsically lower *acuity* than the 'green' mechanism, at least for intensities near the threshold. Some measurements bearing on this point are reproduced in Fig. 10. The test stimulus consisted of a

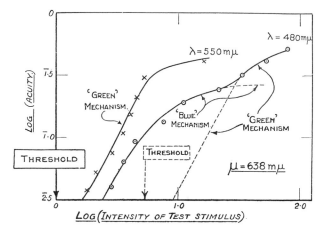

Fig. 10.

Visual acuity for perception of detail in a 1° light patch of wave-length 480 mμ. or 550 mμ. when viewed on an adapting field of wave-length 638 mμ. and intensity 1500 luxons. Intensity of the 1° patch expressed in terms of the threshold value as unit

chess-board pattern of small squares covering in all a square of 1° side. This was exposed in flashes of 1 sec. on an adapting field of wave-length $\mu = 638$ mμ. and of high intensity equal to about 1,500 luxons. The critical intensity of the test stimulus at which the detail in the pattern could just be distinguished was determined for various sizes of detail, and a measurement of the increment threshold for a single light square of 1° side was made at the same time. It is clear from Fig. 10 that for $\lambda = 480$ mμ., where the 'blue' mechanism is responsible for perception at and near the threshold, the acuity at an intensity of say 3 times the threshold intensity is considerably lower than for $\lambda = 550 \, m\mu$. where the 'green' mechanism is responsible for the threshold perception. The curves relating log (acuity) and log (test stimulus intensity) are different in the two cases and a tentative analysis of the curve for $\lambda = 480 \, m\mu$. into 'blue' and 'green' components is indicated by the broken lines in the figure. It is consistent with a threshold of the 'green' mechanism exceeding by approx. 0.75 log units that of the 'blue', which is within 0.1 log unit of the difference to be expected from the theoretical scheme of Fig. 5.

Reverting to increment thresholds proper, the curves of Fig. 11

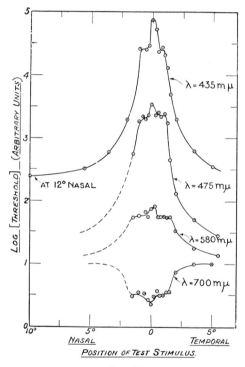

Fig. 11.

Variation of the threshold across the dark-adapted fovea and parafovea for small test stimuli (10′ square) of various wave-lengths: zero adapting field

show the kind of variation in threshold sensitivity across the fovea and parafovea which is obtained when a small test stimulus — in this case 10 min. in diam. — is used. The measurements refer to an eye properly adapted to a field of zero intensity. For $\lambda =$ 435 mμ., the steeply descending outer sections of the curve are certainly to be attributed to rod vision, but the sharp maximum in between is a property of cone vision. Although for the subject used this maximum is rather sharper than for 3 other subjects studied, the central maximum is a general property which many people can observe qualitatively by slightly shifting fixation on and off a small deep-blue test stimulus of near-threshold intensity. According to most subjects the test stimulus at the position of maximum threshold appears relatively green. As the wave-length λ is increased above 435 mμ., the rod sections of the curve are raised relatively, exposing more of the central section. At the same time, the central maximum is reduced and finally in the red it becomes a minimum. The general principle by which we may attempt to explain these variations is suggested in the scheme of Fig. 12 which refers to a test stimulus in the violet. The four curves

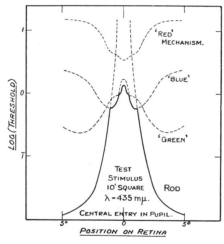

Fig. 12.

Tentative scheme showing the variation of the thresholds of the rods and three cone mechanisms across the fovea and parafovea for a small test stimulus of wave-length 435 mμ.: zero adapting field

represent tentatively the variations in the thresholds of the rod and the three cone mechanisms as the fovea and parafovea is traversed with a small test stimulus. When the wave-length of the test stimulus is changed each of these curves is assumed to move up or down parallel to the axis of log U_λ by an amount determined by the spectral sensitivity curve of the corresponding mechanism. Also if the retina is exposed to an adapting field, say of wave-length μ and intensity W_μ the curves are supposed to be similarly displaced by amounts depending on μ and W_μ, in the same manner as the thresholds of the different mechanisms for a 1° test stimulus are raised by an adapting field according to the scheme of Fig. 5.

However, this simple picture is complicated by several factors. In the first place, when moving the test stimulus from one retinal position to another the rays reaching the end-organs may be absorbed to different extents by pigment in the upper layers of the retina, and even if the end-organs of a given mechanism have an invariable spectral sensitivity function the selectivity of this pigment layer will alter the shape of the traverse curve of that mechanism in Fig. 12, as λ is varied. It can probably be assumed that at a given retinal position pigmentation produces the same proportional change in the threshold for all four mechanisms so that distortions of the traverse curves from this cause will not modify the order in which the mechanisms are arranged, at each retinal point, by the magnitudes of their thresholds.

A sufficiently complicated pigment layer involving two or more pigments of different spectral absorptions would enable the variations with position and wave-length of the threshold on zero field to be explained completely by pigmentation, assuming no variation across the fovea and parafovea of the sensitivity of the under-lying retinal mechanisms. If the absolute sensitivity of these mechanisms (but not the relative sensitivity through the spectrum) is allowed to vary from point to point, a layer containing a single pigment will probably suffice, to the experimental accuracy available. But when thresholds on an adapting field are considered, an explanation in terms of pigmentation breaks down. This is shown by measurements of the t.v.i. curves for the combination $\lambda = 475$ mμ., $\mu = 600$ mμ., made with a small test stimulus imaged (a) on the foveal centre (b) about $\frac{1}{2}$° to the side of the foveal centre (Fig. 13). The pigment hypothesis would predict that the two t.v.i. curves could be brought into superposition as a whole by displacements parallel to the two axes. This is clearly not the case. The 'blue' and 'green' components of the curve require different displacements to bring them together, indicating that there are differences in properties of the

156

underlying mechanisms at different retinal points in addition to such differences as there may be in the pigmentation of the upper retinal layers. The results of colour-matching measurements in the foveal area (Thomson & Wright, 1945) also provide convincing evidence of point to point differences in the retinal mechanisms which cannot be explained by pigmentation.

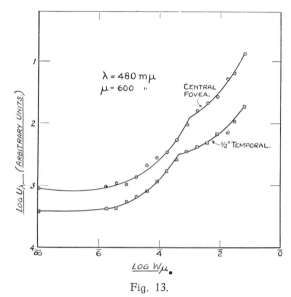

Fig. 13.

Curves of log (threshold) against log (field intensity) for a small test stimulus of wave-length 475 mμ. on a field of wave-length 600 mμ. viewed (a) at the centre of the fovea (b) ½° to the temporal side of the fovea

Fig. 13 illustrates another complication of the simple scheme. Certainly for the 'blue' mechanism, and possibly for the 'green', the component t.v.i. curve is moved along the axis of log W_μ as well as along the axis of log U_λ, when the retinal position is altered. It follows that the threshold traverse curve for the 'blue' has a different form on different adapting fields.

The comparison of thresholds for test stimuli of different sizes brings out further complications of an interesting kind, which will be illustrated by some measurements made recently by Mlle Flamant and myself. They refer to a single eye (F.F., right eye) and it is not yet possible to say how far they represent general properties. The test stimulus was viewed at 3° in the parafovea, a region where the rod mechanism plays a dominating role in vision at low intensities. The t.v.i. curve for a 1° square test stimulus of wave-length 435 mμ. on an adapting field of wave-length 490 mμ. is shown in Fig. 14(a). It is a typical parafoveal curve with low and high intensity components attributable to rod and cone vision respectively. Assuming a close similarity between the foveal and 3° parafoveal cone systems, the upper component with a test stimulus wave-length of 435 mμ. would be associated with the 'blue' cone mechanism. But for a 10' test stimulus a curve of different shape was obtained which could be represented by three components. (Fig. 14b). By other observations on the effects of changing the wave-lengths of the test stimulus and the adapting field it was found that the uppermost component of the curve of Fig. 14 (b) corresponds to a mechanism with a maximum sensitivity at about 440 mμ. i.e. to the 'blue' mechanism, while the middle component corresponds to a mechanism with maximum at about 540 mμ. i.e. to the 'green' mechanism. That the rod mechanism is responsible only for the lowest component was checked by comparing the thresholds obtained when the test stimulus was sent into the eye (a) through the centre (b) near the edge of the pupil. It was found that the point of entry made no difference to the threshold for the lowest component while for the middle and upper components the threshold showed the usual directional sensitivity associated with cone vision. According to these results, the absolute cone threshold for a 10' stimulus deep in the blue and viewed parafoveally is no more than about 10—20 times the rod threshold. This, at first rather surprising conclusion, appears to result from the relatively poor spatial integration of the 'green' mechanism. Comparing curves (a) and (b) in Fig. 14 it is found that the effect of changing from a 60 min. to a 10 min. square test stimulus is to raise the rod component parallel to the log U_λ axis by about 1.3 log units. This is not very different from the shift to be expected (1.5 log units) if the threshold were inversely proportional to the area. For the 'blue' component (uppermost component) there is a similar upward shift of about the same amount but for the 'green' component which is perhaps just detectable in Fig. 14a the shift is less by at least 0.4 log units. It appears therefore that in the parafovea the spatial integration of the rod and 'blue' mechanisms is very similar in amount but for the 'green' it is materially lower. On the

158

basis of this result it seems that .for this subject the 'blue' and 'green' traverses for a test stimulus of wave-length 435 mμ. on a dark field between the central fovea and the 3° parafoveal point must

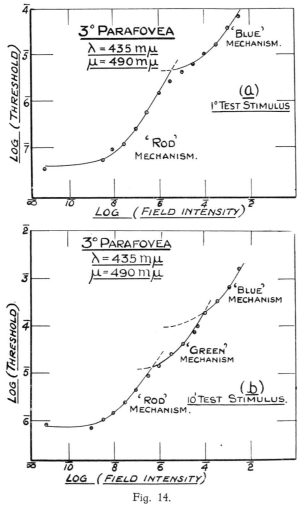

Fig. 14.

Curves of log (threshold) against log (field intensity) for a square test stimulus (a) of 1° side (b) of 10′ side viewed at 3° to the temporal side of the fovea: wave-lengths of the test stimulus and field, 435 mμ. and 490 mμ. respectively

intersect, the 'green' threshold at 3° being of the order of 1 log uniit below the 'blue'. This conclusion has been incorporated in the tentative scheme of Fig. 12. There is some evidence of a similar difference of integrative properties of the 'blue' and 'green' and also of the 'red' mechanism in the actual foveal area. The lower visual acuity of the 'blue' mechanism noted above may also be related to these differences. But intrafoveal variations in threshold sensitivity make it more difficult to draw conclusions about integrative properties in that region.

Because of the complicating factors enumerated above we have only a very rudimentary knowledge of the threshold sensitivities of the various mechanisms in the foveal and parafoveal retina. The sorting-out of the effects of the different factors — pigmentation, variations in sensitivity of the underlying mechanisms, difference in spatial integration, modifications produced by the adapting field — offers a promising field for further experimental work.

In all the foregoing, we have been concerned with the retina in a steady state, fully adapted to the field. For the development of the duplicity theory, measurements of the increment threshold while the condition of the retina is in process of changing have been even more important than observations in the steady state. The most significant feature of work on these lines is the two-phase recovery curve showing how the threshold falls when a high intensity adapting field to which the retina has been exposed is extinguished. Such curves are obtained when the test stimulus falls on regions of the retina containing both cone and rod mechanisms. The initial and final phases of the curve are attributable respectively to these mechanisms. Recently Wald has applied the two-phase recovery curve to the determination of the spectral sensitivity curve of the parafoveal cones. Using monochromatic test stimuli the value to which the initial, cone phase of the recovery curve asymptotes at long times has been determined as a function of wave-length. The spectral sensitivity curve arrived at in this way is generally similar to that of the foveal cones but there are certain differences which Wald relates to differences in retinal pigmentation. *

From the results obtained under steady conditions when different colours are used for the adapting field and the test stimulus, it might be expected that a similar device would yield recovery curves showing the operation of different cone mechanisms. For this purpose recovery curves for foveal (rod-free) vision would of course

---

* Reference may be made to Prof. Wald's paper to the Conference for an adequate account of this work.

be of primary interest. Up to now no foveal recovery curves showing two or more phases which might be related to different cone mechanisms have been reported. It is true that the cones recover much more quickly than the rods and the detection of different phases will certainly be more difficult on that account. But the measurements of Mandelbaum & Mintz (1941) suggest that there is a more radical difficulty. These workers found comparatively little difference in the foveal recovery curves obtained with different colours of the test stimulus and the adapting field when for the latter a fixed intensity of approximately 1600 luxons was used. They compared the recovery curves — log (threshold) against time — by displacing them parallel to the ordinate axis so that the final thresholds coincided. According to Mandelbaum & Mintz, if the spectral sensitivity curves of the three mechanisms were widely separated in the spectrum — as we are led to believe from steady state measurements of various kinds — there should be much greater differences in the recovery curves than were actually observed. For this reason they regard their results as supporting the theory of Hecht in which the spectral sensitivity curves of the three cone mechanisms have their maxima very close together in the centre of the spectrum. Without necessarily accepting the deductions made by Mandelbaum & Mintz, we must admit that their results show the operation of some factor in the recovery of the cone mechanisms which invalidates the simplest application of the notion of three cone mechanisms with widely separated spectral sensitivity curves. A little light is thrown on this point by some recent measurements of foveal recovery made at the National Physical Laboratory. These are no more than preliminary measurements but it is unlikely that uncertainty in the observations can affect the main trend of the results.

In Fig. 15 the circle points represent the observed variation with wave-length of log (sensitivity), i.e. log (1/threshold), for the dark-adapted fovea, obtained with a 1° square test stimulus of exposure time 0.2 sec. The subject is the same as that used for the results summarized in Fig. 5, and the exceptionally low threshold in the red is reproduced. The corresponding variation when the retina was adapted to a high intensity (20,000 luxons approx.) of red light ($\mu = 640$ mμ.) is shown by the cross points. In accordance with the general scheme of Fig. 5, the drop in sensitivity in the blue end of the spectrum where the 'blue' mechanism is responsible for vision of the test stimulus, is much smaller than in the centre and in the red end, where the 'green' and 'red' mechanisms come into play. The reductions in log (sensitivity) are approximately 0.6 for $\lambda = 440$ mμ. 2.2 for $\lambda = 540$ mμ. and 3.5 for $\lambda = 670$ mμ.

The threshold through the spectrum was then determined at a series of times 2, 5, 8, 11, 14 sec. after the abrupt extinction of the high intensity red field, that is to say, at five instants in the initial stages of the recovery process. In Fig. 15 the spectral sensitivity after 2 sec. recovery is shown by the square points. We have the

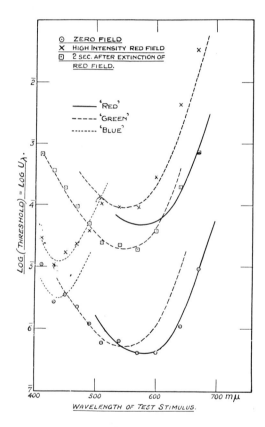

Fig. 15.

Curves showing the variation with wave-length of the threshold of a 1° flashing test stimulus viewed foveally (a) when the retina was adapted to zero brightness (b) when the retina was adapted to a field of wave-length 640 mμ. and intensity 20.000 luxons (c) during the recovery of the retina from condition (b) at 2 sec. after the extinction of the field

remarkable result that while for wave-lengths of the test-stimulus greater than 490 mμ. approx, the sensitivity has increased, i.e. there has been positive recovery, for shorter wave-lengths the sensitivity is actually less than while the adapting field was still exposed. Two other subjects show similar if rather less extreme differences in recovery rate for stimuli in the blue and in the rest of the spectrum.

In Fig. 15 the observations for each condition have been roughly fitted with the three spectral sensitivity curves originally derived for this eye (Stiles, 1939). (To suit the cross points the 'green' curve should be more sharply ascending in the red; there is other evidence that a change in the original curve in this sense is required). In terms of these fitted curves we may say that on the extinction of the adapting field the sensitivity of the 'blue' mechanism instead of increasing progressively over the 0.6 log unit range necessary to reach the final dark-adaptation level, suddenly drops by an amount so great that the 'green' mechanism, whose sensitivity has recovered in a normal manner, takes over threshold vision of the test stimulus throughout the whole of the blue end of the spectrum. As regards the 'red' mechanism the interpretation is much less certain, but it appears that the steady red adapting field depresses the sensitivity of the 'red' so much compared with the 'green' mechanism that the latter is responsible for threshold vision of the test stimulus down to the extreme red. However, in the 2 sec. recovery curve the sensitivity of the 'red' mechanism has begun to catch up on that of the 'green'. The recovery curves at the later times studied are generally similar to the 2 sec. curve except that the sensitivity has increased throughout the spectrum.

The anomalous behaviour of the 'blue' cone mechanism in recovering dark-adaptation after exposure to an intense red adapting field is probably connected with the relatively long time taken for this mechanism to become adapted to high intensities. If the retina is dark-adapted and an adapting field of high brightness is exposed, the increment threshold has initially a value higher than that reached after the eye has become adapted to the bright field. Defining light-adaptation time as the time after exposing the field, for the threshold to drop to twice the final value, it is found that for a red or orange adapting field which ultimately raises the threshold for the 'blue' mechanism by a relatively small amount (say 0.3 log units) the light-adaptation time for blue stimuli is of the order of one minute or more. On the other hand, for green and red test stimuli whose thresholds are raised by the field by much larger factors, the light-adaptation time is of the order of 10 sec. or less. (Stiles, 1946d).

The experiments just described and other similar ones both by the threshold method and also by Wright's method of binocular colour matching, show that the dynamics of the cone mechanisms — the way they behave when the retina is moving from one equilibrium condition to another — are not in accordance with the straightforward notions of recovery curves which work fairly well in dealing with the rod mechanism. Perhaps it is to differences in the dynamics of the different cone mechanisms rather than to a different choice of their spectral sensitivity curves that our attention should be directed by the results of Mandelbaum & Mintz.

This paper is published by permission of the Director of the National Physical Laboratory. The investigations referred to under the author's name were carried out as part of the Research Programme of the Laboratory.

REFERENCES.

Hecht, S. Peskin J. C. & Patt, M. (1938). J. gen. Physiol. *22*, 7.

König, A. & Dieterici, V. V. (1892). Zeits f. Psych. u Physiol. der Sinnesorgane, *4*, 241.

Mandelbaum, J. & Mintz, E. U. (1941). Am. J. Ophthalm. *24*, 1241.

Pitt, J. H. G. (1944). Proc. Roy. Soc. B. *132*, 101.

Stiles, W. S. (1939). Proc. Roy. Soc. B. *127*, 64.

Stiles, W. S. (1944). Proc. phys. Soc. *56*, 329.

Stiles, W. S. (1946a). Proc. Roy. Soc. B. *133*, 418.

Stiles, W. S. (1946b). Proc. phys. Soc. *58*, 41.

Stiles, W. S. (1946c). J. opt Soc. Amer. *36*, 491.

Stiles, W. S. (1946d). Proc. of the Reunion d'Opticiens, Paris 1946 (In the press).

Thomson, L. C. & Wright, W. D. (1945). J. Physiol. *105*, 316.

de Vries, H. (1946). J. opt. Soc. Amer. *36*, 124.

Walters, H. V. (1942). Proc. Roy. Soc. B. *131*, 27.

Wald, G. (1945). Science, *101*, 653.

Willmer, E. N. & Wright, W. D. (1945). Nature, London. *156*, 119.

Wright, W. D. (1939). Proc. Roy. Soc. B. *115*, 49.

Errata

Page 139. Last line: replace β_λ by s_λ.

Page 140. 3rd line below figure caption: replace γ by λ.
4th line below figure caption: replace σ_λ by s_λ.
Last line: replace β_λ by s_λ.

Page 149. Formula 4th line up, right-hand side of equality sign: delete 1, enclose the whole of the following expression in braces and add the upper suffix $^{-1}$ outside the brace. Thus 1 $(W_\lambda I_r \rho_\lambda)\xi(W_\lambda J_r \rho_\lambda)$ is replaced by $\{(W_\lambda I_r \rho_\lambda)\xi(W_\lambda J_r \rho_\lambda)\}^{-1}$.

Paper VIII: Reprinted from Transactions of the Optical Convention of the Worshipful Company of Spectacle Makers, 1948.

THE PHYSICAL INTERPRETATION OF THE SPECTRAL SENSITIVITY CURVE OF THE EYE

By W. S. STILES, O.B.E., D.Sc.

(*The National Physical Laboratory*)

Perhaps the most important single fact in our knowledge of the visual process is the close similarity of the curve showing the relative sensitivity of the dark-adapted eye to light of different wavelengths, as determined by subjective measurements, and the curves showing the spectral absorption and bleaching of solutions of the photosensitive substance, visual purple, which is extracted from the retina. From this similarity it can be concluded that the first stage in the process by which we see with the dark-adapted eye consists in the absorption of light by molecules of visual purple contained in the retinal rods, the chromophore groups of the visual purple molecules, *i.e.* the parts of the molecule responsible for absorption in the visible spectrum and hence for the colour of the substance, being destroyed or radically modified in the process. Although this conclusion was generally accepted, it was not until 1937 that it was pointed out, by Dartnall and Goodeve, that the effect of light on visual purple, like other photochemical reactions, must be governed by quantum principles, and that the basis of comparison of the subjective spectral sensitivity curve and the absorption and bleaching curves of visual purple must be modified. The result of making this modification was to produce a slight improvement in the agreement of the curves. After a brief explanation of Dartnall and Goodeve's important argument, I propose to repeat their comparison of the subjective and physical measurements, using the more recent experimental data now available on all the quantities concerned. In conclusion, some observations will be made on the form of the curves on the red side of the maximum.

In determining the spectral sensitivity of a light-sensitive mechanism such as the eye the general principle is to find for stimuli of different wavelength the intensivies in energy units necessary to produce identical effects on the mechanism. For the dark-adapted retina the most direct method is to measure the smallest perceptible intensity or absolute threshold for a light patch of fixed size and exposed for a fixed time interval, which is observed in such a way that the image falls on a particular extrafoveal area. The extrafoveal retina must be used because in the fovea of the normal eye the mechanism possessing all the properties we associate with dark-adaptation is absent. The results obtained in this way are usually represented by plotting to a log scale the so-called threshold sensitivity, *i.e.* the reciprocal of the absolute threshold $1/W_\lambda$, against the wavelength λ. Instead of measuring the absolute threshold as a function of wavelength we may measure the energy intensity of a monochromatic light which matches in brightness a fixed white light of low intensity in a large bipartite photometric matching field. Alternatively the monochromatic light may be introduced into the visual field as a secondary stimulus and the energy intensity necessary to raise by a given factor the threshold for a primary stimulus of fixed colour may be measured. Provided the conditions are so arranged that it is the action of light on the retinal rods which is concerned, the relative energies of different wavelengths required to produce the same effect are found to be substantially the same in all these methods (Stiles, 1948).

On the hypothesis that it is the absorption of light by the visual purple of the rods which is the first stage in the visual process, we might argue that if different energies $W'_{\lambda'}$ and $W''_{\lambda''}$ of wavelengths λ' and λ'' respectively, produce identical visual effects, this is because the absorption factor of the visual purple layer in the rods has different values for λ' and λ'', so that the energy actually absorbed in the two cases is the same. This would entail

$$p_{\lambda'}W'_{\lambda'} = p_{\lambda''}W''_{\lambda''} \quad \dots\dots\dots\dots\dots\dots\dots\dots\dots\dots\dots(1)$$

where $p_{\lambda'}$ and $p_{\lambda''}$ are the absorption factors. This is not quite right, as the optic media of the eye and the upper layers of the retina through which the light has to pass to reach the visual purple may have different transmission factors $t_{\lambda'}$ and $t_{\lambda''}$ respectively for the two wavelengths. Allowing for such a difference (1) becomes

$$t_{\lambda'}p_{\lambda'}W'_{\lambda'} = t_{\lambda''}p_{\lambda''}W''_{\lambda''} \quad \dots\dots\dots\dots\dots\dots\dots\dots(2)$$

or, in general, $1/(W_\lambda t_\lambda)$ should be proportional to p_λ. This was the original basis of comparison of the subjective and the objective measurements. According to quantum concepts, however, we have to think of a beam of monochromatic radiation, not as a continuous energy flow but as a stream of particles—light-quants or photons as they are called—each of fixed energy content hv, where v is the frequency of the light and h is Planck's constant ($h = 6 \cdot 56 \cdot 10^{-27}$ erg sec.). Absorption of light by a molecule immersed in such a stream can consist only in the capture of a complete light-quant by the molecule, the latter being raised, in the process, from its normal or ground state to a higher excited state of greater energy. Thus if a monochromatic stimulus of wavelength λ comprising N light-quants, *i.e.* of total energy $W_\lambda = Nhv$, is incident on a layer of visual purple molecules of absorption factor p_λ, the number of light-quants absorbed, and hence the number of molecules raised to the excited state, will be $p_\lambda N = p_\lambda W_\lambda / hv$. Assuming that it is the number of excited molecules which determines the subsequent visual effect, the condition for the visual equivalence of two stimuli of different wavelengths becomes

$$t_\lambda' p_{\lambda'}W'_{\lambda'}/hv' = t_\lambda'' p_{\lambda''}W''_{\lambda''}/hv'' \quad \dots\dots\dots\dots\dots\dots(3)$$

or, in general, $hv/(W_\lambda t_\lambda)$ should be proportional to p_λ.

The primary process in excitation by the absorption of a quantum of visible or ultra-violet light consists in the transfer of one of the electrons in the molecule from the orbit of lowest to one of higher energy. At the same time the vibrational energy associated with the relative motion of the different atoms in the molecule, and the rotational energy, if the molecule is free to rotate, will also change. In every case the increase in total energy —electronic, vibrational and rotational—must equal exactly the energy of the absorbed light-quant. As the possible vibrational and rotational energies of a molecule are limited to certain discrete values by quantum conditions, this means, in the case of simple molecules of substances in the gaseous state, that the absorption spectrum corresponding to a particular electronic transfer will consist of a system of fine absorption lines. But it may happen that the electron transfer makes the molecule unstable, so that excitation is followed immediately by the disruption of the molecule. In that case light-quants of all frequencies above a certain minimum can be absorbed, that is to say, a continuous absorption spectrum is obtained as the kinetic energy of the separating parts of the molecule, which is not quantised, always enables the balance-of-energy condition to be satisfied exactly. For complex molecules of substances in the liquid or dissolved states, the broadening and overlapping of lines which occurs may give the appearance of a continuous spectrum even in the absence of dissociation. However, for visual purple, which in fact gives a continuous absorption spectrum, the bleaching action of light provides direct evidence that excitation is followed by a radical change in the molecule—perhaps the breaking-off of a part or some re-arrangement of the atoms—as a result of which a different chemical species is produced having, in particular, different light-absorbing properties.

Our present conception of the visual purple molecule is that it is a conjugated protein—a massive protein molecule (molecular weight estimated at 270,000 by Hecht and Pickels, 1938) to which are conjoined several very much lighter molecular groups (about 10, according to Broda, Goodeve and Lythgoe, 1940) resembling but not identical with molecules of carotene, the organic pigment of the carrot. These carotenoid appendages form the so-called *chromophore groups* where the electron transfer corresponding to the characteristic light absorption of visual purple takes place. It appears that as far as light absorption is concerned, the chromophore groups may be treated as independent centres, very much as though they were independent molecules. Thus after the excitation of a chromophore group by absorption of a light-quant, it is the chromophore group which breaks off or undergoes some re-arrangement of its atoms. But the number of chromophores destroyed does not necessarily equal the number of light-quants absorbed. There is a possibility that after excitation the chromophore may dissipate its excitation energy in " collisions " with the solvent molecules and may slip back to its original state unchanged. On the other hand the destruction of a chromophore group may conceivably initiate a purely chemical secondary reaction leading to the destruction of further chromophore groups. Thus the *quantum yield* γ_λ—the ratio of the number of chromophore groups destroyed to the number of light-quants absorbed—may have a value greater or less than unity. The work of Lythgoe, Goodeve and their collaborators

(1939, 1942) on the bleaching of visual purple solutions by monochromatic light has enabled them to determine, not γ_λ itself, but the product $\gamma_\lambda a_\lambda$ where a_λ is the absorption coefficient per chromophore group. The observed absorption coefficient a_λ of an actual solution of visual purple will equal $a_\lambda C$ where C is the number of chromophore groups per unit volume. Unfortunately the concentration C cannot be measured directly, but for a given solution a_λ will be proportional to a_λ, and by comparison of a_λ with $\gamma_\lambda a_\lambda$ the dependence of γ_λ on wavelength can be derived.

Turning now to the experimental values of the quantities discussed above, the three main curves of Fig. 1 represent the following experimental data:

Curve I.   Log (absorption coefficient) $= \log a_\lambda$ for visual purple solutions.   Mean results of Lythgoe (1937), Wald (1938), Chase and Haig (1938), extended to 365 mμ using the curve quoted by Goodeve, Lythgoe and Schneider (1942).

Curve II.   Log (photosensitivity of visual purple in solution) $= \log \gamma_\lambda a_\lambda$. Results of Schneider, Goodeve and Lythgoe (1939) and Goodeve, Lythgoe, and Schneider (1942).

Curve III.   Log (spectral sensitivity of the dark-adapted parafoveal retina expressed on the quantum basis and corrected for light losses in the optic media) $= \log (h\nu/t_\lambda W_\lambda)$.   Mean curve based on Wald's values of $1/W_\lambda$ by a threshold method (1945) and Crawford's values by a brightess-matching method (1948).   Correction factor t_λ derived from a mean curve based on Ludvigh and McCarthy's direct measurement of total absorption of the eye media (1938) and derivations by Wald (1945) and Wright (1944) of the eye-lens absorption from comparisons of visual thresholds for normal and aphakic eyes.

In each case the quantity plotted has been multiplied by a suitable constant factor to bring its maximum value to unity and the variation with the reciprocal wavelength $1/_\lambda$ rather than with the wavelength λ is shown. This is generally preferable when quantum theory considerations are involved as $1/_\lambda$ is proportional to the energy of a single light-quant of the wavelength in question ($1/_\lambda = h\nu/hc$. $c =$ velocity of light).

In the immediate region of the maximum where the data are most reliable the three curves of Fig. 1 are closely superimposed and their respective maximum-wavelengths are not detectably different.   On the old energy method of representing the subjective data (log ($1/t_\lambda W_\lambda$) plotted instead of log ($h\nu/t_\lambda W_\lambda$), Curve III would be displaced towards the red.   As shown in the subsidiary Curves IV and V the actual displacement is quite small— about 4 mμ shift in maximum-wavelength.   Nevertheless the fact that, as first shown by Dartnall and Goodeve, this small discrepancy is removed by adopting the quantum basis, must be regarded as indicating the correctness of the latter.

In moving out from the maximum it is clear that Curve III falls below the other curves.   Direct comparison of the shapes of the curves assumes that the absorption factor p_λ of the visual purple layer in the actual rods may be taken as proportional to the absorption coefficient a_λ.   This is true only if the absorption factor at the wavelength of maximum absorption is small so that we may put $p_\lambda = 1 - e^{-a_\lambda d} = a_\lambda d$ approx. ($d =$ effective thickness

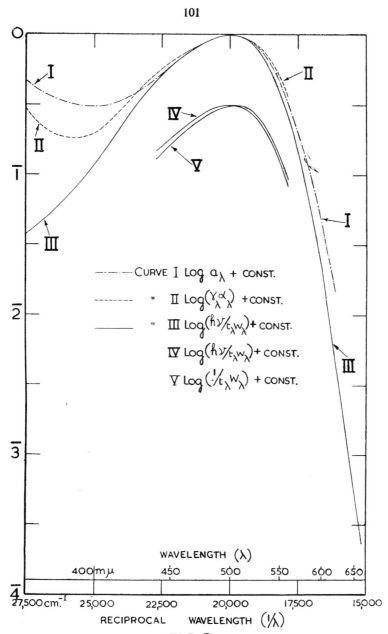

CURVE I $\log a_\lambda$ + CONST.

" II $\log(\gamma_\lambda \alpha_\lambda)$ + CONST.

" III $\log(h\nu/t_\lambda w_\lambda)$ + CONST.

IV $\log(h\nu/t_\lambda w_\lambda)$ + CONST.

V $\log(1/t_\lambda w_\lambda)$ + CONST.

WAVELENGTH (λ)

400 mμ 450 500 550 600 650

27,500 cm.$^{-1}$ 25,000 22,500 20,000 17,500 15,000

RECIPROCAL WAVELENGTH $(1/\lambda)$

FIG. I.

of the layer). A correction of Curve III to allow for the inaccuracy of this assumption must make the curve sharper, *i.e.* it will increase the discrepancy with the other curves, but from estimates which have been made of the density of the visual purple layer in the dark-adapted human retina, it is probable that the extremities of Curve III are not lowered by more than 0·1 log units if such a correction is applied. The position of the maximum-wavelength is unaffected by the correction.

What is the significance of the marked divergence of the three curves as the ultraviolet is approached, *i.e.* as λ falls below about 430 mμ? For wavelengths above 430 mμ the absorption coefficient a_λ (Curve I) and the photosensitivity $\gamma_\lambda a_\lambda$ (Curve II) agree closely. In this range therefore the quantum efficiency is very nearly independent of wavelength and in fact Dartnall, Goodeve, and Lythgoe (1938) have been able to conclude from other evidence that it must be either equal to unity or only slightly less. Below 430 mμ, however, Curve II passes beneath Curve I, that is to say there is a drop in the quantum efficiency. This seems to be associated with the secondary rise in the absorption curve which is attributed by Goodeve, Lythgoe, and Schneider (1942) to an absorption band at 360 mμ corresponding to an electron transition to a higher level than that responsible for the absorption maximum at about 500 mμ. They consider the possibility that excitation to this higher level may bring about the destruction of the visual purple chromophore in a different and less efficient manner (quantum efficiency about 0·5). If this is so, then comparison with Curve III suggests that the break-up of a chromophore group following excitation to the higher level is either incapable of initiating the visual process in the rods or, at least, is much less effective in this respect than the break-up associated with absorption in the 500 mμ band. At present neither the range nor the reliability of the experimental observations is sufficient to press this point, but an interesting question for further study is raised.

On the red side of the maximum, there is no indication of a further electronic absorption band, the deviation of the physical and subjective curves corresponding simply to a rather steeper decline of the latter. The subjective measurements have recently been greatly extended in the red and infra-red by Griffin, Hubbard, and Wald (1947), and from their results the variation of $\log (h\nu/t_\lambda W_\lambda)$ up to a wavelength of 1050 mμ has been plotted as Curve I in Fig. 2. The scale has been reduced compared with Fig. 1 to a quarter on the ordinate and a half on the abscissa, the area corresponding to Fig. 1 being indicated by the broken line frame. A striking feature of this curve is its linear descent on the red side of the maximum over the sensitivity range $(h\nu/t_\lambda W_\lambda) = 10^{-3}$ to 10^{-13}, that is, over the enormous range of ten thousand million to one. We can probably assume that the absorption coefficient of visual purple in the condition in which it exists in the retinal rods follows a similar course. By the application of quantum principles it is possible to explain the intensity distribution in the absorption spectra of simple gaseous molecules, but with increasing complexity of the molecule a rigorous theoretical treatment becomes rapidly intractable. In the case of the visual purple of the rods, we have a substance in a dissolved, or more probably in an oriented adsorbed state, with a main absorption band corresponding to an electron transition at a chromophore group of

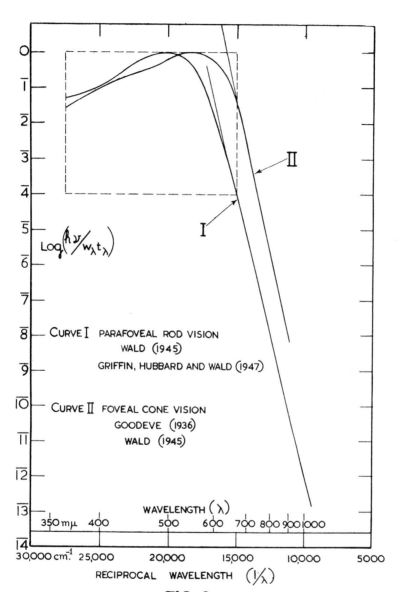

Log$\left(^{h\nu}\!/_{w_\lambda t_\lambda}\right)$

CURVE I PARAFOVEAL ROD VISION
WALD (1945)
GRIFFIN, HUBBARD AND WALD (1947)

CURVE II FOVEAL CONE VISION
GOODEVE (1936)
WALD (1945)

WAVELENGTH (λ)

350 mμ   400   500   600   700 800 900 1000

30,000 cm⁻¹ 25,000   20,000   15,000   10,000   5000

RECIPROCAL WAVELENGTH $(^1\!/_\lambda)$

FIG. 2.

whose exact nature and mode of connection to the protein base we are ignorant, and which breaks up in an unknown way after excitation. There can be no question at present of an adequate theory of the shape of the absorption band. But the simple linear form of the band on the red side of the maximum which is indicated by the subjective sensitivity measurements suggests that some general theoretical explanation of this feature at least might be obtainable.

The following very elementary theoretical picture gives an idea of some of the factors involved. Suppose that to bring about the electron transition at the chromophore group. a minimum energy E_o is required. This must be supplied by the energy $h\nu$ of the absorbed light-quant together with any thermal vibrational energy possessed by the chromophore group in its unexcited ground state. The ground state comprises in fact a whole range of possible energy levels—E_1, E_2, etc., in order of increasing magnitude —corresponding to different quantised states of vibration of the group. In thermal equilibrium the chromophore groups will be distributed among these possible levels in accordance with Boltzmann's law, the number in a level of energy E_i being proportional to $e^{-E_i/kT}$ where T is the absolute temperature and k is Boltzmann's constant ($1\cdot371 . 10^{-16}$ erg sec./deg.). The absorption of a light-quant of frequency ν incident on a chromophore group in the energy state E_i depends on whether $(h\nu + E_i)$ exceeds E_o and to simplify the calculation we will suppose that the absorption coefficient for a chromophore in the ith state has a certain constant value A when $h\nu$ is greater than $(E_o - E_i)$ and is zero when $h\nu$ is less than this quantity. The average absorption coefficient per chromophore, allowing for the relative numbers in the different vibrational levels, is then proportional to the sum

$$\sum_{i=j}^{\infty} Ae^{-E_i kT} \dots\dots\dots\dots\dots\dots\dots\dots\dots\dots\dots\dots\dots(4)$$

where j is the lowest level for which $h\nu$ exceeds $(E_o - E_i)$. If the vibrational levels are very numerous and close together this sum may be replaced by the integrals:

$$\int_{E=E_o-h\nu}^{\infty} Ae^{-E/kT}\left(\frac{dm}{dE}\right)dE \text{ for } h\nu \text{ less than } E_o$$

$$\text{and} \quad \int_{0}^{\infty} Ae^{-E/kt}\left(\frac{dm}{dE}\right)dE \text{ for } h\nu \text{ greater than } E_o \dots\dots\dots\dots(5)$$

where dm represents the number of vibrational levels of energy between E and $E + dE$. If we could assume that A and $\left(\frac{dm}{dE}\right)$ were independent of E we could complete the integration. Making these assumptions tentatively we obtain the result that the absorption coefficient α_λ is proportional to

$$\left(A\left(\frac{dm}{dE}\right)kTe^{-E_o/kT}\right)e^{h\nu/kT}, \quad \text{for } h\nu \text{ less than } E_o$$

and $\qquad A\left(\dfrac{dm}{dE}\right)kT \qquad$, for hv greater than E_o ....(6)

or, as far as variation with frequency is concerned,

$$\log_e a_\lambda = \text{const.} + hv/kT \text{ for } hv \text{ less than } E_o$$

and $\log_e a_\lambda = \text{const.} + E_o/kT = \text{const. for } hv$ greater than E_o.........(7)

This expression reproduces the linear variation of $\log a_\lambda$ with v (or $1/_\lambda$) which is shown on the red side of the maximum in the experimental Curve I of Fig. 2. We proceed to compare the gradients of the experimental and derived results. For the temperature T we must put the body temperature of the human subject, which is approximately $273° + 37° = 310°$Abs. We find then that the experimental Curve I has a gradient in the red corresponding to

$$\log_e a_\lambda = \text{const.} + 0\cdot79 \, hv/kT \text{ ....(8)}$$

Thus the observed gradient is not widely different from that given by this very crude theoretical picture which, it may be noted, takes no account of the structural properties by which the chromophores of different substances must be distinguished.

We may attribute the devation of (7) from the experimental result (8) to the fact that A and $\left(\dfrac{dm}{dE}\right)$ are not, as assumed, independent of E. The variation of $A\left(\dfrac{dm}{dE}\right)$ to give the result (8) is easily obtained: $A\left(\dfrac{dm}{dE}\right)$ must increase exponentially with the energy E according to the law

$$A\left(\dfrac{dm}{dE}\right) = \text{const.} \; e^{\sigma E} \qquad \text{where} \quad \sigma = (1 - 0\cdot79)/k310 = 4\cdot9 \, . \, 10^{12}.$$

Increase of $\left(\dfrac{dm}{dE}\right)$ with E corresponds to a crowding together

of the vibrational levels towards higher energies, an effect which in the case of simple molecules can of course be traced in their spectra and related to the structural constants of the molecule. For the chromophore group the quantity σ may be regarded as a kind of structural constant for the group in its particular environment and probably as independent of temperature. Allowing for an exponential variation of $A\left(\dfrac{dm}{dE}\right)$ we may write in place of (7)

$$\log_e a_\lambda = \text{const.} + hv\left(\frac{1}{kT} - \sigma\right) \text{ for } hv \text{ less than } E_o ....(9)$$

where for the visual purple in the retinal rods $\sigma = 4\cdot9 \, . \, 10^{12}$.

Curve II of Fig. 2 shows the spectral variation of the threshold sensitivity $(hv/t_\lambda W_\lambda)$ for foveal cone vision, as derived from the measurements of Goodeve (1936), Wald (1945) and Griffin, Hubbard, and Wald (1947). In this case t_λ includes not only the correction for light losses in the refractive media of the eye but also a correction for macular pigmentation derived from Wald's comparison of the cone thresholds within and without the macula. The bodily shift of Curve II towards the red with respect to Curve I corresponds of course to the Purkinje effect in passing from rod vision to cone vision. It is probable that for cone vision, unlike rod vision, the threshold sensitivity does not depend on the absorption of a single substance such as visual purple. However, although several photosensitive substances may be concerned, there are good grounds for assuming that in the red the threshold response is dominated by the so-called " red " cone mechanism and the experimental curve may be taken as showing the spectral variation of the absorption coefficient β_λ of a corresponding " red " photosensitive substance. Again over a considerable range (about a million to one in threshold sensitivity or absorption coefficient) the curve is linear and corresponds to

$$\log_e \beta_\lambda = \text{const.} + 0 \cdot 87 \ h\nu/kT$$
$$= \text{const.} + h\nu(1/kT - 3 \cdot 1 \ . \ 10^{12}) \ \ldots\ldots\ldots\ldots\ldots(10)$$

The difference in the values of σ in (9) and (10)—$4 \cdot 9 \ . \ 10^{12}$ and $3 \cdot 1 \ . \ 10^{12}$ respectively—can probably be attributed to the different nature of the chromophore groups concerned which it must be an objective of future work to explain. It is remarkable that the red side of the absorption bands of these many-atom groups belonging to complex molecules not in the gaseous state should be so closely linear.

With diminishing temperature the relative number of chromophores with the higher vibrational energies must diminish by Boltzmann's law, with a consequent increase in the gradient of the absorption band on the long wave side (see (7)). By using as solvent a mixture of glycerol and water Broca and Goodeve (1941) were able to compare the spectral absorption of visual purple at room temperature and at $-73°$ C ($200°$ Abs.). They found a small shift of the maximum wavelength of about 10 $m\mu$ towards the red and, as expected, a more steeply descending absorption curve on the long wave side. Unfortunately their results do not reach the strictly linear range of the $\log \alpha_\lambda$ against $1/_\lambda$ curve. At the long wave limit of their range (550 mμ), the gradient of their curve for $-73°$ C. is about double that of the room temperature curve. Against this, equation (7) would require the gradients in the red to stand in the ratio $1 \cdot 5$ to 1.

In conclusion, it is interesting to observe that while in the case of rod vision we are able to interpret to some extent the subjective sensitivity data in terms of the directly measured physical and chemical properties of the effective photochemical substance, visual purple, the converse is also true. Subjective measurements enable the variation of the spectral absorption coefficient to be followed down to very low values which are likely to remain inaccessible to direct measurement because of the difficulty of obtaining high concentrations of visual purple. In the case of the cone mechanisms, the effective photosensitive substances have not yet been isolated with any certainty, and subjective measurements, provided we can interpret them correctly, may give information about the physical and chemical properties of substances whose existence we can only infer.

REFERENCES

Broda, Goodeve, and Lythgoe (1940): *Journ. Physiol.*, 98, 397.
Broda and Goodeve (1941): *Proc. Roy. Soc.*, A179, 151.
Chase and Haig (1938): *J. Gen. Physiol.*, 21, 411.
Crawford (1948): *Proc. Phys. Soc.* (In publication.)
Dartnall and Goodeve (1937): *Nature*, 139, 409.
Dartnall, Goodeve, and Lythgoe (1938): *Proc. Roy. Soc.*, A164, 216.
Goodeve (1936): *Proc. Roy. Soc.*, A1554, 664.
Goodeve, Lythgoe, and Schneider (1941): *Proc. Roy. Soc.*, B/130, 380.
Griffin, Hubbard, and Wald (1947): *J.O.S.A.*, 37, 546.
Hecht and Pickels (1938): *Proc. Nat. Acad. Sci., Wash.*, 24, 172.
Lythgoe (1937): *J. Physiol.*, 89, 331.
Ludvigh and McCarthy (1938): *Arch. Ophth.*, Chicago, 20, 37.
Schneider, Goodeve, and Lythgoe (1939): *Proc. Roy. Soc.*, A170, 102.
Stiles (1948): *Netherlands Science Times* (In publication).
Wald (1938): *J. Gen. Physiol.*, 21, 795.
Wald (1945): *Science*, 101, 653.
Wright* (1944): Unpublished work.

ADDENDUM

Erratum

The work by Dr W. D. Wright indicated in the final reference was sub-sequently published under the title 'The visual sensitivity of normal and aphakic observers in the ultraviolet', L'Année Psychologique, *50* (Henri Pieron Jubilee Volume), 169 (1952).

* I am indebted to Dr. W. D. Wright for making available to me the results of an unpublished investigation of the visual thresholds of normal and aphakic subjects.

Paper IX: Reprinted from Coloq. Probl. Opt. Vis. (U.I.P.A.P., Madrid), Vol. 1, 1953.

FURTHER STUDIES OF VISUAL MECHANISMS BY THE TWO-COLOUR THRESHOLD METHOD

by W. S. STILES

(The National Physical Laboratory), London.

INTRODUCTION

In a paper to the International Conference on Colour Vision in Cambridge 1947, I developed a general picture of the threshold sensitivity of the retina —particularly of the foveal retina— based on measurements by the two-colour threshold method (Stiles, 1949). This picture will be recalled by the diagram of Fig. 1 to be referred to later. Extensive measurements by the same method have since been made on a group of five subjects and the main modifications of the original picture demanded by the new results will be considered in this paper. A full account of the work is being prepared for publication elsewhere and of the experiments it will be necessary here to give only the following brief description. The quantity measured is the increment threshold or smallest perceptible intensity of a small test stimulus which is superimposed, in flashes, on a much larger stimulus—the conditioning or adapting field—which the subject views steadily and to which he is assumed ideally to have become fully adapted. In general, the spectral compositions of the test and field stimuli are different. In all the measurements discussed below the test stimulus was monochromatic and consisted of a circular patch of 1° diameter exposed in flashes of 0.2 second duration at the centre of an adapting field of 10° diameter. The latter was either monochromatic or a mixture of monochromatic light and filtered light obtained from a narrow-band colour filter. Except for one block of measurements, the test stimulus was viewed foveally, the subjects' gaze being directed by means of four weak red-light «point» sources forming a square of side 3° at the centre of which the test stimulus appeared. The increment threshold was derived from frequency-of-seeing curves (50 per cent threshold), or from a reduced form of this method using series of test stimulus exposures of increasing and decreasing

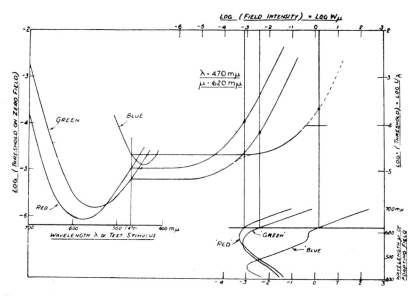

Fig. 1.—Tentative scheme showing how the increment threshold U_λ for a test stimulus of walength λ depends on the intensity W_μ and wavelength μ of the adapting field for foveal cone vision (Stiles, 1949).

intensity, or by subject-setting of the test stimulus intensity to the threshold value. No essential difference in the results given by the different methods was observed except that subject-setting generally gave rather higher threshold values.

The Π_2 mechanism

Perhaps the most interesting new result is one obtained when working with a violet test stimulus and a green, orange or red adapting field. For subject A (the writer) on whose results the original picture was mainly based and who was also one of the subjects in the later work, the variation of the logarithm of the increment threshold with the logaritm of the field intensity (threshold versus intensity, or t. v. i. curve) for a test stimulus of wavelength 430 m μ

and field of wavelength 600 mμ is as shown in Fig. 2 A. It consists of a main branch, attributed to the «blue» mechanism, with a short horizontal section at the highest field intensities. The latter feature (limited conditioning effect of orange or red light on the «blue» mechanism) will be considered further below. For all other subjects

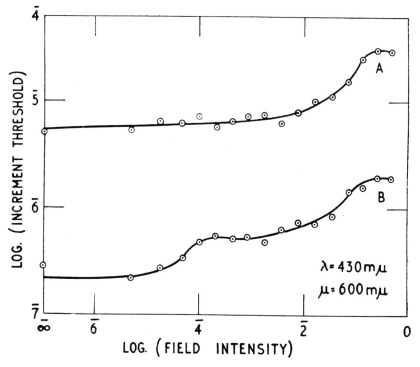

Fig. 2.—Variations of the foveal increment threshold with field intensity for two subjects (λ = 430 mμ, μ = 600 mμ).

studied the t. v. i. for this combination of test and field colours shows a clear division of the curve into two branches, in addition to the limited conditioning effect (Fig 2 B). The difficulty which the appearance of two branches makes for the original picture can be understood from the diagram of Fig. 1. According to this diagram for a test stimulus of wavelength 430 mμ (or any wavelength below about 450 mμ) the observed absolute threshold should be the absolute threshold for the «blue» mechanism and on applying an adapting field of long wavelength (600 or 620 mμ, for example), it should continue to be the increment threshold of the «blue» mechanism which is observed up to the field intensity where the limited conditioning effect sets in. Thus below this intensity the observed t. v. i. curve should consist of one branch only—as is the case for subject A. This branch would belong to the «blue» mechanism, the «red» and «green» branches lying completely above it. The simplest modification of the diagram to suit the results for other subjects would be to suppose that for them the absolute threshold for the «blue» mechanism is always greater than for the «green» or «red» mechanisms down to the shortes test stimulus wavelengths This would explain the appearance of two branches but it would also entail that at or just above the absolute threshold the perception of monochromatic test stimuli throughout the whole spectrum including the blue would be mediated by two mechanisms only, the «red» and the «green». It is difficult to reconcile this with the varying colours of near-threshold stimuli. (Even with three mechanisms sharing the perception of monochromatic test stimuli at the threshold—as in the original scheme—this difficulty remains although it is not so acute). However further measurements suggest an alternative explanation of the two branches for violet test stimuli. Fig. 3 shows a set of t. v. i. curves (single runs) for subject C obtained with a monochromatic field of wavelength 600 mμ. and test stimuli of wavelengths from 405 mμ. to 580 mμ. The field intensity scale is correct for all the curves but for clarity the curves below the top curve have been displaced downwards by varying amounts with respect to the increment threshold scale, which is correct only for $\lambda_{test} = 405$ mμ. As the test stimulus is increased from 405 mμ. the upper («blue» mechanism) branch moves up relative to the lower branch, while maintaining its approximate position with respect to the field intensity scale. This is the behaviour to be expected of a branch belonging to a single mechanism according to the general scheme. The lower branch on the other hand is displaced to the left with respect to the field intensity scale as the test wavelength is changed from violet to blue. By placing a tracing representing the average shape of the upper branch over each t. v. i. curve of Fig. 3 in turn, the position of the tracing with respect to the field intensity scale, which gives the best fit with the experimental points on the upper branch can be obtained. The cross points in Fig. 4 were found in this way and a similar procedure applied to the lower branch gave the circle points. The scatter of the experimental points and small apparently unsystematic variations in the shape of a branch prevent

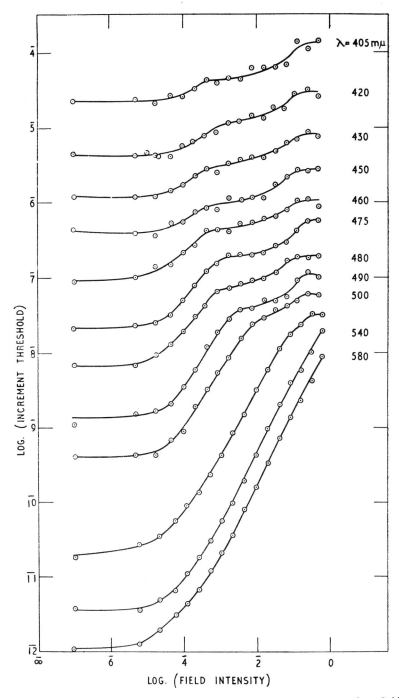

Fig. 3. — Variation of the foveal increment threshold with field intensity for a field of wavelength $\mu = 600$ mμ and various wavelengths λ of the test stimulus.

any very precise fitting but the two main points—the approximate constancy of the position of the upper branch and a shift in the position of the lower branch—are clear. This shift—about 0.8 of a log unit—would not occur if the lower branch were attributable to a single mechanism (in our sense) unless there is some summation

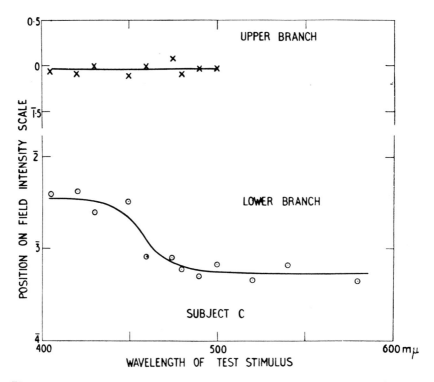

Fig. 4.—Positions of the upper and lower branches of the curves of Fig. 3 along the field intensity scale.

or interaction between mechanism not contemplated in the original scheme. It is unnecessary however to introduce new assumption about possible interaction effects, if it is admitted that a different mechanism may be responsible for the lower branch when the test stimulus is violet and when it is blue or blue-green. The diagram of Fig. 5, constructed on the same principle as Fig. 1, illustrates the way in which the observed t. v. i. curves of Fig. 3 might be generated from component curves or branches associated with three mechanisms: Π_1, the original «blue» mechanism; Π_2, a mechanism responsible for

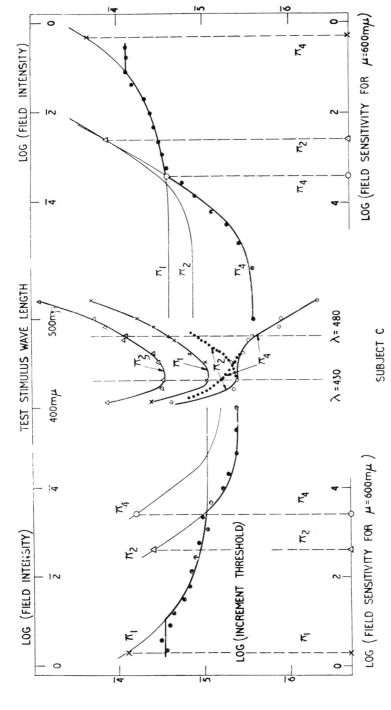

Fig. 5.—Tentative Scheme showing how mechanisms π_1, π_2 and π_4 determine the foveal increment threshold for short wave test stimuli and long wave fields.

189

the absolute threshold when the test stimulus wavelength is below about 450 m μ ; II_4, the original «green» mechanism responsible for the absolute threshold when the test stimulus exceeds about 450 m μ. Neutral symbols have been subtituted for the names previously ap-

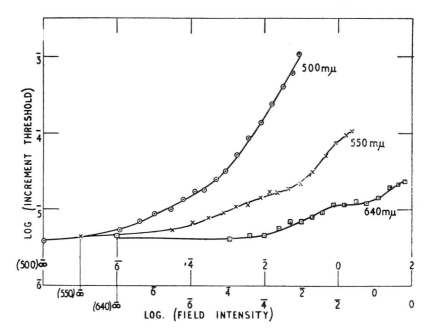

Fig. 6.—Variation of the foveal increment threshold with field intensity for a test stimulus of wavelength λ = 420 m μ and fields of wavelengths 640, 550, 500 m μ respectively.

plied to mechanisms. Although it was made clear, for example, that by «blue» mechanism was meant simply the mechanism with maximum sensitivity in the blue end of the spectrum, it was easy to make the mistake of expecting stimulation of the «blue» mechanism to produce necessarily a blue sensation. The curves in the central panel of Fig. 5 represent the variation with wavelength of the absolute thresholds of the II_1, II_2 and II_4 mechanisms, acting alone (the top curve II_3 indicates the threshold value at which limited conditioning sets in). The II_2 and II_4 curves are supposed to intersect at about 450 m μ, the dotted parts of these curves—not determined by the data of Fig. 3—being sketched in with some help from other evidence. The left and right-hand diagrams show the construction of the resultant t. v. i. curves for $\lambda = 430$ and 480 respectively, from the Π_1, Π_2 and Π_4 components whose position along the threshold scale (ordinate axis) are determined from the central curves. In accordance with a principle of the theory, the positions of the component curves with respect to the field intensity scale are the same for all test stimulus wavelengths and are determined solely by the field sensitivities of the mechanisms to light of wavelength 600 mμ.

If the above explanation of the t. v. i. curves for $\lambda = 430$ and 480 mμ is correct then at some intermediate wavelengths the t. v.i. should be compounded of three branches, a lowest one attributable to Π_2, an intermediate one to Π_4 and an upper one, to Π_1. But on placing the components in the appropriate positions using the diagram of Fig. 5, it is readily seen that it would be very difficult experimentally to distinguish the Π_1 and Π_4 branches, and that the net effect would be of a single lower branch in an intermediate position along the field axis.

For adapting fields of wavelength greater than 600 mμ, the t. v. i. curve for a violet test stimulus is little changed, and the same is true for shorter wavelengths down about 550 mμ. Below this wavelength the transition from the lower to the upper branch becomes less marked and at 500 mμ it is not distinguishable from experimental irregularities (Fig. 6). The modification of the curve in reducing the field wavelength below 550 mμ is consistent with a reduction in the separation of the Π_1 and Π_2 branches along the field intensity scale, their positions along the threshold scale remaining the same.

Because so little of the Π_2 branch shows in the t. v.i. curves, the study of its properties is difficult and the difficulty is accentuated by small changes in the relative position of the branches which occur from time to time in the results obtained under similar conditions for the same subject. In our interpretation such changes point to independent shifts in the sensitivities of different mechanism. One useful result of this variability is to make possible the conclusion that subject A actually possesses a Π_2 mechanism but one for which the absolute threshold is normally equal to or even above that of Π_1 (for violet test stimuli) so that the Π_1 branch generally masks the Π_2 branch. On a few occasions a shallow lower branch has appeared for subject A which from its position along the field can be attributed to a Π_2 mechanism.

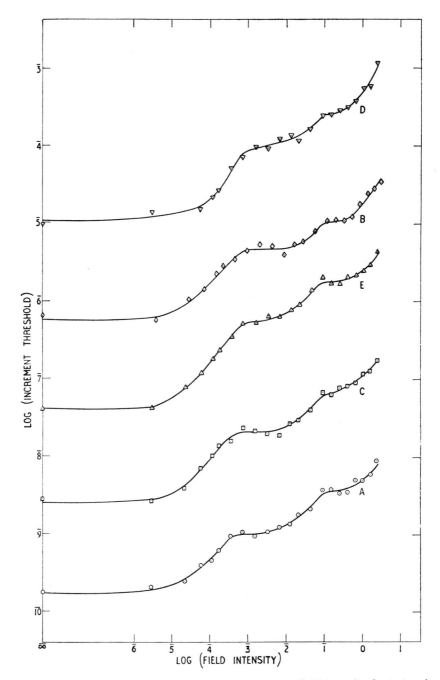

Fig. 7.—Variation of the foveal increment threshold with field intensity for test and field wavelengths 476 and 578 mμ respectively. Five subjects.

To sum up, t. v. i. curves for violet test stimuli and green, orange and red fields show a lower branch which is not consistent with the original scheme but which can be accommodated in it by postu lating an additional mechanism (II_2). This must have a rather higher sensitivity to violet test stimuli than the original «blue» mechanism (II_1) (at least, for most subjects) and a very much higher sensitivity to green, orange and red fields.

The II_3 mechanism (limited conditioning effect)

By the use of a compact source H. P. M. V. lamp to supply the field stimulus, t. v. i. curves showing the limited conditioning effect have been followed up to much higher field intensities than before For field wavelengths 578 and 546 m μ corresponding to the Hg yellow and green lines, field intensities of about 10^6 trolands were obtained in the apparatus. The t. v. i. curves obtained for a blue test stimulus and yellow field (Fig. 7) show that the levelling-out of the curves at high intensities previously noted is no more than the initial part of a third, high intensity branch. The effects of changing to a violet (436 m μ) test stimulus and to a green (546 m μ) field are illustrated in Fig 8. The modifications in the shape of the curve are of the kind to be expected if the high-intensity branch corresponds to a distinct mechanism—maintaining its position with respect to the threshold scale when only the field wavelength is changed, and with respect to the field scale when only the test wavelength is changed. Insufficient field intensity was the reason why the high-intensity branch at field wavelengths below 570 m μ was not observed in the earlier work. When the limited conditioning effect was first reported (Stiles, 1939) it was considered unlikely that it corresponded to a distinct mechanism, because such a mechanism would have the same relative spectral sensitivity in the blue as the II_1 mechanism (this is shown for example by the parallelism of curves II_1 and II_3 in the central panel of Fig. 5), and would have a field sensitivity dropping almost discontinuously with increasing wavelength in the neighbour hood of 570 m μ. This drop is not so sharp as was thought, but otherwise the new results lead to the same conclusions. But as the high-intensity branch moves with changes in test and field wavelengths in the appropriate way it now seems preferable to treat it as the component curve of a distinct mechanism which will be called II_3.

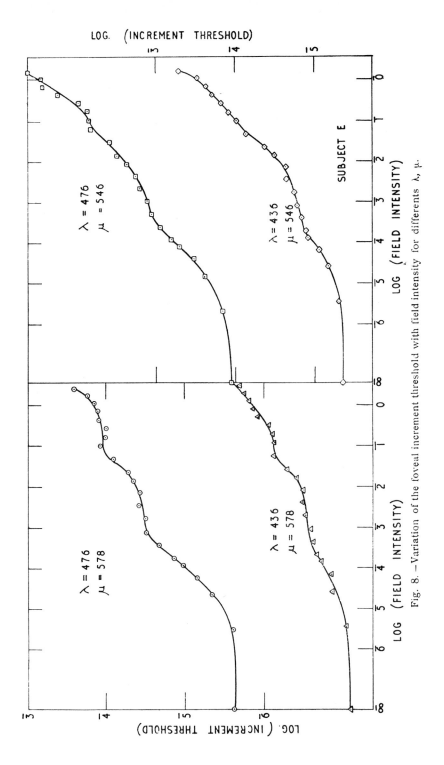

Fig. 8. – Variation of the foveal increment threshold with field intensity for differents λ, μ.

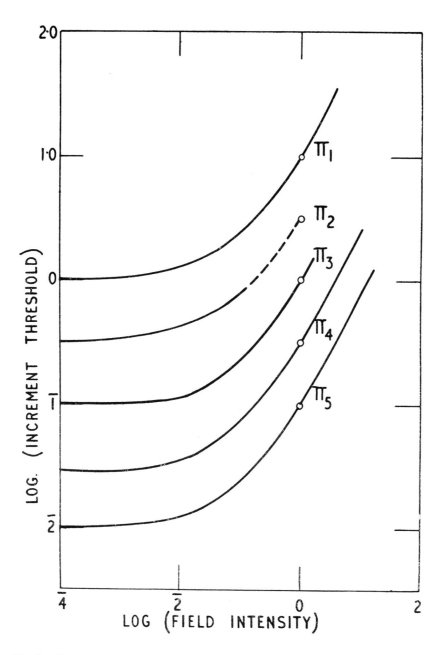

Fig. 9. — Mean shape of the curve relating log (threshold) and log (field intensity) for mechanisms π_1, π_2, π_3, π_4, π_5.

Threshold properties of mechanisms

The threshold properties of a particular mechanism in a particular retinal region for a test stimulus of prescribed area and exposure time are expressed by three curves, the spectral sensitivity to the test stimulus, the spectral sensitivity to the field stimulus and the curve relating the increment threshold and the field intensity. These have to be measured under conditions in which the threshold response is determined by the mechanism in question without appreciable interference from other mechanisms. The relative spectral sensitivities of a given mechanism to test and field stimuli are expected to be the same but it is important to test this by determining both in the region of the spectrum where that is possible. The ratio of field to test sensitivity at a common wavelength (Fechner fraction) is also an important property of a mechanism.

The mean results about to be considered rest on extensive measurements on four subjects (subject B was not available for all the measurements and it will simplify the discussion to omit his results, which as far as they go show no radical difference from those of the other subjects). The measurements for the individual subjects show all the main features of the mean results; there are however some minor differences between subjects which it will not be possible to discuss here.

Threshold properties of Π_1 Π_2, Π_3

(a) *Shape of the t. v. i. curve.*

Using all the observed t. v. i. curves which show a branch assignable to Π_1, Π_2 or Π_3, the mean shapes of these branches have been determined (full line curves of Fig. 9). The transition from the horizontal to the nearly linearly ascending section is rather more gradual than that given by the simple formula (increment threshold) = constant + c_2 (field intensity) which is often used as an approxima-

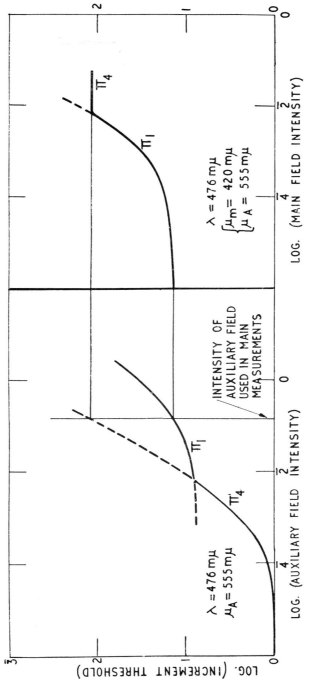

Fig. 10.—Scheme showing the theory of the auxiliary field method

tion. In the case of II_2, the broken line extrapolation has been made by assuming the shapes of II_1 and II_2 to be identical in the extrapolated portion. An extrapolation has been made merely to enable the position of II_2 along the intensity scale to be defined in a similar way to II_1 and II_3 i. e. by the position of the point on the curve at which the increment threshold is ten times the absolute threshold (the reference point). The form of this extrapolated portion is not at present directly determinable, although it is unlikely to differ much from that shown.

(b) *Field sensitivities.*

For fields of long wavelength the field sensitivity—the reciprocal of the field intensity required to raise the threshold to ten times the absolute threshold—has been determined for II_1, II_2 and II_3 by fitting to the appropriate branch of the experimental t. v. i. curve, the mean t. v. i. curve for the mechanism and noting the position of the reference point on the field intensity scale. For fields of short wavelength the branches are no longer distinguishable. For II_1 and II_3 the difficulty has been got over by the use of an auxiliary adapting field. The principle of the method as applied to II_1 is made clear by the diagram of Fig. 10. The t. v. i. curve for a blue test stimulus ($\lambda = 476 \, m\mu$, say) and a field of wavelength $555 \, m\mu$ has the form of the full line curve on the left-hand side of Fig. 10 and is generated it is believed from the component curves of mechanisms II_4, II_1, in the way shown. Thus if an auxiliary field of wavelength $555 \, m\mu$ and of the intensity X marked on the figure is applied, the increment threshold for the II_1 mechanism will be considerably lower (about one log unit) than for II_4. By superimposing on this auxiliary field a main field of any wavelength and of an intensity which is increased from zero to a high value, the observed increment threshold will continue to be the threshold of the II_1 mechanism at least until the increase in threshold caused by the main field reaches one log unit. This should be true even if the main field has a wavelength in the blue or violet where the sensitivity of II_1 has its maximum and where II_4 is relatively insensitive. However ultimately the II_4 mechanism will have the lower increment threshold and a plot of log (increment threshold) against log (intensity of main field) should show a mar-

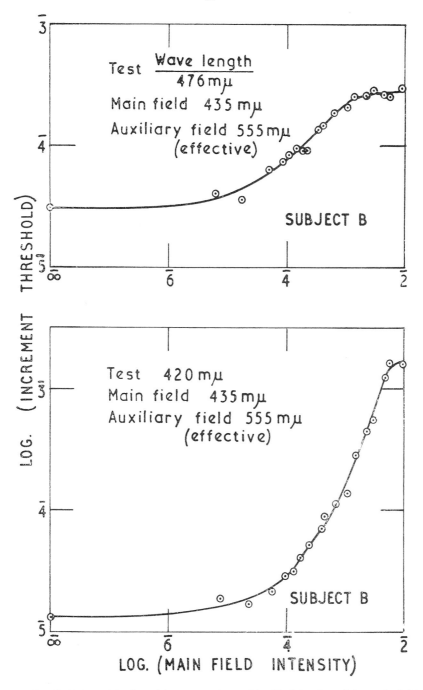

Fig. 11. —Variation of the foveal increment threshold with intensity of the main field in two sets of measurements using an auxiliary field.

199

ked reduction in gradient when this occurs as illustrated in the right-hand half of Fig. 10. Experiment establishes that the effect of the main field is very similar to that expected. The upper curve of Fig. 11 was obtained with test stimulus and main field of wavelengths 476 and 435 mμ respectively and a yellow green auxiliary field of effective wavelength 556 m μ and effective intensity 0.007 ergs per second per square degree. For the lower curve the test stimulus wavelength was changed to 420 m μ and here the transition in the curve is barely reached when the increment threshold has been raised 2 log units, again in accordance with the prediction from the diagram of Fig. 10 modified to suit the new test wavelength. Thus to determine the relative field sensitivity of Π_1 for field wavelengths in the violet, blue and blue-green it is only necessary to find the field intensities which when added to an auxiliary yellow-green field of appropriate intensity will raise the increment threshold for a violet test stimulus by a fixed factor—say 10—above its value for the auxiliary field alone.

To obtain the field sensitivity of Π_3 in the short-wave region of the spectrum, a similar method was employed except that the auxiliary field was red and of sufficiently high intensity to make the increment threshold of Π_3 lower than that of Π_1 and in fact of all other mechanisms. Unfortunately the auxiliary field method is not applicable to the Π_3 mechanism.

In the first instance, the auxiliary field method gives only the *relative* field sensitivity for the different field wavelengths studied but by a slight elaboration of the method, which need not be described here, the absolute values were derived.

The final mean results for the field sensitivities of Π_1, Π_2, Π_3, are given in Fig. 12. It will be noted that the field sensitivities are expressed in quantum units and are plotted against wave number $(1/\lambda)$ instead of wavelength. Considering first Π_1 and Π_3 it is clear that at wavelengths below about 500 mμ the field sensitivities show closely similar variations, with maxima at approximately 440 mμ and slight indentations at 455 and 480 mμ which probably correspond to maxima in the absorption of the macular pigment (see below). At wavelengths greater than 500 mμ, the Π_1 and Π_3 curves diverge gradually until at about 570 mμ a pronounced lobe develops on Π_1. Although in the long wave region only two points on Π_3 (at the wavelengths of the mercury green and yellow lines) could be determined it is certain that there is no corresponding lobe on Π_3. If there were the limited conditioning effect could not possibly show so clearly for orange and orange-red fields.

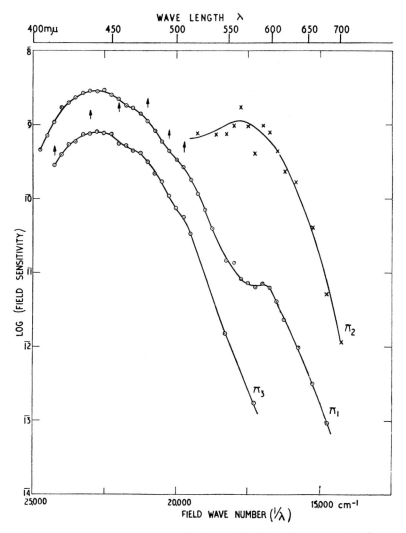

Fig. 12.—Field sensitivity on quantum basis as a function of wave number for π_1, π_3 (Mean of 4 subjects) and π_2 (Mean of 3 subjects).

Only a very approximate determination of the field sensitivity of Π_2 can be made by the present methods and the plotted points (means for 3 subjects only, as subject A normally shows no II_2 branch) are correspondingly irregular. It could be however that the high point at $1/\lambda = 17,750$ cm^{-1} ($\lambda = 563$) and the low point at $17,250$ cm^{-1} (579 mμ) are not just erratic variations—all 3 subjects show similar variations—and, if so, an interesting fluctuation in the sensitivity curve would be indicated, of a kind which recalls the fluctuations in foveal and near-foveal luminosity curves observed by Wright (1946) using very small test stimuli ($5'$ or $20'$ diameter). For field wavelengths below about 520 mμ it has been possible only to determine lower limits for the field sensitivity (shown by arrow-heads in Fig. 12), as in the absence of well-defined branches the interpretation of t. v. i. curves for these wavelengths and with a violet test stimulus is uncertain. One conclusion can be drawn about the field sensitivity of II_2: it has a maximum in the blue or violet and a second maximum or at least a pronounced lobe in the yellow-green.

(c) *Test sensitivities.*

With some slight and unimportant exceptions, an adapting field will raise the increment thresholds of all mechanisms to a greater or less extent. In measuring the relative spectral sensitivity to the test stimulus (relative values of the reciprocal threshold) of a particular mechanism the colour and intensity of the field should be chosen so that the increment threshold for this mechanism is below those of the other mechanisms for as great a range of test stimulus wavelengths as possible. Which mechanism is responsible for the observed increment threshold has to be judged from the particular branch of the t. v. i. curve on which the measured point is located. The main measurements of the test sensitivity of II_1 were made with an adapting field of wavelength 550 mμ and an intensity of approximately 3000 trolands. With this, the observed increment threshold corresponds to the increment threshold of II_1 for test wavelengths from the violet end of the spectrum to 500 or 510 mμ. A little larger range (at the most, up to 530 mμ) could have been obtained with a higher field intensity but the intensity must not be too great if the increment threshold of II_1 is to be kept well below that of II_3. Independent measurements showed that the form of the test sensitivity curve of II, did not depend on the colour and intensity of the adapting field provided the condition just discussed was satisfied.

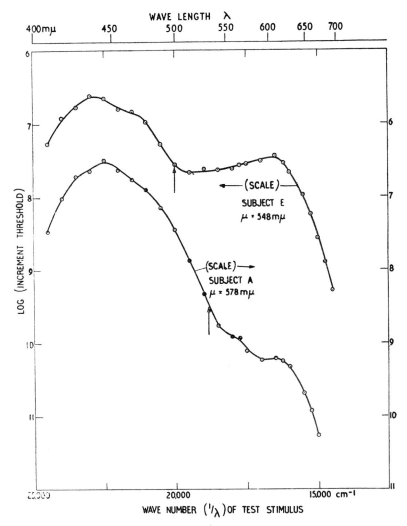

Fig. 13.—Variation of the increment threshold for foveal vision (note inverted ordinate scale) with wave number $1/\lambda$, for two high intensity adapting fields, $\mu = 548$ mμ and $\mu = 578$ mμ.

For the II$_3$ curve, a field of longer wavelength and of as high an intensity as possible is required and yellow light ($\mu = 578$ mμ) provided by the compact source Hg lamp was used. Fig. 13 shows preliminary curves of log (increment threshold) against test stimulus wave number (extending through the whole spectrum) for two subjects, the upper curve for the adapting field used in the main measurements on Π_1 and the lower curve for an adapting field of the same colour but about double the intensity used in the main measurements on Π_3. The intensity was reduced because after the long period of exposure to the high intensity yellow light (about 10^5 trolands), the subject for the lower curve had a persistent after-image which did not disappear completely until a week later. The short-wave ranges of the curves of Fig. 13 to the left of the points marked can probably be safely ascribed to Π_1 and Π_3 respectively. The difference in shape of the short-wave ranges of the two curves arises, it is believed, from a difference in the degree of macular pigmentation in the two subjects and not to a difference in the spectral response of the underlying Π_1 and Π_3 mechanisms.

The final mean values for the relative test sensitivities of Π_1 and Π_3 are shown as the plotted points in Fig. 14. In each case the curve shown is the relative field sensitivity of the corresponding mechanism (from Fig. 12). It is clear that for both Π_1 and Π_3 the form of the relative spectral sensitivity curve is closely the same whether the «field» or the «test» method is used in determining it. The biggest discrepancy occurs at $1/\lambda = 19000$ ($\lambda = 526$ mμ) on the interpolated section of the field curve of Π_3, about which there must be some uncertainty.

For Π_2, the best determination that can be made of the relative test sensitivity is to take the threshold on zero field i. e. the absolute threshold, for those subjects who show a Π_2 branch. But it is uncertain up to how large a test stimulus wavelength this will correspond to the threshold of Π_2. The curve shown in Fig. 13 has been taken to 460 mμ ($1/\lambda = 21750$) but may not represent Π_2 quite up to this value. Thus the wavelength of maximum sensitivity of Π_2 remains uncertain.

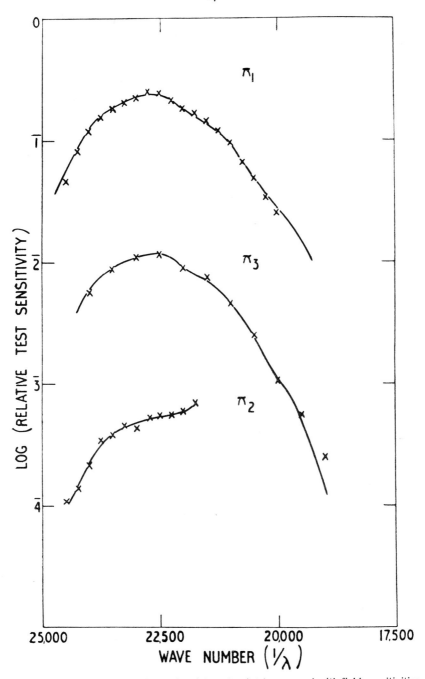

Fig. 14.—Test sensitivities of π_1 and π_3 (plotted points) compared with field sensitivities of the same mechanisms (line curves for π_1 and π_3). Test sensitivity for π_2 (points and curve). Means for all subjects.

Absorption of the Macular Pigment

When measurements of the increment threshold for extrafoveal vision are made for high intensity adapting fields of long wavelength, the variation with wavelength follows a similar course to that illustrated in Fig. 13, and in particular shows the pronounced peak in the blue associated with the Π_1 or Π_3 mechanisms. If this peak arises from a similar mechanism in the extrafoveal retina, the form of the relative spectral sensitivity curve should be the same except for differences in the absorption of light in its passage through the retina before the photosensitive substance on which vision depends is reached. It is of course the so-called macular pigment which is expected to modify the spectral sensitivity curve in this way. To test the point a series of measurements of the increment threshold was made under precisely similar conditions to those used in determining Π_1, except that the observations were made at a point 8° to the nasal side of a fixation point instead of foveally. The mean results for the four subjects are plotted in Fig. 15, which also shows, for test wavelengths between 400 and 500 mμ, the difference in log (test sensitivity) between the foveal and 8° extrafoveal values. This difference cannot be attributed wholly to the effect of macular pigment: even in the absence of the latter, the actual sensitivities of the same mechanism under the same adapting field may well differ at different retinal points but the difference should be the same for all test wavelengths.

Wald has suggested that the macular pigment consists of a carotenoid pigment—probably xanthophyll, and has obtained in support much evidence from subjective observations and direct absorption measurements (Wald, 1949). The differences between foveal and extrafoveal sensitivities plotted in the lower graph of Fig. 15 accord well with Wald's view. The continuous line represents the optical density of a solution of leaf xanthophyll in chloroform (Wald's measurements), and it is clear that the characteristic contour of this curve is simulated by the experimental points. A very fair fit has been obtained by a suitable choice of the concentration of the xanthophyll solution to which the continuous curve applies, and by admitting a difference in the sensitivities of the Π_1 mechanisms beneath the pigment layer at the foveal and 8°-extrafoveal points under the field

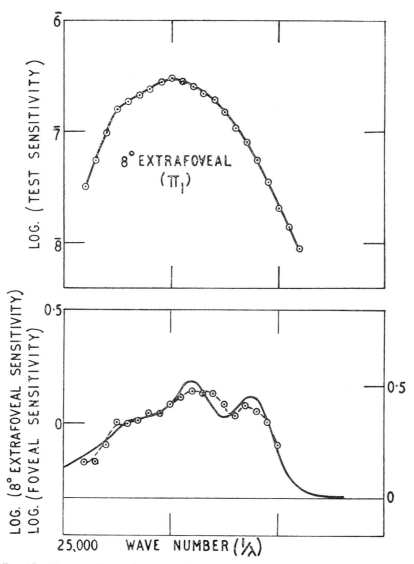

Fig. 15. —Test sensitivity of π_1 in the 8° extrafoveal retina (temporal side in external field): difference between log (test sensitivities) of π_1 in the fovea and the 8° extrafovea, and the optical density of a solution of xanthophyll in chloroform (Wald's measurements).

conditions used, equal to 0.34 log units, the sensitivity being higher at the fovea. On this interpretation, the macular pigment, on the average for the four subjects concerned, has a density—at the wavelength of maximum absorption—greater by approximately 0,48 log units at the foveal than at the 8°-extrafoveal point. This is practically the same as Wald's estimate (0.52 log units), based on more subjects (10), obtained by a related but not identical method.

'RED' AND 'GREEN' MECHANISMS (II_5 AND II_4)

According to the scheme of Fig. 1, for no choice of test and field wavelengths would the branches attributed to the 'red' and 'green' mechanisms intersect sharply so as to produce a well-defined division of the t. v. i. curve. The reasons for this are firstly the comparatively small separation of the spectral sensitivity curves of the 'red' and 'green' mechanisms along the wavelength scale, and secondly the nearly identical values of the Fechner fractions of the mechanisms (see below). The most favourable case would occur for a test stimulus in the orange with a red adapting field, but even here a slight lowering of the resultant increment threshold by summation effects when the 'red' and 'green' thresholds have nearly the same value, would blur the transition so as to produce an apparently simple curve. This curve however would not have the properties of a branch associated with a single mechanism and, in particular, it would not maintain its position along the threshold or field scales when, respectively, only the field or only the test wavelength was changed. The new work using green, orange and red test stimuli and fields of all colours has shown that a distinction must be drawn between fields of moderate intensity (up to about 150 trolands) and more intense fields. For the moderate fields the results are consistent with the original scheme: no well-defined transitions in the t. v. i. curve are observable but the effect of changing test and field wavelengths is to alter (or leave unchanged) the position of the observed curve relative to the field and test scales in the way to be expected if the curve really arises from 'red' and 'green' branches with a blurred intersection. We shall return to this case later. For high intensity fields on the other hand small anomalies in the t. v. .i curves regularly appear which cannot be reconciled with the original scheme. An example is given in Fig. 16 where the upper curve is the t. v. i. curve for a red test stimulus and a red adapting field both of wavelength 667 mμ. The curve is apparently simple and

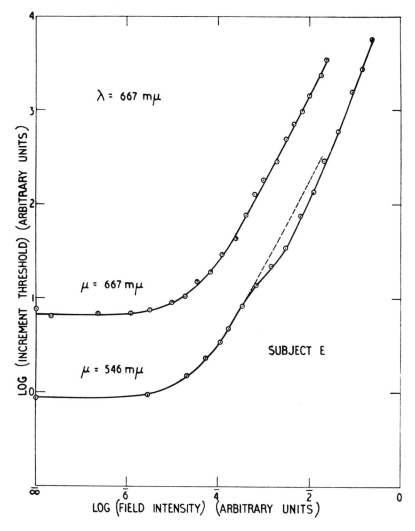

Fig. 16. — Variation of the foveal increment threshold for a red test stimulus ($\lambda = 667$ mμ) with field intensity for two field wavelengths 667 mμ and 546 mμ.

would be interpreted in our scheme, both at moderate and high field intensities, as the t. v. i. curve of the 'red' mechanism. It is certainly conceivable that at high field intensities the t. v. i. curve of the 'green' mechanism passes slightly below that of the 'red' (the

209

effect of a red field in raising the increment threshold being much greater for the 'red' than for the 'green' mechanism), and, in that case, although no transition from one branch to another is apparent

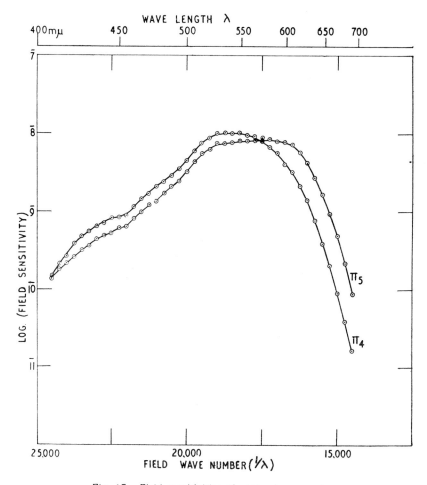

Fig. 17.—Field sensitivities of mechanims π_5 and π_4

the upper part of the experimental curve might represent the increment threshold of the 'green' mechanism. The t. v. i. curve for the same test stimulus but a green adapting field (lower curve of Fig. 16) shows a division into low and high intensity branches. The lower branch can be assigned to the 'red' mechanism but the 'green' mechanism can hardly account for the upper branch. Fitting the two curves together in the low intensity range (broken line of Fig. 16), it is clear that changing from a red to a green field gives thresholds at high field intensities, which are relatively too low. This is the opposite of what would occur if the 'green' mechanisms were responsible for the upper branch. The anomalous effect is small but all the subjects show it. A corresponding anomaly is observed for green test stimuli. The t. v. i. curve for a green field is apparently simple but with a red field the thresholds are a little too low at high field intensities. A full discussion of measurements made at high field intensities, which throw further light on these anomalies must be left to another occasion but the following general remark may be made Tre anomalies can probably be explained by admitting an additional 'red' and an additional 'green' mechanism just as additional 'blue' mechanisms have had to be admitted. But the relative spectral sensitivities of the additional 'red' and 'green' mechanisms would have to differ comparatively little from those of the main 'red' and 'green' mechanisms respectively.

Reverting to fields of moderate intensity, the results of an elaborate series of measurements to determine the field sensitivities of the main 'red' and 'green' mechanisms (here renamed Π_5 and Π_4 mechanisms respectively) are plotted in Fig. 17. The curve for Π_5 was obtained by finding the field intensity for different field wavelengths necessary to raise the threshold for a red test stimulus (667 mμ) by 1 log unit above the value for zero field. Π_4 was similarly determined but with a blue-green test stimulus (500 mμ). Both curves show slight indentations at about 544 mμ and 480 mμ associated with the absorption maxima of the macular pigment. It is remarkable that the Π_4 and Π_5 curves run very nearly parallel between 510 and 430 mμ. If the two curves are fitted together in this region, the Π_5 curve is slightly higher in the violet and of course considerably higher from the yellow to the red.

FECHNER FRACTIONS

Before discussing briefly the relative spectral sensitivity curves of the various mechanisms, a reference must be made to their Fechner fractions. The Fechner fraction is defined as the ratio of the field intensity when test and field have the same wavelength. As the field intensity is increased the Fechner fraction diminishes and if the t. v. i.

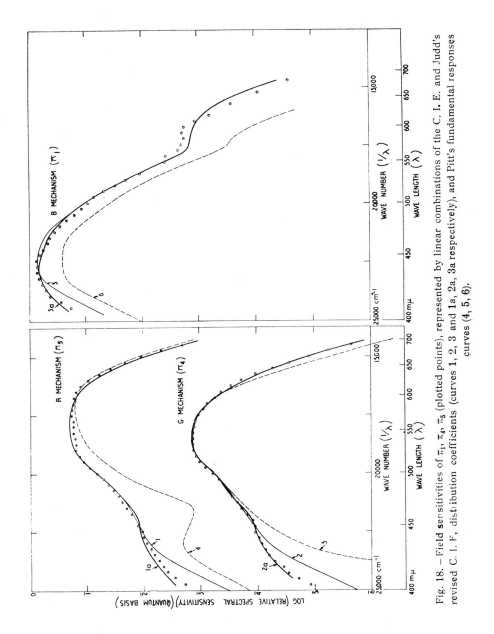

Fig. 18. — Field sensitivities of π_1, π_4, π_5 (plotted points), represented by linear combinations of the C. I. E. and Judd's revised C. I. F. distribution coefficients (curves 1, 2, 3 and 1a, 2a, 3a respectively), and Pitt's fundamental responses curves (4, 5, 6).

curve has unit gradient (*d* log (threshold)/*d* *log* (field intensity) = 1) at high intensities, the Fechner fraction tends to a limiting value. In earlier work, this limiting Fechner fraction was discussed, but it now seems preferable to consider the Fechner fraction at a standard field intensity, that required to raise the threshold by 1 log unit above the value on zero field. If the relative spectral sensitivities of a mechanism to test and field are identical, the wavelengths for which the Fechner fraction is determined will be immaterial.

The mean values (four subjects) for the Fechner fraction of the mechanisms at the standard field intensity, as determined in the new work, are as follows:

II_1 8.7 per cent measured at wavelength 435 m μ.
II_3 8.7 » » » » » 435 m μ.
II_4 1.9 » » » » » 500 m μ.
II_5 1.8 » » » » » 667 m μ.

The main points of interest are that the II_4 and II_5 mechanisms have nearly the same Fechner fraction, but the values are only about one fifth those for the II_1 and II_3 mechanisms. This substantially confirms the result previously obtained for subject A only (Stiles, 1939), except that no value for II_3 was derivable from the measurements then made. The implications of this considerable difference in Fechner fractions, in the theory of the relative visibility curve, and of hue and general colour limens have already been discussed (Stiles, 1946). Unfortunately it has not yet been possible to determine the Fechner fraction for II_2 and all that can be said from indirect evidence, is that the value is probably not materially lower than for II_1 and II_3.

SPECTRAL SENSITIVITIES OF MECHANISMS AND COLOUR-MATCHING DATA

It is well-known that the data of monocular colour-matching do not determine uniquely the relative spectral sensitivities of the basic processes, but only three experimental functions of wavelength—the distribution coefficients $\bar{x}$, $\bar{y}$, $\bar{z}$—in terms of which the spectral sensitivities in question are expressible in linear form ($a\,\bar{x} + b\,\bar{y} + c\,\bar{z}$). Should the spectral sensitivities of visual mechanisms derived by the two-colour threshold method be similarly expressible, assuming of

course that the colour-matching and the threshold measurements refer to the same retinal area? No simple answer can be given. In the

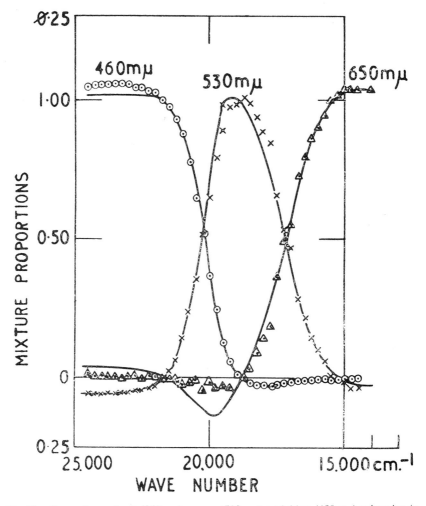

Fig. 19. — Proportions of red (650 mμ), green (530 mμ) and blue (460 mμ) primaries to
match the spectrum colours: points, derived from threshold sensitivities of π_1, π_4, π_5,
curves mean results of Wright's colour-matching investigation.

first place, the laws of colour-matching and the associated distribution coefficients do not apply without some restriction on the stimulus conditions. Some of the fields used in the threshold work are
sufficiently intense to upset colour matches made at more moderate

stimulus levels. But even if there were no limitations to the colour-matching data, it would not follow that visual mechanisms in our sense would necessarily have linear combinations of the distribution coefficients for their relative spectral sensitivity curves. The colour-matching laws would be satisfied if there were just three photosensitive substances concerned in vision, each absorbing light under 'dilute solution' conditions; it would not matter where they were located in the end-organs or how the end-organs were organised in the neural network by which the visual response was passed on to the brain. The spectral absorption curves of these substances would be linear combinations of the distribution coefficients (corrected for selective absorption by inert materials in the eye) but apart from this, colour-matching data would give no information about the make-up of the visual mechanisms. The mechanisms with which particular branches of the t. v. i. curves must, we believe, be associated, are not necessarily served by end-organs containing one and the same photosensitive substance, and their spectral sensitivities might therefore be composites of the spectral absorption curves of two or three substances. In such cases the resultant spectral sensitivity of the mechanism need not be a linear combination of the component spectral absorption curves and is perhaps unlikely to be so on physiological grounds. On the other hand, a composite spectral sensitivity curve is also unlikely to remain undistorted under extreme stimulus intensities. It is obviously difficult to draw any useful theoretical conclusion about the comparability of spectral sensitivites of mechanisms on the one hand and linear combinations of the distribution coefficients on the other, but a practical trial can be made. In Fig. 19, the plotted points represent the field sensitivities of Π_5, Π_4, Π_1, and the curves 1, 2, 3 suitable chosen linear combinations of the C. I. E distribution coefficients to fit the points. The curves 1a, 2a, 3a, which in the blue deviate appreciably from 1, 2 and 3 respectively, are linear combinations of modified C. I. E. distribution coefficients, computed by Judd (1951) to bring the colour-matching data more in line with current views on the form of the relative visibility curve at short wavelengths. The fit with the field sensitivity points in the blue is distinctly better with Judd's distribution coefficients. For Π_4, the agreement between points and curve 2 is rather close through the whole spectrum, but for Π_5 and Π_1 the corresponding differences are larger. It must be remembered that data for different groups of individuals are being compared and in the blue where lens and pigment absorptions are important some of the difference may have arisen in this way. Fig. 19 also gives the R, G and B fundamental response curves (curves 4, 5 and 6 respectively), derived by Pitt (1944) by combining the monocular colour-matching data with results from measurements by the binocular method and on colour-defectives. These are linear combinations of the original C. I. E. distribution coefficients. It is clear that Pitt's fundamentals R and G and the field sensitivities of II_5 and II_4 differ much more radically than can be related to the imperfect agreement of II_5 and II_4 with their best representations in terms of the distribution coefficients.

A comparison of a different kind may be made by imagining an individual whose colour-matching is determined by the field sensitivities II_1, II_4 II_5, and by computing the proportions of three spectral primaries (650, 530 460 mμ) which he would match with the spectral colours. By fixing the units of the primaries in the way devised by Wright, spectral coefficient curves for the hypothetical individual are obtained which may be compared with those directly measured by Wright for 10 observers. In this treatment of the field sensitivities, those features of the data which go beyond what colour-matching can give have been jettisoned to get a clearer comparison with the colour-matching measurements. The treatment also eliminates the effects of pigmentation of the retina and optics media. In Fig. 20 the curves are the mean coefficient curves of Wright and the plotted points are the corresponding coefficients calculated from the field sensitivities of II_1, II_4, II_5. Although the deviations do not appear considerable this is partly because each coefficient curve (measured or derived) must pass through three fixed points, and the '460' and '530' curves must intersect at 494 mμ, the '530' and '650' curves at 582.5 mμ. The deviations are however too great to class the hypothetical individual as a normal colour-matcher. For example, in the neighbourhood of 500 mμ, the '650' coefficient has a negative value which for the hypothetical subject is only about one quarter that for Wright's mean curve. The range for Wright's 10 subjects is approximately — 0.11 to — 0.18, and the derived value, — 0.04, lies well outside this range. Diminished negative red it may be noted is a characteristic of protanomalous vision (McKeon and Wright, 1940).

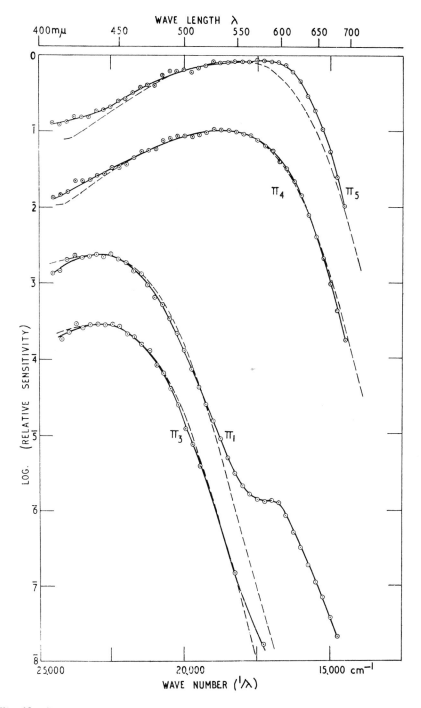

Fig. 20 — Relative spectral sensitivity curves of mechanisms π_1, π_4, π_5 corrected for optic media and macular pigment absorption: broken curves represent attempt to fit the similarly corrected rod sensitivity curve to π_1, π_4, π_5 by suitable displacements along the spectrum.

SPECTRAL SENSITIVITIES CORRECTED FOR PIGMENT ABSORPTIONS

There is evidence, both histological and from subjective observations, that at $8°$ from the fovea the absorption of light by the macular pigment is slight. If the absorption here is neglected the estimate made above of the difference in optical density at the foveal and $8°$-extrafoveal point (average for the four subjects) represents simply the optical density at the fovea, and may be used to correct the foveal spectral sensitivities to the values they would have if there were no macular pigment. No measurements on the subjects were made which enable a similar correction to be applied for light absorption by the optic media of the eye. But in the violet the correction is an important one and although individual variations are known to be large it seems worth while to apply an average correction based on estimates by different methods by Ludvigh and McCarthy (1938), Wald (1941) and Wright (1952) The values of this correction in the region where it is considerable are as follows:

$1/\lambda$	24500	24000	23500	23000	22500
Optical density of optic media	.82	.55	.34	.24	.10
$1/\lambda$	22000	21500	21000	22500	20000
Optical density of optic media	.14	.12	.10	.08	.05

The corrected relative field sensitivities for Π_1, Π_3, Π_4 and Π_5 are plotted in Fig. 21, and in each case an attempt has been made to fit a similarly corrected curve for the spectral sensitivity of the rod mechanism (Π_0) to the plotted points by displacing the latter along the wave number scale by a suitable amount. The interest of this procedure resides in the fact that the spectral sensitivity of the rod mechanism is known to correspond to the spectral absorption of the photosensitive visual pigment rhodopsin and it is at least plausible to expect that if the spectral sensitivity of any of the other mechanisms should correspond to the spectral absorption of a single visual pilgment, the form of the sensitivity curve would be similar to that of the rod mechanism although with its maximum at a different wavelength. For Π_1, there is a rather close similarity of form with the

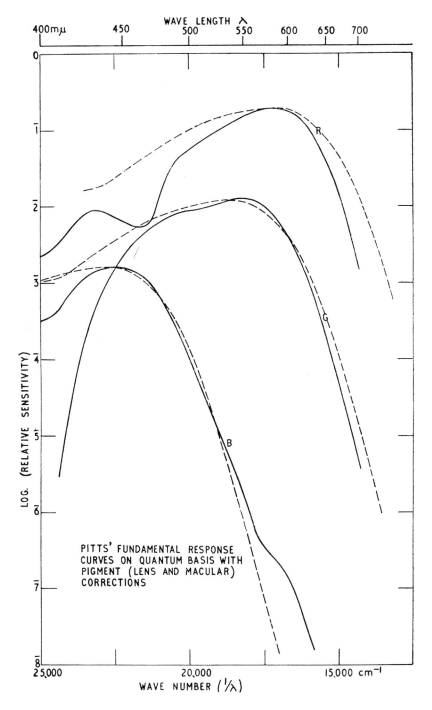

Fig 21.—Pitt's fundamental response curves corrected for optic media and macular pigment absorption, and their attempted representation by displaced rod sensitivity curves.

displaced rod curve, and for II_1 and II_3 excepting the long wave lobe on II_1 there is some similarity. The greater uncertainty of the curves in the violet, on account of the large correction for the optic media, must be kept in mind. The rod curve is a poor fit to the II_5 results, however it is placed. II_5 in fact has more the appearance of a composite curve, of a curve of «rod» shape with a lobe high up on the red side. (Wright has considered the possibility that the red fundamental response curve of colour-matching is a composite curve, and has brought forward in support evidence from colour-matching measurements under special conditions, notably small matching fields (20')). The appearance of lobes on the red side of the spectral sensitivity curves of II_1 and II_5, does not necessarily mean that different photosensitive pigments, perhaps in different end-organs, are concerned in the response of these mechanisms. The enhancement of the red sensitivity of photographic sensitisers by the polymerisation of a single dye may be a relevant analogy here and there are other possibilities. But where a sensitivity curve like II_4 follows so closely the form of the rod curve and hence of the rhodopsin absorption curve it is clearly favourable to the view that the sensitivity curve does correspond to the spectral absorption curve of a single photosensitive pigment.

As a matter of interest, the lens and macular pigment corrections have been applied to Pitt's fundamental response curves to obtain the continuous line curves of Fig. 21. Pitt's curves rest on the original C. I. E. distribution coefficients: if they were recalculated using Judd's revised distribution coefficients the curves of Fig. 21 would be raised in the violet (compare curves 1, 2, 3 and 1a, 2a, 3a in Fig. 20) but in the rest of the spectrum the change would probably be small. The corrected B fundamental of Pitt can be fitted with the rod curve at least as well as can II_1 in Fig. 20, but the fit for curve G is less satisfactory than for II_4 in Fig. 20. Like II_5 in Fig. 20, Pitt's corrected R curve cannot be fitted with the rod curve, and the deviations are perhaps less easy to understand physically, if a single photosensitive pigment is concerned.

CONCLUSION

Although it has been necessary to extend the scheme of Fig. 1 by admitting additional mechanisms, the main principle has continued to prove a useful working hypothesis. According to this principle, the observed increment threshold is equal approximately to the lowest of the increment thresholds of several component mechanisms for each of which the dependence of the threshold on the wavelength and intensity of the field and the wavelength of the test stimulus follows fairly simple laws, involving a relative spectral sensitivity curve. These spectral sensitivities of foveal mechanisms provide perhaps the most likely visual properties for linking up subjective with electrophysiological and photochemical data on cone vision.

Acknowledgements.

Acknowledgement is made of the assistance given by Mr. J. Bull, B. Sc., Miss P. Bailey, Miss E. Kinrade and Miss P. Fowler who acted as subjects and helped in the measurements. The work described forms part of the general research programme of the National Physical Laboratory and this paper is published by permission of the Director of the Laboratory.

REFERENCES

JUDD: «Compte Rendu, Com. Intern. Eclairage», 1951.

LUDVIGH & McCARTHY: «Arch. of Opthalmol.», 1938, 20, 37.

PITT: «Proc. Roy. Soc.», B, 1944, 132, 101.

STILES: «Docum. Ophthalm.», 1949, 3, 138.

— — «Proc. Roy. Soc.», B, 1939, 127, 64.

— — «Proc. Roy. Soc.», B, 58, 41.

WALD: «Science», 1945, 101, 653.

WRIGHT: «Trans. Opt. Soc.», 1928-29, 30, 1.

— — *Researches on Normal & Defective Colour Vision*, 1946, London, H. Kimpton.

— — «L'Annee Psychologique», 1952, 50, 169.

WRIGHT & McKEON: «Proc. Phys. Soc.», 1940, 52. 464.

Errata

Page 65. 6th line up: replace durantion by duration.

Page 70. 8th line up: replace assumption by assumptions.

Page 73. 20th line down: insert to between down and about.

Page 86. 4th line up: replace Fig. 13 by Fig. 14.

Page 97. 14th line up: replace Fig. 19 by Fig. 18.
5th line up: replace $\Pi_?$ by Π_4.

Page 98. 2nd line down: replace Fig. 19 by Fig. 18.
16th line up: replace Fig. 20 by Fig. 19.

Page 100. 12th line up: replace Fig. 21 by Fig. 20.

Page 102. 11th line up: replace Fig. 20 by Fig. 18.

Paper X: Reprinted from Farbe, Vol. 4, 1955.

W. S. Stiles:

Remarks on the Line-Element

(National Physical Laboratory, Teddington, Middlesex)

DK 535.646

Die übliche Darstellung der Linienelemente beruht auf nur drei unabhängigen Rezeptoren mit verschiedenen spektralen Empfindlichkeitskurven. Hier wird die Möglichkeit näher ausgeführt, weitere Rezeptoren in Betracht zu ziehen.

All the line-elements usually discussed imply just three independent mechanisms with different spectral sensitivities. Here a possible method of dealing with further mechanisms is explained.

On a coutume de discuter les éléments linéaires en les déduisant de seulement trois récepteurs indépendants, à sensibilités spectrales différentes. Ici on développe la possibilité d'envisager d'autres récepteurs.

All the line-elements considered in Dr. WYSZECKI's valuable review rest on the notion that at an early stage in the visual process, three linearly independent spectral sensitivity functions come into play and in such a way that, for all subsequent stages, the effect of a stimulus is determined by the three weighted integrals of the energy distribution of the stimulus, with the respective sensitivity functions as weighting factors. The work on colour adaptation presented to the Conference by Dr. MACADAM suggests that in fact more than three independent spectral sensitivities are involved. There is also evidence, obtained by the two-colour threshold method, of more than three visual cone mechanisms with different spectral sensitivities, although the extent to which the latter are truly linear and independent is not known.

Can the conception of the line-element be extended to a situation in which there are four or more independent spectral sensitivities while colour-matching by means of mixtures of three primaries is still possible? We have made some trials of this question, not it is true directed in the first instance to the case of multiple cone mechanisms, but concerned with the long-standing problem of colour-matching in a large field where the four independent spectral sensitivities correspond to three cone mechanisms and one rod mechanism. In that case the neural mechanism beyond the site of the spectral sensitivities must be so constituted that a compromise can be made and the two halves of the matching field can be brought to the same colour by the adjustment of just three mixture primaries. This statement ignores colour break-up at the central fovea which is visible for some test colours, but in practice the small area involved can be disregarded when making large field matches.

The simplest generalisation of a line-element of HELMHOLTZ type to include a fourth mechanism (the rod mechanism), may be written:

$$F^2 = \underbrace{(\delta R/T_R)^2 + (\delta G/T_G)^2 + (\delta B/T_B)^2}_{\text{three cone mechanisms}} + \underbrace{(\delta S/T_S)^2}_{\text{rod mechanism}}$$

asserting that the difference of appearance on the two sides of the matching field, specified by F, is the resultant, by a root mean square summation, of the differences of response of four mechanisms, specified respectively by the terms $(\delta R/T_R)$, etc. For each mechanism the difference of response is defined as the difference of stimulation of the mechanism on the two sides ($\delta R = R_2 - R_1$, say) divided by the smallest difference of stimulation T_R which would produce a perceptible difference of appearance if the mechanism in question were alone in action and was adapted to the average stimulation ($R = (R_1 + R_2)/2$, say). T_R is a function of R, T_G of G, etc. The notion of a "mechanism acting alone" may prove inadmissible and a more general line-element in which T_R say, depends on R, G, B and S may be required. However our trials have been confined to the simpler case. If for example a spectral yellow of energy intensity Q_1 is being matched by adding to it an intensity Q_2 of a spectral-blue desaturating primary and by comparing the desaturated yellow so obtained with a mixture of Q_3 of a spectral green and Q_4 of a spectral red primary, then

$$\delta R = Q_1 r_1 + Q_2 r_2 - Q_3 r_3 - Q_4 r_4$$
$$R = \tfrac{1}{2}(Q_1 r_1 + Q_2 r_2 + Q_3 r_3 + Q_4 r_4)$$

where r_1, r_2, r_3, r_4 are the spectral sensitivities of the R mechanism to the yellow, blue, green and red spectral stimuli; similarly for δG and G, δB and B, δS and S. With the intensity Q_1 of the yellow test colour fixed, it is in general impossible by varying the quantities Q_2, Q_3, Q_4 of the primaries to reduce the resultant "difference of appearance" F to zero. But it is possible to reduce F (or F^2) to a minimum, and it is at least plausible that, in some way, the neural mechanism beyond the receptors operates so as to achieve this result when a match is made. I have no clear picture of just how this could happen but I have thought it worth while to explore the implications of such a mode of action. For F^2 to be a minimum we must have

$$\frac{\partial F^2}{\partial Q_2} = \frac{\partial F^2}{\partial Q_3} = \frac{\partial F^2}{\partial Q_4} = 0$$

as the conditions for a match. To solve any particular case we need to know the relative spectral sensitivities of all four mechanism — the actual physiological ones not just linear combinations of them. For the rod mechanism the spectral sensitivity is well established. For the cone mechanisms we might adopt the new set of fundamentals recently derived by THOMSON and WRIGHT [1] or alternatively — and this is what we have done — use a set obtained by means of the two-colour threshold method [STILES (1955): mechanisms π_1, π_4 and π_5]. The latter method is also capable of supplying the requisite information about the way in which for each mechanism the threshold difference T depends on the level of stimulation of that mechanism. For the rod mechanism we have some fairly recent results on the variation of T with stimulus level extending to quite high scotopic levels (AGUILAR and STILES [3]). For the cone mechanisms corresponding data for a large test stimulus are not available and it has been necessary to make use of results for a 1^0 test stimulus with a reasonable allowance for the size factor. The actual calculations are very laborious on desk machines, but by the cooperation of my colleague at the N.P.L., Mr. R. P. HARVEY, the Laboratory's electronic computer (ACE) was brought to bear.

The matching of a yellow test colour (581 mμ) has been principally studied. Suppose first that this has a very high intensity, 5000 photopic trolands or more. At colour-match as derived from the line-element by the minimising procedure, the resultant quantities Q_2, Q_3 and Q_4 are negligibly different from those obtained by ignoring the rod term in the line-element and by solving $\delta R = \delta G = \delta B = 0$. This is because the average stimulation of the rod mechanism in the matching field for these values of Q_2, Q_3, Q_4 corresponds to about 5000 s c o t o p i c trolands[*] and, as shown in the work of AGUILAR and STILES [3], the rod mechanism at this level is 'saturated' and incapable of producing a differential response, i. e. $\delta S/T_S$ is effectively zero. Suppose all intensities (Q_1, Q_2, Q_3, Q_4) are now reduced in the same

---

[*] It is a coincidence that the average photopic and scotopic intensities in the field have nearly the same numerical value in their respective units.

proportion until Q_1 corresponds to a photopic intensity of the test colour of 100 photopic trolands. In the rod mechanism response,

$$\delta S/T_S = \frac{\delta S}{S} \bigg/ \frac{T_S}{S}$$

the factor δS is unchanged but T_S/S (the FECHNER fraction of the rod mechanism) is now very much reduced as we have moved out of the saturation region of the rods. The rod term in the line-element is no longer negligible and when Q_2, Q_3, Q_4 are allowed to vary keeping Q_1 constant the minimising procedure leads to new values for the ratios $\dfrac{Q_2}{Q_1}, \dfrac{Q_3}{Q_1}, \dfrac{Q_4}{Q_1}$. The change however is confined almost entirely to Q_2/Q_1, which increases, i. e. more desaturating blue is required. Of the three cone mechanism terms, the one corresponding to the blue mechanism,

$$(\delta B/T_B)^2 = \left(\frac{\delta B}{B} \cdot \frac{T_B}{B}\right)^2$$

can best tolerate a δB not equal to zero, since T_B/B is relatively large. The two reasons for this are: (a) the FECHNER fraction of the "blue" mechanism is about four times that of the "green" and "red" mechanisms at corresponding levels of stimulation, and (b) the level of stimulation of the "blue" mechanism in a yellow match is in any case much lower than for the "green" and "red", and the FECHNER fraction is larger on that account. The net result is that if the rod term in F^2 is to be reduced in making F^2 minimal, it will occur in the main by a change in the relative amount of desaturating blue (specified by the ratio Q_2/Q_1), since such a change affects $\delta B/B$ but does little to $\delta G/G$ and $\delta R/R$.

On reducing the intensity level still further, the increase in the relative amount of desaturating blue (Q_2/Q_1) continues until finally at a luminance of about 1 photopic troland, Q_2/Q_1 has about 80 times its value for high intensities and there is no further change. The computed relative amounts of the green and red primaries (Q_3/Q_1 and Q_4/Q_1) undergo only very slight changes (less than 10 per cent) in passing from very high to very low levels.

In recent tests of the effect of field intensity on colour-matching in a large field (10⁰), the case of a yellow test colour, discussed above, was included. The modifications of the match as intensity was reduced were much as predicted, at least as regards the major effect — the increase in the relative amount of desaturating blue. The ratio Q_2/Q_1 begins to increase at about

200 photopic trolands and rises to about 30 times its original value as 1 troland is approached. The observed changes in the relative amounts of the green and red primaries are small, as expected, but it was a disappointment to find that experimentally the amount of green primary diminishes slightly, instead of increases slightly as the calculation predicts. Although this first trial has proved only partially successful, some further tests are planned.

Any line-element can be applied to derive the step-by-step V_λ function. Some time ago I calculated the change in the V_λ curve in passing from scotopic through mesopic to photopic levels, using a line-element (of HELMHOLTZ type) comprising two terms — a rod term and a single cone term representing the lumped effect of all the cone mechanisms (STILES [4]). The results were in general agreement with WALTERS and WRIGHT's experimental measurements of V_λ in the parafovea [5]. A similar calculation could be made with the present four-term line-element and it can be foreseen that the mode of variation of V_λ with intensity would be substantially the same as derived from the two-term element.

It is an open question whether additional cone mechanisms present similar problems in colour-metrics to those arising from the addition of the rod mechanism. But the present method of attack — naive though it is — interests me because it shifts the "trichromatic principle" over to operators $\left(\dfrac{\partial}{\partial Q_2}, \dfrac{\partial}{\partial Q_3}, \dfrac{\partial}{\partial Q_4} \right)$ and leaves the operand free to embody as many independent spectral sensitivities as may be required.

Bibliography:

1. THOMSON, L. C., a. W. D. WRIGHT, The convergence of the tritanopic confusion loci and the derivation of the fundamental response functions. J. opt. Soc. Amer. **43** (1953), p. 890...891
2. STILES, W. S., Further studies of visual mechanisms by the two-colour threshold method. Printed in: Union Internationale de Physique pure et appliquée. Coloquio sobre Problemas Opticos de la Vision. Madrid 1953. P. 65...103
3. AGUILAR, M., a. W. S. STILES, Saturation of the rod mechanism of the retina at high levels of stimulation. Optica Acta **1** (1954/55), p. 59...65
4. STILES, W. S., Current problems of visual research. Proc. phys. Soc. **56** (1944), p. 329...356
5. WALTERS, H. V., a. W. D. WRIGHT, The spectral sensitivity of the fovea and extra-fovea in the Purkinje range. Proc. Roy. Soc. **131 B** (1943), p. 340...361

Paper XI: Reprinted from the Proceedings of the National Academy of Sciences, Vol. 45, 1959.

COLOR VISION: THE APPROACH THROUGH INCREMENT-THRESHOLD SENSITIVITY

By W. S. Stiles

NATIONAL PHYSICAL LABORATORY, TEDDINGTON, MIDDLESEX, ENGLAND

I am most sensible of the honor of addressing this meeting and of the generosity of the National Academy of Sciences in bringing me here as their guest. The invitation to contribute to the present symposium came just as I had finished a rather elaborate study of the color-matching properties of the average observer. However, that work I believe to be of more colorimetric interest, and I have elected, therefore, to deal with a quite different approach to color vision by a method which does not rest on actual color-matching—the method of increment thresholds.

Consider, to take first the simplest case, a subject whose eyes are fully adapted to a completely dark field. The increment threshold is then just the smallest perceptible quantity of a certain test light which is applied at a particular part of the visual field. For convenience, I use the expression "smallest perceptible quantity," although, of course, thresholds are definable only statistically, for example as critical values of the stimulus variable at which the chance of a perception equals 50 per cent. In the general case, the increment threshold is still the smallest perceptible quantity of a certain test light, but now this is added to another stimulus—the conditioning stimulus—which consists of any distribution of brightness and color to which we may choose to expose the eye. The conditioning stimulus need not be an unvarying one: the increment threshold is, in fact, often measured while the eye is adapting itself to a change from one constant stimulus to another constant stimulus, the whole spatial and temporal pattern of stimulation being considered to form the conditioning stimulus. The increment threshold (or, better, its reciprocal, the threshold sensitivity) is a measure of visual sensitivity which can be varied in different ways to bring out particular properties of the visual response system. We may, for example, vary the angular size and exposure time of the test stimulus, to determine how well the visual system integrates over area and over time. Most important, we may change the spectral composition of the test stimulus, in order to determine the spectral sensitivities that are active in the response system. So far, only changes in the parameters of the test stimulus have been mentioned. In addition, any number of different conditioning stimuli may be used. However, there is evidence that the modifications of the increment threshold by more complex patterns of brightness and color are similar to those obtained with a very simple pattern, namely, a uniform stimulus which extends over and around the area of the field where the test stimulus is applied. We should regard the action of a more stimulus, including stimuli applied at some distance from the test area, as *equivalent* to that of a suitably chosen uniform stimulus of the kind mentioned if, for all possible test stimuli (of various sizes, colors, exposure times, etc.), the observed increment threshold was the same for the two conditions. The equivalence is probably not generally complete, but it has been found to hold approximately in some cases, and we are justified in concentrating, in the first instance, on the simple stimulus pattern. This has the advantage that much bigger effects on the increment threshold can be obtained with "covering fields" than with conditioning stimuli confined to the surrounding retina.

For probing the color mechanisms of the eye, the method that has been extensively used is to apply, in flashes, a small monochromatic test stimulus of wave length λ to a uniform monochromatic conditioning field of wave length μ and intensity M_μ extending over the test area (the two-color threshold technique). Most work has been done for the case when the eye is fully adapted to the conditioning field, although several recent investigations (particularly by Boynton[1]) as well as some earlier ones have considered non-equilibrium situations. If all the other possible experimental variables (size and exposure time of test stimulus, angles of incidence on the retina of test, and conditioning stimuli, etc.) are kept constant, the increment threshold N_λ, i.e., the smallest perceptible intensity of the test stimulus, will be a function $f(\lambda, \mu, M_\mu)$ of the three variables λ, μ, M_μ. The function f is certainly not simple, and its determination for the whole range of possible values of the three variables is a considerable undertaking. Some progress has been made, however, which suggests that the function may be put in a form involving separate terms identifiable, on certain reasonable assumptions, with the contributions to the increment threshold of component visual mechanisms having different spectral sensitivities and some other differences in their properties. The possibility of "separating" the function f in this way does not, of course, prove that there exist in the eye separate structures and processes corresponding to the different terms. The psychophysical analysis has to be related to objective observations on the visual pigments, on the types of end-organ and the ramifications of the nerve pathways through the higher neurons, on the electrophysiological response, etc., before the "component mechanisms" can begin to acquire a real existence. Despite the wealth of information on the visual system generally that is provided by these objective techniques, there has until recently been little which could be applied directly to the psychophysical data of color vision. The important new development is the objective detection and measurement of bleachable visual pigments, other than rhodopsin, in the living human eye (Rushton).[2] Some repercussions of this work on the increment-threshold analysis will be mentioned later.

The guiding principle in interpreting increment thresholds is that in the retinal area on which the test stimulus is imaged there are several component mechanisms, any one of which may be the means of triggering off the response "seen" when the test flash is applied. Each component mechanism is conceived of as an association of a selected proportion of the end-organs (rods and cones) in the area, the association being effected somewhere in the neural system through which the nervous activity, initiated by light absorption in the end-organs, is transmitted to the brain and finally to the effector nerves of the external response. It is not assumed that the end-organs of a component mechanism are necessarily all of the same kind or contain just one photopigment, nor that end-organs belong exclusively to one component mechanism, but the mechanisms are assumed to have sufficient independence for the idea of a particular component mechanism acting alone to have a meaning. It is assumed, in fact, that the response of all but one component mechanism could be blocked (ideally; it may not be practicable to do it), leaving the remaining mechanism to respond in its normal way. For a given test stimulus and given conditioning stimulus, the observed increment threshold in the retinal area is assumed to depend only on the respective increment thresholds of the component mechanisms that would be observed under the same conditions if they were acting alone. In particular, it is assumed that the observed increment threshold will not exceed any of the component increment thresholds and will generally approximate to the smallest of these. Finally, each component mechanism is assumed to have a characteristic relative spectral sensitivity function, so that the effect on the mechanism of an intensity I_1 (in energy units) of one wave length λ_1, forming the whole or part of the test or conditioning stimulus, is just the same as that of an intensity I_2 of any other wave length λ_2 that may be substituted for it, provided that I_1 and I_2 are in the inverse ratio of the relative spectral sensitivity values at these wave lengths.

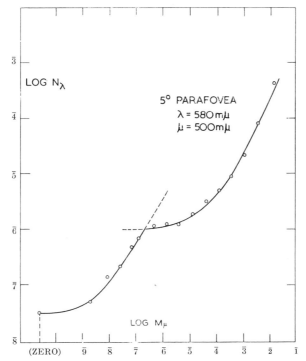

FIG. 1 —Increment threshold, $N\lambda$, versus field intensity, $M\mu$, for 5°′ extrafoveal vision. Test stimulus: 1°, 0.06 sec. Subject: W. S. S. ($N\lambda$ and $M\mu$ expressed in erg sec^{-1} [deg. of arc]$^{-2}$.)

The analysis of increment-threshold measurements on the above lines may be illustrated by examining briefly the case of extrafoveal vision, for which there is the ample evidence of the duplicity theory of vision for the operation, in some sense, of distinct rod and cone mechanisms. Figure 1 gives an example of a so-called threshold-versus-intensity (t.v.i.) curve, in which the logarithm of the increment threshold is plotted against the logarithm of the uniform conditioning stimulus for a particular pair of test and conditioning wave lengths, $\lambda = 580$ mμ, $\mu = 500$ mμ. In this case the test stimulus (1°, 0.06 sec.) was imaged 5° from the

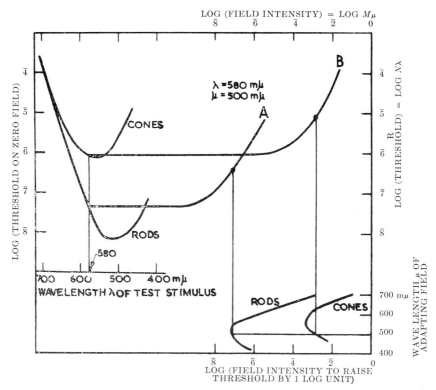

Fig. 2.—Diagram illustrating how t.v.i. curves like that of Fig. 1 result from the t.v.i. curves of two component mechanisms, A (rod) and B (cone), whose positions with respect to the axes of log $N\lambda$ and log $M\mu$ for any test and field wave lengths λ and μ are determined by the respective spectral sensitivity curves of the mechanisms shown in the auxiliary diagrams.

fovea.   Figure 2 shows diagrammatically the tentative interpretation of the curve of Figure 1 in terms of two component mechanisms of the kind contemplated above.[3] Curves A and B (Fig. 2) represent, respectively, the t.v.i. curves assumed for the A (rod) and B (cone) component mechanisms when acting alone.   At each field intensity the observed increment threshold is put equal to the lower of the values appropriate to the A and B curves.   The crucial question now is What happens if λ and μ are changed?   According to the assumption about the spectral sensitivity curve of a component mechanism, a change in λ, keeping μ constant, should merely displace the curves A and B—without change of shape—parallel to the ordinate axis, by amounts determined by their respective relative spectral sensitivities.   A change in μ, keeping λ constant, should, on the other hand, displace the curves parallel to the axis of abscissae by amounts also fixed by the respective spectral sensitivity curves.   The spectral sensitivity curves are also shown in the diagram, and it is easy to visualize the effects of changing λ and μ.   The experimental t.v.i. curves obtained for various combinations of test and field wave lengths show that the branch of the curve attributed to the A mechanism conforms satisfactorily to these *displacement rules*, the displacements parallel to the two axes being controlled by the same spectral sensitivity curve.   For the B branch, however, the displacement rules fail to hold, and it is impossible to represent the increment threshold for extrafoveal vision as arising from just two component mechanisms in the way proposed. The next step would be to see whether the B branch could be represented as the resultant of two or more branches, but this is difficult because the form of the B branch for many of the interesting (λ, μ) combinations is not accessible to observation: it is masked by the A branch, which has the lower threshold.

We now examine the various component mechanisms which we are led to postulate for the fovea, the area of the retina where color discrimination is most highly developed and where the absence of rod end-organs eliminates (probably) any participation of a "rod" component mechanism. (This last simplification is not quite a certain a priori, as the adapting field extends into the retinal area containing rods, but it seems to be so in fact.) Consider, first, the t.v.i. curves obtained with test stimuli of short wave length $(\lambda < 510 \text{ m}\mu)$ and with conditioning stimuli of medium or long wave length $(\mu > 520 \text{ m}\mu)$. These show a division into two branches $(\mu < \text{about } 560 \text{ m}\mu)$ or of three branches $(\mu > 560 \text{ m}\mu)$, an example of the latter being given in Figure 3. The three branches are provisionally ascribed to three component mechanisms, denoted by the neutral symbols π_4, π_1, π_3 marked in the figure. The changes in the t.v.i. curve when λ and μ are altered establish that the branch π_1 obeys the displacement rules. But if λ becomes too large or μ too small, the π_1 branch is masked by the π_4 branch; thus the displacements observable by changing λ and μ correspond to non-overlapping spectral ranges of the spectral sensitivity curve of the mechanism, and it is not possible immediately to check that a single spectral sensitivity curve determines displacement of both kinds. The difficulty can be largely overcome by the "auxiliary field method." In this we use as conditioning stimulus a mixture of a fixed auxiliary field of long wave length sufficiently intense to bring the increment threshold to the π_1 branch of the curve, and a main field of wave length μ, which may be as short as desired. The comparative effects of main fields of different wave length in moving the increment threshold higher up the π_1 branch can then be determined.[4] It is found that in the overlapping region $(\lambda < 500 \text{ m}\mu)$ the λ and μ displacements correspond to a common relative spectral sensitivity curve and that this curve has a maximum at approximately 440 mμ (energy expressed in quantum units). The evidence on the π_3 branch is more limited because of the difficulty in obtaining the very high field intensities needed to reach it. The results again indicate a branch obeying approximately the displacement rules and with consistent λ and μ displacements in the overlap region

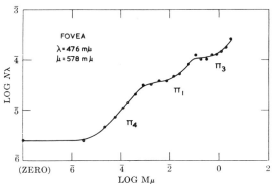

Fig. 3.—Foveal t.v.i. curve. Test stimulus: $1°$, 0.2 sec. Subject: E. K. ($N\lambda$ and $M\mu$ in erg sec^{-1} [deg. of arc]$^{-2}$.)

($\lambda < 500$ mμ).   As can be seen in Figure 4, the spectral sensitivities of the π_1 and π_3 component mechanisms (derived from μ-variation displacements) agree closely in shape in the region of their maxima ($\lambda < 500$ mμ) and differ only at long wave lengths.   (The curves of Figure 4 and later figures refer to the mean results of the same four subjects.)   But for test stimuli in the short-wave region the two mechanisms still differ in their absolute thresholds, i.e., the values to which their increment thresholds tend as the conditioning stimulus is reduced to zero: the absolute threshold for π_3 is about four times that for π_1.   It was unexpected to find two com-

ponent mechanisms with maximal and closely similar spectral sensitivities in the blue.   But there is also some evidence of a third component mechanism (π_2) with maximal sensitivity in the same spectral region.   This is indicated by a breakdown in the displacement rules for the branch π_4 when, for conditioning fields of long wave length (e.g., 600 mμ), the wave length of the test stimulus is reduced below about 460 mμ.   The discrepancy would be consistent with a π_2 mechanism with the spectral sensitivity curve (by the μ-variation method) in the range 510–700 mμ, as shown in Figure 4.   For $\mu <$ 510 mμ, the curve must lie above the points of the arrows shown in the figure.   Unfortunately, the auxiliary field device is not applicable in this case, and the form of the curve has not been determined in the neighborhood of the maximum, although the latter can hardly lie outside the range 440–480 mμ.

As the wave length λ of the test stimulus is increased above about 450 mμ, the branches of

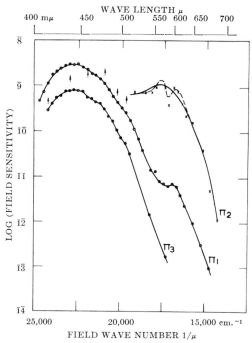

FIG. 4.—Field spectral sensitivity of foveal cone mechanisms π_1, π_2, and π_3. Field sensitivity is defined as the reciprocal of the field intensity in quanta sec^{-1} (deg. of arc)$^{-2}$ required to raise the increment threshold of the mechanism to ten times its zero-field value. For $\lambda < 510$ mμ, the arrow points indicate values below which the undetermined part of the π_2 curve cannot fall. Means for four subjects, π_1 and π_3; for three subjects, π_2.

the t.v.i. curve associated with mechanisms having maximal sensitivity in the blue move upward with respect to the π_4 branch, and for λ greater than 520 mμ they move completely above it and are inaccessible to measurement, whatever the wave length of the conditioning stimulus.   For these test stimuli of longer wave length, the π_4 branch does not obey the displacement rules, although the well-marked transitions obtained at shorter wave lengths are not in evidence.   It was originally thought that the results would be explained by admitting that there were, in fact, two branches—a π_4 and a π_5 branch—with associated spectral sensitivities not very widely separated along the spectrum, so that sharp transitions from one branch to the other would not be expected. Further measurements indicated, however, that, while this explanation is fairly satisfactory if attention is confined to conditioning stimuli below about 150 trolands, it leads to discrepancies with observations made at higher intensities. The spectral sensitivities of π_4 and π_5 derived by the μ-variation method from measurements in the lower-intensity range are shown in Figure 5. These sensitivities, like those of Figure 4, represent at each wave length the reciprocal of the field intensity (in quantum units) required to raise the increment threshold of the particular mechanism to ten times its zero-field value. If we also know the shape of the branch of the t.v.i. curve appropriate to the mechanism and the absolute threshold of the mechanism for some test wave length, we can derive the curve showing the variation of the increment threshold

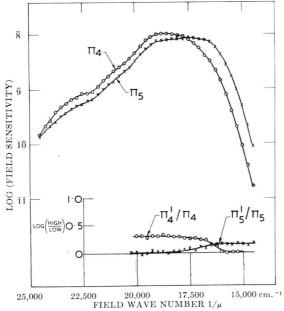

or its reciprocal, the threshold sensitivity, with test wave length for any intensity and wave length of the field. This calculation has been made in Figure 6 for the five component mechanisms π_1–π_5 for the case of a field of wave length 667 mμ and intensity 29 trolands. The observed threshold sensitivity at each test wave length should equal approximately the highest of the component threshold sensitivities, and it is apparent that only π_4 and π_5 are concerned in this instance. The circle points represent the directly observed threshold sensitivities and are in satisfactory agreement with the prediction. The comparison of the predicted and observed curves when the field intensity is raised by a factor of nearly 100 is shown in

Fig. 5.—Field spectral sensitivities as in Fig. 4 for cone mechanisms π_4 and π_5. The inset diagram shows the log (ratio of the sensitivities: high-intensity level/low-intensity level) for the π_4 and π_5 mechanisms. Means for four subjects.

Figure 7. The discrepancy is not only in the absolute values (which might arise from uncertainty in the shape of the π_4 branch) but also in the shape of the observed curve in the wave-length range where it should be at least parallel to π_4. The indication is that, with a high-intensity red field, the π_4 mechanism is relatively more sensitive on the short-wave side of about 580 mμ than the calculation treating π_4 as a single component mechanism with its low-intensity properties would predict. This deviation is independently confirmed by t.v.i. curves taken to high intensities. An analogous, although smaller, effect for π_5 is shown by observations with low- and high-intensity green conditioning fields (Figs. 8 and 9) and is again confirmed independently by t.v.i. curves. The π_5 mechanism under high green stimulation is relatively more sensitive on the long-wave side of about 580 mμ than the calculation treating π_5 as a single component mechanism with its low-intensity properties would predict.   Insufficient is yet known of these deviations from single component properties of π_4 and π_5 to say whether they could be explained by assuming additional component mechanisms.   For the present, it is advisable merely to recognize modified high-intensity conditions of these mechanisms, denoted by π_4' and π_5', respectively.   The differences in spectral sensitivity in the low- and high-intensity conditions of π_4 or π_5 are not large compared with the differences between π_4 and π_5.   A first determination of the ratio of the high- to the low-intensity spectral sensitivity is shown in the inset diagram of Figure 5.   A tentative deduction

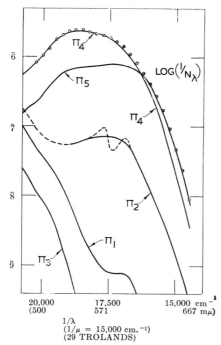

Fig. 6.—*Points:* Increment-threshold sensitivity by $\cdot 1/N\lambda$ versus test stimulus wave number 15,000 cm^{-1} (wave length 667 mμ) and intensity 29 trolands. Test stimulus: 1°, 0.2 sec. Means of four subjects. *Curves:* predicted threshold sensitivity versus wave-number curves at this conditioning stimulus for the component mechanisms π_1–π_5.

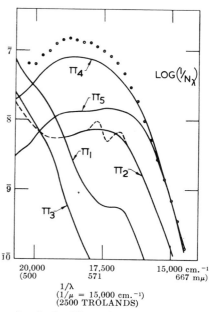

FIG. 7.—As for Fig. 6, but for conditioning field of intensity 2,500 trolands.

from other observations is that the transitions $\pi_4 \rightarrow \pi_4'$ and $\pi_5 \rightarrow \pi_5'$ occur in a range of conditioning intensities of the order of 1 log unit centered on an intensity of about 300 trolands.

The scheme of component visual mechanisms indicated by increment-threshold analysis is summarized in Table 1.   The Fechner fraction quoted in the final column is defined as the ratio of the increment threshold to the field intensity when the conditioning field has the same color as the test stimulus ($\lambda = \mu$) and the increment threshold is raised by it to ten times the zero-field value.   There are interesting differences between the Fechner fractions of different component mecha-

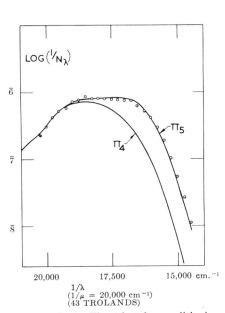

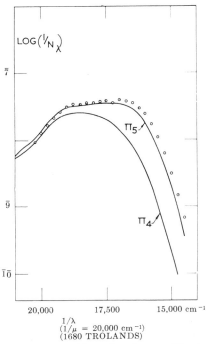

Fig. 8.—As for Fig. 6 but for conditioning field of wave number 20,000 cm⁻¹ (wave length 500 mμ) and intensity 43 trolands.

Fig. 9.—As for Fig. 8 but for conditioning field of intensity 1,680 trolands.

nisms: the "blue" cone mechanisms have values four to five times those for the "green" as "red" cone mechanisms. In applying the present ideas of component mechanisms to the explanation of other psychophysical measurements on color discrimination and brightness matching, this difference plays an important part: it corresponds to the small contribution to luminance of short-wave stimuli, despite their strong coloring value.

TABLE 1

Mechanism	Symbol	Remarks		Wave Length of Maximal Sensitivity (mμ)	Fechner Fraction (1°, 0.2 Sec. Test Stimulus)
Rod	π_0	Absent at the fovea		503	(30)
"Blue" cone	π_1	Ratio of blue to yellow sensitivity (440/590)	approx. 2.6 log units	440	8.7
	π_2	Ratio of blue to yellow sensitivity (440/590)	order of 1 log unit	? (Between 440 and 480 mμ)	? (Probably as for π_1 and π_3)
	π_3	Ratio of blue to yellow sensitivity (440/590)	approx. 4.0 log units	440	8.7
"Green" cone	π_4			540	1.9
	π_4'	Modified high-intensity state		540	. . .
"Red" cone	π_5			575 (very flat max.)	1.8
	π_5'	Modified high-intensity state		587	. . .

The discussion so far has been concerned with the breakdown of the three-variable function $f(\lambda, \mu, M_\mu)$, all the parameters of the test stimulus other than color being assumed constant. If one of these is allowed to vary, the effects on the different branches of the t.v.i. curves can be compared, and more information on the properties of the component mechanisms can be obtained. For example, it is known that the response of the cone end-organs of the retina is highly directional, and, by determining the change in increment threshold on altering the angle of incidence on the retina of the rays forming the test stimulus (keeping, of course, the retinal area stimulated the same), differences in the directional properties of different mechanisms can be studied. The differential effects are small, and more measurements are needed, but the early work indicates that π_1 is more directional in its reponse than π_4, that π_4 is more directional than π_5 for stimuli in the green and yellow, but that this position is reversed for red stimuli. Changes in the relative response of different mechanisms as the angle of incidence is varied may be expected to produce changes of color even of monochromatic stimuli. The small changes, observed are, in fact, in general agreement with the relative directional properties of the mechanisms obtained by the threshold observations.

Two outstanding questions are: (a) What is the relation of the increment-threshold mechanisms to the three processes of trichromatic color-matching? and (b) Do the spectral sensitivities of the component mechanisms represent photo-sensitivities of visual pigments? We limit ourselves to foveal vision, so that the complication of the rod mechanism does not arise. The two questions are closely related, as the three small-field color-matching functions which sum up the color-matching properties of the foveal retina (conditions of very high intensity excluded) are almost certainly linear combinations of the spectral photosensitivities of three visual pigments, although the coefficients in these combinations are not determinable by straightforward color-matching measurements. Thus, if the spectral sensitivity of a component mechanism could be represented as a linear combination of the color-matching functions, it would also be a linear combination of the pigment photosensitivities. This would indicate that the end-organs of the mechanism contained the pigments represented in the linear combination (i.e., those having non-zero coefficients) and that the effects of light absorption in these different pigments added up linearly. Electrophysiological evidence makes it unlikely that this last state of affairs could come about unless all end-organs of the mechanism contained the pigments in a mixture of the same composition, including the specially simple case of a "mixture" comprising just one pigment. The rigorous application of the argument is hampered by the difficulty of obtaining "hard" data from increment-threshold measurements. However, tests made on the mean spectral sensitivity curves (Figs. 4, 5) indicate that π_4 or π_4' can be expressed fairly well as linear combinations of the small-field color-matching functions. For π_5 the linear representation is less satisfactory, particularly for the high-intensity condition π_5'. For π_3 and for π_1 in the main (short-wave) region of the curve, a linear representation is acceptable, and even with the inclusion of the long-wave lobe on the π_1 sensitivity curve it could not certainly be excluded. The actual shapes of the sensitivity curves also have a bearing here. The spectral absorption and spectral photosensitivity curves that have now been obtained for many visual pigments from animal retinas, by measurements on retinal extracts or complete excised retinas, differ little in shape from the absorption curve for the pigment of rod vision, rhodopsin; to a first approximation, they correspond to the rhodopsin curve (log absorption factor against wave number) displaced along the wave-number axis so that its maximum occurs at the appropriate position. Before physical absorption and photosensitivity curves can be compared with psychophysical sensitivity curves, the latter must be corrected for the selective light losses in the eye that precede the actual absorption by the photosensitive pigment. The correction is uncertain in the violet but is probably not seriously in error in the blue and green: it is negligible at longer wave lengths. It is found that the corrected π_4, π_4', and π_3 spectral sensitivity curves and the π_1 curve ignoring the long-wave lobe are fairly well represented by displaced rhodopsin absorption curves (Fig. 10: the broken lines are, in fact, the corrected spectral sensitivity curves of the rod mechanism, but the latter has substantially the same shape as the rhodopsin absorption curve in the relevant spectral region). An attempt to represent the complete π_1 curve by the addition of a second rhodopsin-shaped absorption curve whose absorption combines linearly with that of the first is not quite acceptable: the linear summation produces too smooth a transition. But it is for π_5 and π_5' that the representation is least satisfactory: neither a simple rhodopsin-shaped curve nor a linear summation of two such curves (however displaced along the spectrum) will represent the spectral sensitivity of the "red" cone mechanism in low- or high-intensity conditions. It

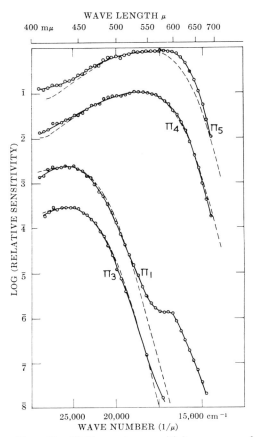

Fig. 10.—Field spectra sensitivity curves of mechanisms π_1, π_3, π_4, π_5 corrected for pre-receptor light losses and compared in each case with the similarly corrected sensitivity curve of rod vision displaced parallel to the two axes to give the best fit.

seems certain that the end-organs of π_5 cannot be equipped either with a single rhodopsin-type pigment or with a simple mixture (the same in all end-organs) of two such pigments. It has already been noted that the π_5 and π_5' spectral sensitivities are not adequately represented by linear combinations of the small-field color-matching functions, and the failure to fit rhodopsin-type curves might result from the fact that the increment-threshold spectral sensitivity is not uiblt up linearly from the spectral absorption curves of the pigments contained in the end-organs of the π_5 mechanism. It is most improbable, however, that this is the sole cause.   Other proposed fundamental (pigment) spectral sensitivities for color vision obtained as strict linear combinations of the color-making functions for which the coefficients have been derived from the properties of the three kinds of dichromatic color defectives and other psychophysical measurements demand a similar non-rhodopsin-type "red" curve, usually including still more striking deviations from the rhodopsin shape at short wave lengths (Fig. 11).

Rushton's[2] objective measurements of bleachable pigments in the human fovea have established the presence in protanopes, deuteranopes, and color normals of a pigment he has named *chlorolabe* with a difference spectrum and action spectrum having a maximum at 540 mμ.   As he has pointed out, the spectral sensitivity of the π_4 mechanism is a fair approximation to the spectrum of chlorolabe.   The

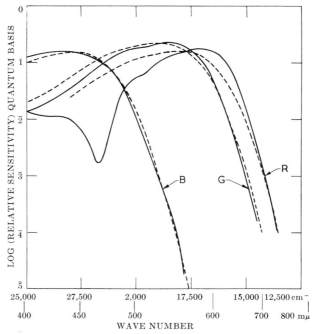

Fig. 11.—Thomson-Wright colour fundamentals corrected for light losses and compared with the displaced rod curve as in Fig. 10.

π_4' spectral sensitivity curve lies still closer to the objective curve.   In fact, we have here a convergence, onto a common curve of rhodopsin type, of four spectral sensitivities: the objective spectrum of chlorolabe, the "green" fundamental derivable from the small-field color-matching functions of normal and dichromatic subjects,[5] the increment-threshold sensitivity π_4', and, finally, the sensitivity of a normal eye in a state of "artificial monochromasy" produced by exposure to very intense violet and red stimuli (Brindley[6]).   The implication for the "green" cone mechanism is that, in the high-intensity condition, its end-organs contain, or at least are activated by the light absorption of, just one pigment—chlorolabe.   Why, then, should the spectral sensitivity π_4, attributed to the mechanism in the low-intensity condition, be different?   If exactly the same end-organs were concerned at all intensity levels, either these would have to contain—probably in relatively small amount—a second pigment more red-sensitive than chlorolabe, or, alternatively, the effective spectral absorption curve of the latter pigment in its situation within the end-organs would have to vary with the intensity of stimulation. A variation of the kind required would occur if at low levels of stimulation the optical density of the pigment in the end-organ was high enough for self-screening to occur and if the reduction of density by bleaching at high levels of stimulation substantially reduced the self-screening. "Self-screening" denotes here the selective filtering of the light reaching the deeper pigment layers in the end-organ, in its passage through the upper pigment layers. Brindley has considered the possibility that the breakdown of metameric color-matches after the eye has been exposed to high intensities may be explained by the reduction of self-screening present at low and moderate intensities.[6] The difference between the π_4 and π_4' spectral sensitivities would correspond—very approximately—to a change in self-screening if in the low-intensity condition the chlorolabe in the end-organs had an optical density at the maximum wave length 540 mμ of about 1.0 and if this was reduced to about 0.2 in the high-intensity condition. However, the existence of self-screening in the end-organs of the green cone mechanism is contrary to all the evidence: Brindley's results show that the breakdown in metameric color-matches in the green-yellow-red range is associated with an anomaly not of the "green" process but of the "red" process only; the transition from π_4 to π_4' occurs in an intensity range lower than that required to produce appreciable breakdown in color-matches; the requisite density of the chlorolabe under zero-field conditions and the necessary degree of bleaching in passing from the π_4 to the π_4' intensity level are both improbably high, according to Rushton's objective data on chlorolabe. As a more red-sensitive pigment, *erythrolabe*, has been shown objectively to be present in the retina (Rushton),[2] the suggestion that the end-organs of the "green" cone mechanism might contain a small proportion of it mixed with chlorolabe is, at first sight, promising. The difficulty here is to understand why the red-sensitive pigment should be bleached or rendered ineffective by an increase in intensity corresponding to the transition π_4 to π_4'. The objective data on erythrolabe would point to a comparatively small reduction—not more than 10 per cent—in its density by bleaching in this intensity range. We are led, therefore, to the other main possibility that, at low intensities, additional end-organs, not containing only chlorolabe, have contributed to the spectral sensitivity derived for the "green" cone mechanism. Many ways can be imagined in which this might come about, but it would be pointless to enlarge on them, as there is at present little evidence to distinguish different suggestions. One general observation may be made: whatever the way in which the non-chlorolabe end-organs are associated with the chlorolabe end-organs in determining π_4, the association is broken as a result of increasing the level of stimulation.

It is possible that in three blue-sensitive mechanisms—π_2, π_1, π_3—we have something like the same principle in operation. If we accept π_3 as the "blue" cone mechanism with end-organs containing just one blue-sensitive pigment of rhodopsin type (cyanolabe? not yet detected objectively), the spectral sensitivities of the other mechanisms would correspond to associations of cyanolabe with non-cyanolabe end-organs, these associations being broken at higher levels of stimulation by long-wave light. On this view, only one of the three mechanisms would be in being at any moment, and this represents formally a radical change in our working hypothesis. But, while it can be shown from the steady-state increment-threshold measurements that the mechanisms π_1 and π_4 are present together, the relationship of the spectral sensitivity curves of π_1, π_2, and π_3 prevents a similar proof that any two of these are simultaneously present.

Comments generally similar to those made on π_4 and π_4' apply to the change from π_5 to π_5', but there are some differences. There is an additional objection to the use of self-screening as an explanation of the change; bleaching of the self-screening pigment would lead to a change in the spectral sensitivity curve even qualitatively different from that observed. This is not necessarily in conflict with Brindley's conclusion that, at higher-intensity levels, a change in self-screening of the end-sensitive pigment accounts for the breakdown of metameric color-matches, although the objective data on the erythrolabe in the retina do not support this theory. There is no convergence of the different spectral sensitivities with maxima at long wave length on a common rhodopsin-type curve. The π_5 curve does not agree with the objective spectrum of erythrolabe: Rushton has shown that π_5 can be fitted by the absorption curve of a mixture of erythrolabe and chlorolabe in the proportion $1:0.6$.[2] For π_5', the corresponding proportion would be about $1:0.3$, so that π_5' is nearer the objective curve of erythrolabe. The fact that both erythrolabe and chlorolabe have been shown to be present in the deuteranopic eye favors the Fick hypothesis of red-green fusion for the explanation of deuteranopia. The character of dichromatic color vision as a reduction form of normal color vision means that the spectral sensitivity of the red-green fusion in the deuteranope must be a linear combination of the normal's color-matching functions and hence almost certainly of the spectral absorption (strictly photosensitivity) functions of the normal's pigments. Deuteranopia would then be explained by the presence in all the end-organs of the fused red-green system of a mixture in an invariable ratio of the chlorolabe and erythrolabe pigments; any other explanation would encounter linearity difficulties. If, as is sometimes assumed, the normal also has the fusion process of the deuteranope but, in addition, the simple "green" process (and, of course, the "blue" process also possessed by the deuteranope), then the appearance in the normal eye of a $\pi_5-\pi_5'$ mechanism supplied by end-organs containing a mixture of chlorolabe and erythrolabe would fit in very well. But there are difficulties: on the one hand, the pigment mixture appears unexpectedly stable when very high-intensity colored stimuli are used in increment-threshold and artificial monochromasy measurements, and, on the other hand, the breakdown of color-matches at high-intensity levels could not correspond merely to an alteration of the composition of a pigment mixture in the end-organs of the "red" cone mechanism.

This review has been devoted mainly to the spectral sensitivities of the color-vision mechanisms of the fovea arrived at by increment-threshold measurements made under steady-state conditions. The spectral sensitivities are perhaps of special interest at this time in the light of the new objective data on cone pigments. The summation properties of different color mechanisms, the way the mechanisms are modified in moving out from the fovea, and their behavior when the conditioning stimulus is suddenly changed have all been studied by the increment-threshold method to a limited extent. There is an interesting field here for further work.

[1] R. M. Boynton, *J. Opt. Soc. Amer.*, **46**, 172, 1956.

[2] W. H. A. Rushton, *Visual Problems of Colour* (N.P.L. Symposium, No. 8) (in Press).

[3] W. S. Stiles, *Documenta Ophthal.*, **3**, 138, 1949.

[4] W. S. Stiles, *Coloquio sobre problemas opticos de la vision* (Madrid: Union Internationale de Physique Pure et Appliquée, 1953), **1**, 65.

[5] L. C. Thomson, and W. D. Wright, *J. Opt. Soc. Amer.*, **43**, 890, 1953.

[6] G. S. Brindley, *J. Physiol.*, **122**, 332, 1953.

Erratum

Page 108. Table 1, title of final column: replace Fechner Fraction by Percentage Weber-Fechner Fraction.

Paper XII: Reprinted from Anales Real Soc. Espan. Fis. Quim., Series A, Vol. 57, 1961.

ADAPTATION, CHROMATIC ADAPTATION, COLOUR TRANSFORMATION *

BY

W. S. STILES

(Lecture delivered at Madrid on 3rd may, 1960).

RESUMEN

Se discute el problema de la formulación de conceptos cuantitativos en el estudio de la adaptación visual.

¿Hasta qué punto es posible especificar mediante una o varias variables el estado de adaptación del aparato visual, o más precisamente de aquella parte de él que toma parte en la visión en una región limitada del campo visual? ¿Hasta qué punto las variables de adaptación pueden relacionarse a propiedades objetivas del aparato visual, tales como las concentraciones de los pigmentos visuales en los órganos terminales o las condiciones fisiológicas de partes del sistema nervioso más atrás de dichos órganos? En lugar de la noción insostenible de que la adaptación del mecanismo escotópico o de bastones está determinada por una sola variable relacionada de un modo simple con la concentración de la rodopsina en los bastones, hemos de considerar un sistema de adaptación en el cual tomen parte tanto la concentración de la rodopsina como las condiciones neurales, pero aún quedan sin aclarar varias cuestiones.

Para el sistema escotópico existe la gran simplificación de que los estímulos luminosos de diferentes distribuciones energéticas son visualmente equivalentes si sus valores escotópicos basados en la función de eficacia luminosa escotópica son los mismos. Para el sistema de conos, fotópico, de respuestas coloreadas, existe una simplificación análoga, aunque en menor grado, mediante el principio según el cual son equivalentes los estímulos que tienen los mismos valores triestímulos. Estos tres valores, transformados linealmente a un sistema de referencia apropiado, se han tomado frecuentemente como representantes respectivos de las estimulaciones de tres mecanismos visuales que actúan al mismo tiempo, pero independientemente. Por tanto, la adaptación del sistema fotópico puede corresponder a un cambio interno del estado de cada uno de estos mecanismos —en general no el mismo para los diferentes mecanismos—, como resultado del cual sus sensibilidades luminosas efectivas se modifican sin que quede efectuado el modo en que las respuestas que ellos transmiten se elaboran después por la retina y el cerebro. Los investigadores de la adaptación cromática por las dos técnicas principales—medidas de umbrales de color y medidas de claridad y cromacidad aparente—comenzaron con esta idea, pero la han encontrado inadecuada en diferentes modos. Se examinan algunos de estos fallos.

Los fenómenos de contrastes simultáneos y sucesivos pueden considerarse incluídos en la adaptación cromática. Pero queda todavía por resolver la cuestión si pueden entrar otros factores en la visión de sistemas de estímulos complejos y con significado. Como cuestión de interés actual se dan interpretaciones cuantitativas recientes de los trabajos de Land sobre proyecciones de color con dos primarios.

Mr. Chairman, Ladies and Gentlemen :

May I first say what a pleasure and distinction it is for me to address on this occasion the combined meeting of the International League of Opticians and the Institutes of Optics of Florence, Madrid and Paris.

In this lecture I want to say something of the elementary ideas underly-

---

* Conferencia pronunciada en el Instituto de Optica «Daza de Valdés». Madrid.

ing the study of visual adaptation and to consider the extent to which they can be made precise and quantitative. It is perhaps not inappropriate to review these ideas at this time because the adaptation concept is faced with certain difficulties.

Adaptation, in its widest sense, is concerned with the fact that what we perceive at a particular moment in a certain region of the visual field — for example, the apparent brightness and colour of an object in that region — depends not only on the light stimuli originating in the test area but also on what we will call the conditioning stimuli, that is, the stimuli from the other regions of the field and the stimuli to which the eyes have previously been exposed.

The essential idea of adaptation goes beyond this. It supposes that what is perceived in the test area is determined by the stimuli acting there and by the condition — the state of adaptation — of the visual apparatus, or more precisely of that part of it concerned with vision in the test area. The conditioning stimuli are regarded as influencing perception in the test area solely by modifying the state of adaptation there. It is by no means certain that this idea of adaptation will cover all adaptational phenomena. The idea becoms helpful if we can go on to say two things. Firstly that many different sets of adapting stimuli will produce the same state of adaptation in the test area. It will then be possible, at least in principle, to express state of adaptation more economically than by the complete specification of the actual conditioning stimuli. Put slightly differently, we anticipate that a small number of variables — adaptation variables — will define the condition of a particular visual area at a given time, instead of the indefinitely many that would be required to specify the conditioning stimuli. The adaptation concept — if it works — divides the original problem into two : what are the values of the adaptation variables corresponding to different sets of conditioning stimuli, and how does adaptation, so defined, modify the visual response to given test stimuli.

The second thing we have in mind in trying to specify adaptation quantitatively, is to identify the adaptation variables with objective properties of the visual apparatus. These properties might be the concentrations of photosensivite visual pigments in the retinal receptors, or the physiological conditions of parts of the nerve system beyond the receptors. We have to admit immediately one failure. That is the celebrated attempt to represent the state of adaptation of the scotopic or rod mechanism of vision by a single variable, identifiable with the concentration of the visual pigment, rhodopsin, contained in the outer segments of the rods. No equally definite theory of scotopic adaptation has yet taken its place. I propose to spend some time on the adaptation of the scotopic mechanism before turning to the more complicated photopic, colour — responding mechanism.

We recall the traditional method for following the dark adaptation of the scotopic mechanism by the determination of threshold recovery curves. The recovery curves A and C shown in Fig. 1, which is taken from a recent paper by Arden and Weales (1954), refer to white light test stimuli of very different diameters — 2.7 min. of arc and 420 min. of arc respectively. For these curves the test stimulus was imaged on an extrafoveal area, 8° from the fovea. Curves B refer to foveal vision of the test stimulus and will not concern us. The conditioning stimulus was a large uniform field of white light of intensity corresponding to about 3000 photopic trolands, which was abruptly extinguished at the time $t=0$. Ignoring the initial sections, covering the first eight minutes, of the curves A and C — which can be attributed to cone vision — it is apparent that the subsequent drop in threshold for the small test stimulus is considerably less in amount than for the large test stimulus — about 2 log units as against 3 log units. The ratio of the thresholds for large and small test stimuli, at any moment during the recovery process, is a measure of the extent to which neighbouring retinal receptors are able to combine their responses in determining the threshold. In Fig. 1 this ratio increases by about 1 log unit from the 8 minutes point to the final steady values of the recovery curves, and it may be concluded that the power to summate possessed by the rod mechanism has materially increased during dark adaptation. This important point, illustrated by the Arden and Weale data, has been established in a number of investigations including studies which show a corresponding deterioration of visual acuity during the recovery process.

It is difficult to account for such a change of summation in terms of a change in rhodopsin concentration in the rods, or indeed of any change of condition confined to the individual receptors. It would, I think, be impossible to do so if we were sure that all the receptors in the retinal area concerned had nearly identical properties. But if receptors differed widely in their individual recovery curves and if the neural connections by which summation operates were suitable organised so as to achieve in effect different summation properties for receptors with different recovery curves, an apparent change in summation during dark adaptation could result. This would not entail the assumption that there occur adaptive changes (so-called «switching», for example) in the lateral connections of the neural system with the long recovery times involved in scotopic adaptation. The idea of different neural grouping of rod receptors has been suggested by Pirenne (1953) to explain certain acuity measurements and Otero, Aguilar and their collaborators (1953) have explored similar conceptions. However, the notion that the different groupings

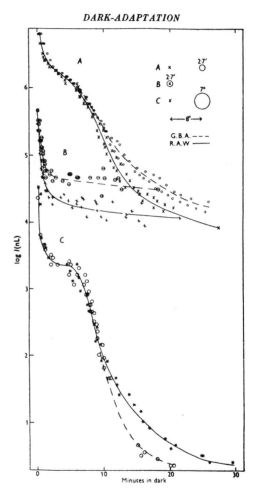

DARK-ADAPTATION

Figure 1.

Threshold recovery curves (two subjects) for test stimuli of different diameters (2.7' and 7°): A and C, 8° — extrafoveal vision: B, foveal vision (Arden and Weale, 1954).

select out receptors of different individual recovery properties, is no more than a conceivable possibility.

Having made this reservation, we may revert to the more likely view that the condition of the post-receptor neural system of the scotopic mechanism does change, and that one adaptation variable defines the ability of the system to summate the responses of neighbouring receptors. There is also evidence, although less clear-cut, of adaptational changes in temporal summation, that is, the extent to which the response of the receptors to the light received during the first part of the exposure of a test stimulus summates with the response to the light received later. But these changes in summation properties are not the only adaptation variables and are probably not the dominant ones. Measurements of the threshold for test stimuli of progressively smaller angular size and shorter exposure time show that below certain limits of size and time the total light in the flash at threshold becomes constant. The limiting size is normally interpreted as defining the extent of the retinal area within which the receptors summate completely. In the near extrafoveal retina (5° to 10° from the fovea, say) the limiting diameter is not less than about 10 min. of arc for the fully dark-adapted condition : the limit is lower when adaptation to darkness is not complete.—If the threshold recovery curve is determined for a test stimulus sufficiently small and brief to lie within the complete summation limits at every stage of the recovery process, any variation in threshold must be ascribed to an adaptational change in the effective sensitivity of the individual receptors or at least of the groups of receptors that act together as perfectly summating units. Experiment shows that with very small and brief test stimuli we still observe a large increase of more than 1 log unit in the extrafoveal threshold during dark-adaptation, and the inference is that the effective receptor sensitivity has undergone a corresponding change. This argument assumes that the limiting size for complete summation is never so small that we could explain the complete summation that is observed as simply the result, of the inevitable spreading of the retinal image of very small stimuli by diffraction, light scattering and optical aberration in the eye. More evidence on this point for the early stage of dark-adaptation is needed but the main conclusion that during dark-adaptation there is a substantial increase in effective receptor sensitivity is unlikely to be modified.

Changes in the effective sensitivity of the rod receptors were attributed in the old photochemical theory of vision to changes in concentration of rhodopsin in the rods. In its simplest form, this theory regarded the average total light absorbed by the photosensitive pigment in the receptors as the sole determinant of visual response. Thus to explain an adaptational change in the threshold that was not attributable to summation changes, a corresponding change in the rhodopsin concentration was demanded. Thanks to the fine work of Rushton and his associates (1955, 1956 a, 1956 b), measurements of the rhodopsin density in the living eye have been obtained by a fundus reflection method. Their results give us the means of calculating the approximate rhodopsin density during and following a wide range of adapting stimuli. The kinetics of rhodopsin bleaching in man were shown to conform to the very simple law of a first order photochemical reaction and the values of the constants in the law — the rate of bleaching and the rate of regeneration — were determined :

$$\frac{dx}{dt} = \frac{(1-x)\,\mathrm{I}}{1\cdot57\cdot10^7} - \frac{x}{519}$$

where x = fraction of rhodopsin bleached ;

   I = the external stimulus expressed in scotopic trolands ;

   t = time in seconds.

Simple calculations from this law show that the changes in rhodopsin density that occur while the effective receptor sensitivity is rising during dark adaptation by more than 1 log unit, are very small. For the Arden and Weale experiments of Fig. 1, the rhodopsin density at the end of the preliminary adaptation to 3000 trolands is still about 90 per cent of maximum. The density changes in the period from the 8 minutes point of the recovery curves to the final steady values, from about 0.97 to 1.00, or 3 per cent. The conclusion — established by Rushton's work — that apparently insignificant changes of rhodopsin density may accompany quite large adaptive changes in the effective receptor sensitivity is in line with earlier evidence of various kinds. I would specially mention the arguments and calculations of Baumgardt published in 1950.

An interesting theory has been advanced by Wald (1954) to extricate us from the dilemma just noted. It rests on the idea that the rhodopsin molecules in the outer segments of the retinal rods are segregated into compartments. These might possibly be associated with the protein layers or membranes in the outer segments described by W. J. Schmidt and demonstrated by the electron microscopic studies of Sjöstrand (1959). There are probably about 2000 such layers in each outer segment. It is assumed by Wald that for a particular compartment to contribute to the response of the rod it must absorb a quantum of light when all the rhodopsin molecules of the compartment are in the unbleached condition. After absorption of a light quantum by one molecule — with the consequent bleaching of that molecule — the compartment is temporarily incapable of further response however many light quanta it may absorb. Its power to respond is restored only when by regeneration all its rhodopsin molecules have resumed their unbleached condition. Thus on this theory the adaptation variable is not the actual density of rhodopsin in the rods but the number of intact compartments i. e. those which have all their rhodopsin molecules in the unbleached condition. Wald's theory leads to the conclusion that after an intense conditioning stimulus, sufficient to bleach many molecules in most compartments, practically all the rods will be put out of action. The first part of the recovery process will be occupied in restoring rhodopsin without producing completely intact compartments. It is only in the later stage, when in each rod most of the rhodopsin has been regenerated, that intact compartments will begin to be produced. When that happens there will be a fairly rapid increase in rod sensitivity accompanied by a quite small change in the total content of unbleached rhodopsin. This is qualitatively the kind of result required. Following Wald we may put the visual threshold inversely proportional to the fraction of the compartments that are intact. Assuming Rushton's results for the regeneration of rhodopsin, the shape of the threshold recovery curve can be calculated : it is exponential. The single adjustable constant in the theory is the number of rhodopsin molecules in each compartment. In Fig. 2 is shown family of extrafoveal threshold recovery curves determined by Hecht, Haig and Chase (1937) for different initial white light adaptations. If we take the curve for adaptation to 400,000 trolands and ignore the initial cone section, it is clear that the rod section is approximately exponential. It can be fitted by Wald's theory. But the number of molecules in a compartment would have to be quite small — about 30 — so that the compartments could not be Schmidt-Sjöstrand layers which contain of the order of 20,000

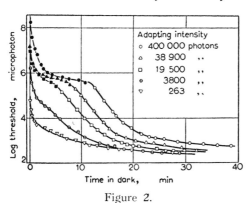

Figure 2.

Threshold recovery curves for 30° — extra-foveal vision, after adaptation to various levels of white light. (Hecht, Haig and Chase, 1937).

rhodopsin molecules. Moving in turn to the lower adaptation intensities, the appropriate number of molecules in a compartment must be increased to 80, 90, 300 and finally to some very large number (greater than 10,000) which cannot be closely estimated from the data. Actually some allowance to eliminate the effects of changes in summation should be made to the experimental curves before applying Wald's theory, but an estimate of the correction indicates that the conclusions from the calculations would be little affected. A similar dependence of the number of molecules per compartment on the particular adapting stimulus used, has been pointed out by Rushton (1959) using other experimental data. It is the variavility of this number that is one outstanding difficulty in Wald's theory : if the number were constant but much smaller than the number of molecules in a Schmidt-Sjöstrand layer, the theory would be equally attractive.

So far, four adaptation variables in scotopic vision have been recognised : degree of summation, lateral and temporal, the modification of effective receptor sensitivity and change in rhodopsin density. However, these are not necessarily independent variables. If Wald's theory were correct, the receptor sensitivity would be uniquely determined by the rhodopsin density even though it might depend on changes of density so small that they would be impossible to measure objectively. Other evidence on scotopic adaptation is provided by recovery curves obtained from different conditioning stimuli, in particular from comparisons of short exposures to very intense adapting stimuli with long exposures to weaker adapting stimuli.

Suppose the adapting variables just mentioned were not really indepen-dent and suppose in particular that they where all functions of a single variable. Then the recovery curves for a particular test stimulus from different conditioning stimuli would all be parts of a single recovery curve. The details of the conditioning stimulus would merely determine from which point on this common curve recovery for that particular case would commence. It has long been believed however that scotopic recovery curves obtained with a common test stimulus are not similar in this way : they cannot be brought into superposition simply by a displacement parallel to the time axis. This point is I think already discernible in the Hecht, Haig and Chase recovery curves. It is apparent in a more striking form in the families of recovery curves determined by my colleague Dr. Crawford (1946) and shown in Fig. 3. These show that, for conditioning stimulus consisting of exposures in which the product of intensity and time is kept constant, the recovery curves for long, low-intensity exposures may actually cross these for short, high-intensity exposures. The existence of such cross-over effects was first demonstrated by Winsor and Clark in 1936. The early explanations were all couched in terms of the simple conception of rhodopsin concentration changes, that we know is untenable. The essential element was that there were two ways of restoration of bleached rhodopsin: a rapid way which would be dominant when bleaching had been intense but brief and a slow way which would take charge when bleaching had been weak but prolonged. Without entering into details of the various schemes, we may ask whether the kinetics of rhodopsin bleaching and regeneration in the living eye, as obtained by Rushton, provide any suport for two modes of regeneration. It appears not: as far as the experiments have gone they show that bleaching and regeneration follow fairly closely the simple first-order process. However measurements on long period bleaching exposures to moderate intensities have not, I think, been made. No appeal to Wald's theory in its original form would explain the cross-over of scotopic recovery curves. The Wald theory indicates a unique relationship between rhodopsin density and the number of intact compartments at any moment whatever the previous stimulation history of the receptors.

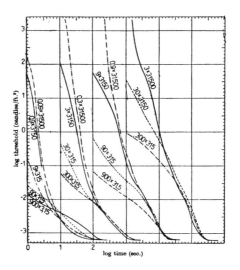

Figure 3.

Threshold recovery curves for extrafoveal vision after adapting flashes of white light. For each family of curves the product of flash exposure time (sec.) and flash intensity (C./ft²) was kept constant (values shown on curves). Counting from the left, the families of curves have been displaced on the axis of log time by 0, 1, 2 and 3 log units to the right. (Crawford, 1946).

It would be particularly interesting to find out if the cross-over can be obtained with test stimuli of widely different areas and exposure times. If it can, and if cross-over occurred at diferent points of time, that would indicate that summation and effective receptor sensitivity were independent adaptation variables. On the other hand, if cross-over always occurred at the same point, the two independent factors producing cross-over would have to be associated either with the effective receptor sensitivity or with the rhodopsin concentration and we have just seen that the latter alternative is improbable.

New problems arise if we consider the condition of a retina at a moment when it is actually being stimulated, for example, when it is continuously exposed to a uniform field. It seems obvious that a retina receiving light stimulation is in some sense in a different state from a retina not doing so. But some adaptation variables may be equally applicable in either situation. The concentration of a visual pigment such as rhodopsin in the receptors would appear to be of this kind. But it is not crear that this is true of neural variables. However we know from studies of brightness difference thresholds (or increment thresholds) made for steady uniform fields of different intensities, that summation diminishes as the brightness level is raised. The valuable work of M. A. Bouman (1954) and his associates on this question I would particularly mention. I want however to lay stress on the quantitative correspondence between changes in threshold by recovery curves and the changes of threshold (difference threshold) measured on steady fields of different brightness. There are few direct data on this correspondence. Fig. 4 shows some results obtained by Crawford (1947) for the threshold recovery of the eye from an intense adapting light flash and—for the same subject—the change in increment threshold measured on steady fields at a series of brightness levels, white light being used for all stimuii. The date were obtained for a practical application and fixation was not controlled. But over most of the range slightly indirect vision was certainly being used. The family of curves

refers to a series of test stimuli of diameters increasing from 0.18° to 5.7°. The similar way in which both families of curves converge indicates a similar change of summation whether the threshold objects is exposed

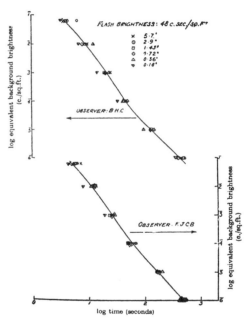

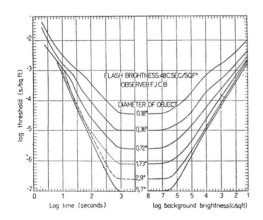

Figure 4.

Threshold recovery curves and curves of increment threshold against background brightness, compared for test stimuli of different angular sizes. (Crawford, 1947).

Figure 5.

Equivalent background brightness as a function of time derived from the family of curves of Fig. 4 and a similar family for another subject. (Crawford, 1947).

on a dark field during recovery or whether it is exposed on a uniform steady field whose brightness is progressively changed. For each test object size, the steady background brightness giving the same increment threshold as at a given moment in the recovery can be determined, and a plot can be made of this so-called equivalent background brightness against time. This is done in Fig. 5. The curves of equivalent background against time are practically the same for all test object sizes.

This would imply that for these two different conditions, the change of summation and the change of effective receptor sensitivity go together, and are determined by a single variable. The equivalent background idea, although quite old has not in my opinion been used as much as it deserves. It may be that for many possible tests the only effect of an extended uniform field is to modify the state of adaptation of the test area, and that the fact that the receptors are actually responding to the uniform fields is not material.

The reason why a uniform field raises the increment threshold is now often discussed in relation to the inevitable fluctuations in the number of light quanta from the field that are absorbed by individual receptors, or strictly by completely summating groups of receptors. The test stimulus intensity must somewhat exceed these fluctuations, if it is to be detected. This is certainly true. But since we do not in fact see the fluctuations as such we must also suppose that somewhere in the neural chain a barrier is raised high enough to prevent the fluctuations passing into consciousness. The raising of this barrier corresponds to an increase in the effective sensitivity of the receptors or summating receptor groups. It would seem that this is the true adaptational change. The fluctuations theory merely places a lower limit on the height of the barrier: its nature remains to be explained.

As may be expected the old photochemical theory is equally ineffective in explaining the rise of increment threshold with brightness level as it is in explaining recovery curves. Fig. 6 (left-hand curve) shows the variation of extrafoveal increment threshold with brightness level [Aguilar and Stiles (1954)] determined by a method that enables the response of the scotopic mechanism to be followed up to high intensities. The right-hand curve shows what would be the expected relation between log (increment threshold) and log (field brightness) if the old photochemical theory held. This curve is based on Rushton's data for rhodopsin kinetics. There is an enormous separation on the log field basis of some 7 log units — between the experimental curve and the predicted curve. (Again a correction for summation should be applied to the experimental curve before the comparison is made but estimates show that it can hardly reduce the separation to below 5 to 6 log units). More interesting is

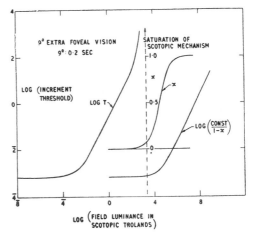

Figure 6.

Variation with logarithm of the field luminance in scotopic trolands of (i) logarithm of increment threshold (data of Aguilar and Stiles, 1954), (ii) fraction x of rhodopsin bleached, (iii) log $\dfrac{\text{(const)}}{(1-x)}$, the log (increment threshold) according to the old photochemical theory.

the fact that even at the brightness level — 2000 scotopic trolands — where the rod mechanism has virtually lost its discriminatory power — where it has become saturated — the fraction x of rhodopsin bleached is only some 6 per cent (see middle curve).

I have reviewed some of the complexities and difficulties in our ideas of the adaptation of the scotopic mechanism. Others, that I have passed over are concerned with the situation within a second of abrupt changes of conditioning stimulus or near a sharp boundary in a steadily exposed field. But there is one major simplification in dealing with scotopic vision. We do not need to concern ourselves with the different colours — the different spectral composition — of the light stimuli. Provided two light stimuli of energy distributions $E_\lambda d_\lambda$ and $E'_\lambda d_\lambda$ have the same scotopic values determined from the scotopic luminous efficiency function V'_λ — a well-established function — i. e. provided $\int E_\lambda V'_\lambda d_\lambda = \int E'_\lambda V'_\lambda d_\lambda$, they will be in every way equivalent in their effects on the scotopic or rod mechanism. For the photopic, colour responding mechanism a corresponding but more limited simplification is secured by the trichromatic principle in its stronger form. Accordingly to this, two stimuli are equivalent in their effects on the photopic mechanism if they have the same tristimulus values. These are derived from the energy distributions, using three empirical functions, $\bar{x}_\lambda$, $\bar{y}_\lambda$, $\bar{z}_\lambda$, the so-called colour-matching functions which again are well established from experimental colour-matching studies.

$$\text{Tristimulus value} \quad X = \int E_\lambda \bar{x}_\lambda d_\lambda = \int E'_\lambda \bar{x}_\lambda d_\lambda$$

$$\text{''} \qquad \text{''} \qquad Y = \int E_\lambda \bar{y}_\lambda d_\lambda = \int E'_\lambda \bar{y}_\lambda d_\lambda$$

$$\text{''} \qquad \text{''} \qquad Z = \int E_\lambda \bar{z}_\lambda d_\lambda = \int E'_\lambda \bar{z}_\lambda d_\lambda$$

But how far is this trichromatic equivalence true in all circumstances for the actual eye? Some qualifications have to be made. For extrafoveal stimuli falling on regions containing the rod mechanism, the equivalence will not usually hold unless the intensities are high enough to exclude rod vision : ideally the conditions should be such that the saturation limit of rod vision is exceeded. Even then the exent to which the photopic mechanism in the more distant extrafoveal areas can be regarded as trichromatic, is uncertain. However, in studying photopic vision we are usually concerned with what is seen in the foveal rod-free area and with adapting stimuli that, although perhaps extending to the periphery, produce their effects on foveal vision mainly by stimulating a zone surrounding the fovea. Such adapting stimuli have tristimules values that can be computed with only a small modification of the foveal colour-matching functions, a change attributable to the smaller effects of macular pigmentation.

There is one limitation of the trichromatic principle which it is important to keep in mind in studying chromatic adaptation. This is the fact, first clearly shown by W. D. Wright in 1936, that after adaptation to high intensities, colour matches between stimuli of dissimilar energy distributions break down. For example, in the foveal match between a monochromatic yellow and a mixture of monochromatic green and red, the match is seriously upset — the amount of red in the mixture has to be doubled — if the eyes have just been exposed for half a minute to an intensity of yellow light of about 100,000 trolands. Intensities one tenth as large may produce just perceptible effects. These are high intensities but they may often be exceeded outdoors where sunlit pavements can reach a brightness of about 200,000 trolands. Recently Brindley (1953) has shown, from a study of the breakdown of colour matches after intense adaptation that probably just one of the photosensitive pigments of photopic vision — the pigment of the red sensitive mechanism — is principally responsible for the breakdown. His theory is that the total spectral absorption of pigment in the red receptors corresponds normally to that of a dye solution of high concentration, but, after intense adaptation, it corresponds to a dye solution of low concentration. The change of concentration alters the effective spectral absorption curve.

Fortunately many of the characteristic phenomena of chromatic adaptation are observable under conditions where the equivalence predicted by the trichromatic principle is valid.

It is now fully realised that the trichromatic principles will certainly be true if the retinal receptors of photopic vision contain just three photosensitive pigments of different spectral absorption. It will not matter how these pigments are distributed among the receptors — in the extreme case, all receptors might contain in varying proportions all three pigments — nor will it matter how selections of receptors are grouped into more or less distinct mechanisms by the neural connections beyond the receptors. However, most investigators of chromatic adaptation have started out with the idea — in one form or another — that there are three fundamental colour-mechanisms, the receptors associated with each of these mechanisms being of one kind and probably containing just one photosensitive pigment. The tristimulus values if transformed to a suitable reference system would represent the stimulations of the three mechanisms. On these views adaptation would be regarded as producing internal changes in the respective mechanisms which would alter their overall sensitivities — but not of their relative spectral sensitivities — and which would not affect the way in which the responses of the three mechanisms were further elaborated at higher levels in the neural systems of retina and brain. The internal changes in the mechanisms have generally been identified with changes in concentration of the photosensitive pigments in their respective receptors, brought about by the conditioning stimuli.

Rushton's remarkable extension of his work by the fundus reflection method, to the objective measurements of photopic visual pigments in the living eye, enables us now to see how far changes in pigment concentration might play a part in chromatic adaptation. While there can be little doubt that *three* photopic or cone pigments are concerned in an eye possessing normal colour vision, we have objective data for only two of them. These have the maxima in their difference spectra at approximately 540 mμ and 590 mμ respectively. They may be described as the green-sensitive and the red-sensitive pigments. The expected third cone pigment, with maximum in the blue region of the spectrum, has not so far been satisfactorily "isolated" by the fundus reflection method. Rushton's late work (1958) on the red and green-sensitive pigments leads to the conclusion that as for rhodopsin the bleaching and regeneration processes follow the simple laws of a first order reaction. The regeneration rate is found to be the same for both pigments : 0.77 per cent, or (1/130)th, of the bleached pigment is restored per sec. He also finds that white light leads to a rate of bleaching that happens to be the same for the two pigments. Naturally, for lights of other spectral compositions, their bleaching rates will be different, depending on the different spectral absorption curves of the pigments.

[Kinectics of bleaching (white light) and regeneration of two cone pigments:

$$\frac{dx}{dt} = \frac{I(1-x)}{5 \times 10^6} - \frac{x}{130}$$

x = fraction bleached,

I = bleaching stimulus intensity (white light) in photopic trolands,

t = time in seconds].

Using Rushton's results the fraction bleached, x, when the retina has been exposed to a uniform field of white light sufficiently long for equilibrium to be reached, can be computed, and from this can be determined the quantity $\log\left(\dfrac{\text{const}}{1-x}\right)$ which should equal, on the old photochemical theory, the increment threshold. The middle and right-hand curves of Fig. 7 show the variation of x and $\log\dfrac{\text{const}}{1-x}$ obtained in this way. The left-hand curve shows the results of measurements of the foveal increment threshold, yellow test stimulus on yellow field, extended to the very high intensity of nearly one million photopic trolands. The fact that yellow and not white light was used makes no significant difference in the comparisons to be made.

As in the analogous comparison for rod vision, the displacement along the log I axis of the third curve $-\log\left(\dfrac{\text{const}}{1-x}\right)$ — with respect to the experimental curve, a displacement of over 3 log units, shows the failure of the simple photochemical theory to explain the results for cone vision, just as the previous comparisons showed it to fail for rod vision. The displacement is certainly somewhat less but it is still impossibly large. It will be noted that there is no indication of saturation in the photopic threshold curve. In the brightness range from about one thousand to one millions photopic trolands, the bleaching of the photopigments increases from nearly zero to nearly 100 per cent. But there is no indication from the increment threshold curve that anything remarkable occurs which is related to the incidence of the bleaching process.

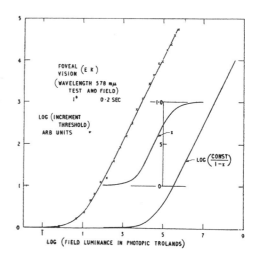

Figure 7.

Variation with logarithm of the field luminance in photopic trolands of (i) logarithm of the foveal increment threshold for a 1°, 0.2 sec. test stimulus (Stiles, unpublished data), (ii) fraction x of photopic pigments bleached, (iii) $\log\dfrac{(\text{const})}{(1-x)}$, the log (increment threshold) according to the old photochemical theory.

Over the whole of the range mentioned the Weber fraction (ratio of threshold to field intensity) is substantially constant.

It seems that the discriminating power of the photopic mechanism defined by the Weber fraction is just about as good when all but a few per cent of the pigment is bleached as when none of it is bleached. Nevertheless there are other visual observations—the apparent colour of the field in particular—that show changes round the region where the bleaching is becoming marked.

The experimental threshold curve just shown is typical of much work on colour-adaptation done by methods not involving actual colour-matching. One development with which we have been particularly concerned at the National Physical Laboratory is the use of different colours (usually monochromatic) for the test stimulus and the conditioning field—the two-colour threshold method. For certain combinations of the two wavelengths, the curves relating the logarithm of the increment threshold to the logarithm of the field intensity show two or three branches which can be attributed to the action of different cone mechanism. This is with strictly foveal vision of the test stimulus so that for this and other reasons it is certain that the rod mechanism played no part. An example of such multibranch curves is shown in Fig. 8.

It was at first thought that by investigating the number and positions of the branches of such curves for different wavelengths pairs, we should arrive at just three distinct branches that could be attributed to just three cone mechanisms. However, the actual situation turns out to be a good deal more complicated. It appears that five cone mechanisms must be recognised and two of these show somewhat different properties for lower and higher ranges of adaptation intensities. In the accompanying Table 1 these mechanisms are list. It would be quite unjustifiable to insist on the details of the present tentative scheme of cone mechanisms be-

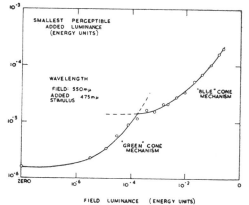

Figure 8.

Two-branch curve of log (increment threshold) against log (field intensity) for foveal vision.

cause the overlapping of their spectral sensitivity curves is such that we cannot obtain for all of them clearly defined branches like those shown in Fig. 8. The inference from threshold measurements then becomes less direct and less certain. Nevertheless, the threshold methods do provide the same kind of evidence for the existence of different cone mechanisms, possessing some degree of independence, as they provide for a separate rod mechanism, although the evidence is a good deal less strong and complete. Where we have a distinct branch in increment threshold curves, it is possible in principle to study the lateral and temporal summation properties—and some other properties— of the corresponding cone mechanism, including the possible variation of these properties as the state of adaptation of the mechanism is changed. Something has already been done on these lines (Stiles, 1949, Brindley, 1953), and the greater lateral summation of the «blue» mechanism compared with the «green» mechanism has been demonstrated. The low precision of threshold methods is however

TABLE 1

Mechanism	Symbol	REMARKS		Wave Length of Maximal Sensitivity (m μ)	Fechner Fraction (1.°, 0.2 Sec. Test Stimulus)
Rod	π_0	Absent at the fovea		503	(30)
«Blue» cone	π_1	Ratio of blue to yellow sensitivity (440/590)	approx. 2.6 log units	440	8.7
	π_2	Ratio of blue to yellow sensitivity (440/590)	order of 1 log unit	? (Between 440 and 480 mμ)	? (Probably as for π_1 and π_3)
	π_3	Ratio of blue to yellow sensitivity (440/590)	approx. 4.0 log units	440	8.7
«Green» cone ...	π_4			540	1.9
	π_4'	Modified high-intensity state		540	...
«Red» cone	π_5			575 (very flat max.)	1.8
	π_5'	Modified high-intensity state		587	...

a serious limitation and with the recognition of more than three cone mechanisms it becomes increasingly difficult to discriminate between them.

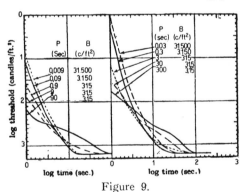

Figure 9.

Threshold recovery curves for foveal vision after adapting flashes of white light. For each family of curves the product of flash exposure time (sec.) and flash intensity (C./ft²) was kept constant (values shown on curves. (Crawford, 1946).

Before leaving threshold methods of studying chromatic adaptation, I must refer to two further points.—Firstly, foveal threshold recovery curves obtained by Crawford for flash conditioning stimuli (white light) with a constant product of intensity and flash time, show an analogous cross-over to that already noted for extrafoveal vision (Fig. 9). Apart altogether from colour effects, this would indicate that the adaptation of the photopic mechanism, like the scotopic mechanism, depends on two variables and involves a fast and a slow process. New measurements confirming this important result would be most valuable.

The second point concerns photopic threshold recovery curves. Shouldn't it be possible to obtain multibranch recovery curves by appropriate choice of the intensity and colour of the initial adaptation and the colour of test stimulus. Only quite small differences in photopic recovery curves had been observed, until, in 1954, Auerbach and Wald, by using extremely high adapting intensities of the order of ten million trolands did succeed in obtaining multibranch cone recovery curves. Some of their results are shown in Fig. 10. One such branch they associate with the «blue» mechanism derived by the two-colour threshold method (probably π, or π₃) and there may be further correspondences. Measurements made by myself in 1948 and recently confirmed, in essentials, by Mr. Das working in my laboratory, point to a quite different behaviour of the «blue» mechanism after the extinction of a red adapting field. Instead of dominating the initial part of the recovery curve as indicated by Auerbach and Wald's results, the «blue» mechanism appeared to be abnormally slow in recovering. The red field had the comparatively moderate intensity of 20,000 trolands against Auerbach and Wald's ten million. Presumably the use of these extremely high intensities brings out quite different properties.

As compared with threshold measurements for the study of chromatic adaptation, the measurement of apparent brightness and colour has two main advantages. It provides simultaneous determinations of three quantities — tristimulus components — whose relative values are important in themselves. Secondly it gives answers in terms of brightness and colour that seem more immediately relevant to ordinary experience. This second advantage however carries with it a corresponding disadvantage. Colour perceptions are interwoven with every part of our daily life. As a result, in judging apparent colours we may be influenced, entirely unconsciously and automatically, by the information conveyed to us by our eyes about the nature of the object bearing the colour and of how it is placed with regard to the light source, and by similar information about other objects in the field. The extent to which these unconscious influences will modify our colour perceptions depends, we believe, on how we arrange our experiments. We may ask subjects to

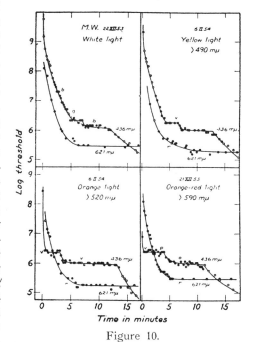

Figure 10.

Threshold recovery curves — 6° — extrafoveal — for 1° test stimuli of different wavelengths, following adaptation to very intense fields of white, yellow, orange and orange-red light. (Auerbach and Wald, 1954).

give judgements of the colours of ordinary objects under naturalistic conditions. We must then expect the results to depend on factors operating at a higher level in the nervous system than if we present stimuli on flat structureless surfaces in simple and biologically meaningless patterns with all clues removed which might show how the stimuli are brought into the visual field. There is of course no sharp line between these different methods but it is easy to see that experimenters with a physical or physiological background and those most interested in the more peripheral parts of the visual mechanism will normally choose the meaningless observing situation. We will consider mainly studies made from the physicist's or physiologist's standpoint.

It will be remembered as part of the trichromatic principle that the match between two stimuli of dissimilar spectral compositions, imaged side-by-side in the foveal area is unaffected by changing the adaptive state of the eye. This is true, provided the conditioning stimuli are symmetrically disposed with respect to the two halves of the matching field, and provided very intense stimuli are avoided. Although the match between the two stimuli is unaltered, their apparent brigtness and colour depend strongly on the conditioning stimuli — as well as on their own intensity — and it is these changes that have to be measured. What is essential is some method of asymmetric matching in wich one stimulus — the test stimulus, say — viewed under one set of conditions can be made to match another — the comparison stimulus — viewed under a different set. The crudest procedure is merely to ask the subject to describe the colour and brightness of the test stimulus, the «comparison stimulus» being his mental recall of the sensations corresponding to various colour names. This unpromising procedure has been refined by Bouma and Kruithof (1947) by a preliminary training of his subject to familiarise him with the appearance of the samples of a colour atlas. Then, in the actual experiment, the subject was asked to name, *by memory*, the sample corresponding to the apparent brightness and colour of the test object exposed under the test conditions. As against memory matching, the binocular matching, developed originally by W. D. Wright (1934) and used in most current research, makes use of the approximate independence of the sensations induced by stimuli applied to the left and right eyes. The test stimulus and one set of conditioning stimuli are presented to the left eye, the comparison stimulus and a different set of conditioning stimuli are presented to the right eye. This may mean that in the combined binocular field two different conditioning stimuli are superimposed. With training, subjects find no serious difficulty in making matching under these conditions. In a third method, which may employ monocular or binocular vision, the test stimulus and its conditioning stimuli and the comparison stimulus and its conditioning stimuli form parts of the same display. Vision may be switched backwards and forwards from test to comparison stimulus as in much older work or a recent technique of MacAdam's (1956) may be adopted. In this, accurate fixation of the midpoint of the dividing line of juxtaposed test and comparison stimuli is maintained, but the actual test and comparison stimuli are exposed only in brief periods (1 sec.) the relatively long intervening periods (9 sec.) being used to apply different adapting stimuli in the two juxtaposed fields.

Although of course there are many differences in conditions of observation by these methods as used by different investigators, there are certain common features in the interpretation of the results. These are conveniently introduced by looking at the general form of the quantitative conditions for a match.

In addition to the tristimulus vectors $\xi = \begin{pmatrix} X \\ Y \\ Z \end{pmatrix}$ and $\xi = \begin{pmatrix} X' \\ Y' \\ Z' \end{pmatrix}$ of the test

and comparison stimuli, we need to represent the two sets of conditioning stimuli, say by vectors C and C'. These latter vectors must be assumed, in general, to have a large number of components as the surrounding and preceeding stimuli can be varied in all kinds of ways. It may reasonably be assumed that in making an asymmetric match we are equalising a function $F(\xi\,;\,C)$ of test stimulus ξ and conditioning C with the same function $F(\xi'\,;\,C')$ of the comparison stimulus and the conditioning C'. Experience shows that asymmetric matching, like ordinary matching, is three-dimensional in the sense that there will be a considerable domain of test vectors ξ for which a satisfactory match can be made by comparison stimuli consisting of mixtures in suitable proportions of three well-chosen primaries of high colour saturation, while the use of mixtures of just two primaries will not serve. The function $F(\xi\,;\,C)$ must therefore be thought of as a three-dimensional vector function, and the relation $F(\xi\,;\,C) = F(\xi'\,;\,C')$ implies three ordinary equations. But depending on C and C' there will be some test stimuli ξ that cannot be matched directly by the three-primary comparison stimulus. This resembles superficially the impossibility of matching certain too saturated stimuli in ordinary symmetric matching. However the unmatchable stimuli in asymmetric matching are not necessarily well described by the expression «too saturated», and the device of desaturating the test colour with a small quantity of one of the matching primaries is not applicable in all cases. An important difference from symmetric matching, is that there may occur test stimuli that are not only unmatchable by any comparison mixture of three fixed primaries but which are unmatchable by a comparison stimulus of any spectral composition whatever.

The form of the matching condition, already implies the property of transitivity: if ξ under condition C matches ξ' under conditions C', and ξ' under C' matches ξ'' under conditions C'', then ξ'' under conditions C'' matches ξ under conditions C. For binocular matching, the evidence is fairly conclusive that interaction between the eyes — which would upset transitivity — is slight. In MacAdam's method using juxtaposed and differently adapted fields, we should not expect the adaptation of one field to leave the condition of the other unchanged and direct tests of the transitive property seem necessary. Perhaps Dr. MacAdam's data would enable such tests to be made, but I believe they have not been applied. If transitivity is not valid a still more general matching condition:

$$G\,(\xi\,;\,C\,;\,C') = G\,(\xi'\,;\,C'\,;\,C)$$

would have to be assumed. For memory matching, transitivity can hardly fail to hold.

The important additivity law is not generally true for asymmetric colour-matching although it has been found in some investigations to be quite closely obeyed for certain pairs of conditioning stimuli. The scheme of Table 2 shows the relation of the additivity law for symmetric matching — which is valid for matches between stimuli both exposed under conditioning C or both under C' — to the additivity law for asymmetric matching for the conditioning pair $C:C'$. The implications of obedience to the additivity law for asymmetric matching are farreaching, and have played a vital part in the study of chromatic matching adaptation. If the law is true, the matching stimulus vectors under the two conditioning C and C' are related by a constant linear transformation $T_{cc'}$:

$$\xi = T_{cc'}\,\xi'$$

TABLE 2
The Additivity Laws

Adaptation by conditioning stimuli C		Adaptation by conditioning stimuli C′
If .... $A_1 \overset{s}{=} B_1$	$\overset{a}{=}$	$C_1 \overset{s}{=} D_2$
And .... $A_2 \overset{s}{=} B_2$	$\overset{a}{=}$	$C_2 \overset{s}{=} D_2$
Then ...... $(A_1 + A_2) \overset{s}{=} (B_1 + B_2)$		$(C_1 + C_2) \overset{s}{=} (D_1 + D_2)$

(additive law for symmetric matching)

$(C_1 + C_2) \overset{s}{=} (D_1 + D_2)$ $\qquad$ $(A_1 + A_2) \overset{s}{=} (B_1 + B_2)$

(persistence of colour equations)

but, not necessarily, $\quad (B_1 + B_2) \overset{a}{=} (C_1 + C_2)$

(additive law for asymmetric matching)

The symbols $A_1 \ldots D_1$, $A_2 \ldots D_2$ represent stimuli, generally of different spectral compositions.

$\overset{s}{=}$ means «matches under asymmetrical conditions».

$\overset{a}{=}$ means «matches under symmetrical conditions».

$T_{cc'}$ or, dropping the suffix, T can be determined, in principle, by making asymmetric matches for three independent test stimuli ξ, although in most recent work a larger group of test stimuli has been used and the best values of the matrix element of T have been determined by a least squares method.

It is assumed in the above equation that the tristimulus values of all the stimuli, that is the components of the vectors ξ and ξ', are expressed initially in a practically convenient reference system, chosen without appeal to any ideas of visual theory. But on the simplest conception of chromatic adaptation, which I have already mentioned, we should be able to trans-form the tristimulus vectors $\xi = \begin{pmatrix} X \\ Y \\ Z \end{pmatrix}$ to new vectors $\eta = \begin{pmatrix} R \\ G \\ B \end{pmatrix}$ $(\eta = M\xi)$ in which the components R, G, B, represent respectively the stimulations of three fundamental colour mechanisms that act independently in adaptation. The different conditioning stimulations, on this view, merely modify the overall sensitivities of the mechanisms so that the asymmetric matching conditions have the simple von Kries form

$$K_{rc} R = K_{rc'} R'$$
$$K_{gc} G = K_{gc'} G'$$
$$K_{bc} B = K_{bc'} B'$$

Here the two sets of constants K_{rc}, K_{gc}, K_{bc} and $K_{rc'}, K_{gc'}, K_{bc'}$ depend only on the respective conditioning stimuli C and C′. This form is consistent with the empirically determined linear relation between ξ and ξ' if a transformation M can be found that makes the triple matrix product MTM^{-1} a diagonal matrix i. e. one of the simple form $\begin{pmatrix} \alpha_1 & 0 & 0 \\ 0 & \alpha_2 & 0 \\ 0 & 0 & \alpha_3 \end{pmatrix}$

Mathematically it is in general * possible to do this whatever the empirical matrix T we may have obtained from the asymmetric colour-matching experiments. But in some cases the values obtained for the constant α_1, α_2, α_3 and the coefficients in the transformation matrix M come out to be complex imaginary. Suppose however that all real values are obtained: then the matrix M enables us to calculate in the initial tristimulus system the particular vectors $(\xi)_1$, $(\xi)_2$, $(\xi)_3$ that each stimulate one fundamental colour mechanism, and the values α_1, α_2 and α_3 are identifiable with the ratios of the adaptation constants $K_{rc}/K_{rc'}$, $K_{gc}/K_{gc'}$, $K_{bc}/K_{bc'}$. Knowing all three of the fundamental vectors the spectral sensitivity curves of the three colour mechanisms can be calculated.

This attractively simple view of colour adaptation has not proved very successful and it is perhaps in trying to understand the manner in which it breaks down that most can be learnt. Wright's pioneer application of binocular matching to the recovery of the test eye from highly saturated conditioning stimuli — the comparison eye being kept adapted to darkness — led to the derivation of fundamental mechanisms with spectral sensitivities in general agreement with what might be expected if each were equipped with a single photopic pigment, the spectral maxima being located at 445, 540, 575 mμ. Walters' further work (1942) by the same method (confined to stimuli of medium and long wavelengths and treating colour vison as approximately dichromatic under those conditions), produced some results giving complex solution for M. He was able to show however that his data were not consistent with the additivity law, the discrepancies increasing with the intensity of the test stimulus. By extrapolating back to test stimuli of zero intensity, he obtained real solutions corresponding to fundamental spectral sensitivities (two only) in fair agreement with Wright's.

The more recent studies have dealt with the situation when the adaptations of the test areas are maintained in steady states either by surrounding them with a uniform adapting field, or by intermittent stimulation by the adapting field (MacAdam) or by a combination of both techniques. Generally, the adapting stimuli have been less strongly coloured — daylight adaptation compared with tungsten light adaptation for example — and more refined computational methods for obtaining the empirical transformation T have been used. A distinction must be drawn between studies in which the results are consistent with the truth of the additivity law and studies for which this is not the case. The investigations of Brewer (1954), Burnham, Evans, Newhall (1957) and Wassef (1958, 1959) belong to the former category. As Wassef has emphasised they do not lead to a unique set of real fundamental vectors for various pairs of conditioning stimuli, a result illustrated by Wassef's own determinations of fundamental vectors (Table 3).

The appearance of different fundamental vectors in experiments using different conditioning stimuli, suggests that the way in which receptors

---

* There are certain exceptions: if the determinant of T is zero or if the secular equation of T has repeated roots the procedure breaks down. These exceptions represent physiologically special cases that I shall not discuss.

TABLE 3

CIE Chromaticity Co-ordinates of Fundamental Vectors derived from Chromatic Adaptation

(Results of E.G.T. Wassef using binocular matching)

CONDITIONING STIMULI	(1)			(2)			(3)			REFERENCE
	x	y	z	x	y	z	x	y	z	
Tungsten colour (A) : Daylight-colour (C)	.700	.375	−.074	.924	−.664	.740	.149	.041	.810	WASSEF *Opt. Acta* 5 pp. 101-108 1958
Tungsten (A) : Daylight (C) (Black background)	.702	.345	−.047	<	complex values	...... >				
Tungsten (A) : Daylight (C)	.641	.342	017	<	complex	values	...... >			WASSEF *Opt. Acta*
Magenta : Daylight (C)	555	.200	.245	.156	.359	.485	.132	.014	.852	6 pp. 378-386 1959
Yellow : Daylight (C)	.684	.335	−.019	<	complex	values	...... >			
Green : Daylight (C)	Complex values			2.481	−.856	−.625	Complex values			

containing different photopigments are associated together in the quasi-independent mechanisms whose responses are equaled in asymmetric matching, may vary with the conditioning stimulus. Physiologically this would not be hard to accept. Threshold studies on summation in rod vision suggest that the lateral neural connections of receptors are changed as the adaptation level is raised, and, if it is granted that the effective colour-mechanisms in asymmetric matching need not be associations of receptors all containing the same photosensitive pigment, the possibility of some change in the neural association under different conditioning is not unreasonable. But if this is admitted, the method of handling the data of asymmetric matching must be changed. The transformation for converting tristimulus values to a system in which each component stimulates just one mechanism, will be different for the two conditionings C and C' and the matching equations must be written : $M_c \xi = M_{c'} \xi'$ or $\xi = (M_c)^{-1} M_{c'} \xi'$. The experimental transformation T has merely to be of the form $T = M_c^{-1} M_{c'}$. There is no way of determining M_c and $M_{c'}$ from T ; indefinitely many pairs of transformation M_c and $M_{c'}$ will satisfy. Naturally the matrix T contains some information on the relationship of the possible pairs of transformations M_c and $M_{c'}$ but the information takes no very simple or striking form. There is the slight satisfaction of seeing the physiological implication in the case of a matrix T which leads to complex values when processed on the von Kries assumption. It must be that the two conditionings have modified differently the way in which receptors containing different pigments are organised into the systems whose responses are equated in making asymmetric matches. But it then follows that even when the matrix T leads to all real solutions on the von Kries method, we must regard this in a way as a fortunate accident. The two matrix transformations M_c and $M_{c'}$ just happen to yield a product $M_c M_{c'}$ for which a third matrix M can be found such that $MTM^{-1} = M (M_c^{-1} M_{c'}) M^{-1}$ is a diagonal matrix. Put briefly, the continual appearance of complex solutions makes the interpretation in the von Kries way of even the all real solutions doubtful.

The discussion so far has related to colour adaptation measurements obeying the additivity and the transitivity laws. It is puzzling that the additivity law should remain valid when neural rearrangements of the different receptors under different conditionings have to be assumed. In other work by the binocular matching method, additivity is certain not valid. In the interesting studies of Hunt, atention was concentrated mainly on the effect of using conditioning stimuli C and C' of different intensities but of the same colour-white. He expressed his results by plotting in the CIE chromaticity chart, the chromaticity of the comparison stimulus — seen in a conditionning surround of fixed intensity (75 trolands)—that matched a test stimulus of fixed chromaticity, seen under a wide range of surround intensities (zero, 0.7 to 6300 trolands). The approximately radial lines in Fig. 11 show the change of apparent chromaticity of eight test colours, as the surround intensity was changed, the circle point on each line representing the chromaticity when the surrounds of test and comparison stimuli were the same — the symmetrical situation. The very large increase in colorimetric saturation of all the test stimuli as the surround was increased from the lowest to the highest intensity (marked Z to A on one of the lines), is evident. The test stimulus and comparison stimulus for the data of Fig. were of 1^e linear extent and foveal vision was used. Hunt's conclusion that no participation of the rod mechanism could explain the observed large changes in saturation can safely be accepted.

Hunt discusses a possible explanation of the change of saturation with intensity which rests on essentially the same idea as the interpretation just given of the complex imaginary solutions obtained in applying the von Kries principle in studies of differential colour adaptation. He supposes in effect, that in the dark-adapted state, the receptors (cone receptors only), containing among them all three kinds of pigments, are neurally grouped into three mechanisms that determine the perceived brightness and colour of a test stimulus, i. e. the quantities equated in the asymmetric match. The three groupings are not identical so that stimuli of different spectral composition can produce different perceived colours, but because each mechanism incorporates some receptors of all kinds, there is extensive overlapping of their relative spectral sensitivity curves and the range of possible colour perceptions is limited. Adaptation to higher levels, by breaking down some of the neural links, tends progressively to limit the receptors of a particular mechanism to those containing just one pigment a different one for each mechanism. The effective spectral sensitivity curves are then much narrower, and highly saturated as well as unsaturated perceived colours can be produced by suitable test stimuli.

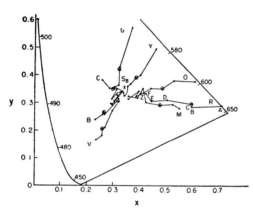

Figure 11.

Change in apparent colour of eight stimuli (R, O, Y, G, C, B, V, M), of fixed CIE chromaticity, as the equal test and test-surround luminances were decreased together in steps from A (6300 trolands) to F (0.7 trolands). An additional observation with zero test-surround and a test luminance of 0.7 trolands is also included (Point Z). For the chromaticity R, the points for the different test intensity levels are labelled A, B, C, D, E, F, Z. (Hunt, 1953).

For the results plotted in Fig. 11 the luminance of the test colour was always adjusted to be the same as that of the surround being used. However, Hunt's observations included matches on the whole measurable range of test luminances of each test-colour, for each surround luminance. These fuller results were not published, but Dr. Hunt has kindly suplied me with some examples of the additional data. They show that for a given pair of test and comparison surrounds, the relation between the test vector ξ and the comparison vector ξ' is not a linear one : it is not possible to express the relation in the form $\xi = T \xi'$. The plot of the components of ξ against those of ξ' for one pair of conditioning surrounds and one test chromaticity (Fig. 12) illustrate this non-linearity. It is of interest to note that departures from linearity, if they were of the right kind, could lead to an increase of the colorimetric saturation of all test colours with increase in the (white) adaptation level, while still retaining the principle of three receptor mechanism each equipped with one photosensitive pigment only. It is not clear how much of the desaturation observed by Hunt could be explained on these lines as the result of non-linearity, but it seems probable that the non-linearity effects could not be large enough to provide a complete explanation.

I have already referred to MacAdam's studies of adaptation by a method in which the adapting stimuli and the stimuli to be matched are presented alternately in an accurately fixated bipartite field. As MacAdam has shown an analysis of his data that assumes transitivity and additivity leads to the conclusion that more than three independent spectral sensitivities must be involved in the adaptation process, a result difficult to reconcile with generally admitted trichromatic principles. It is, however, questionable whether even transitivity is valid for the MacAdam data. Later MacAdam (1957) devised a model intended to explain a large body of results on the appreciation of subjective colour and brightness, including the effects of chromatic adaptation. Although it is not entirely clear, from what Mac Adam has published, how chromatic adaptation is introduced into his model, failure of additivity in asymmetric matching is certainly assumed and changes in the groupings of the receptors containing different photosensitive pigments, following changes in adaptation, are implied. MacAdam reports that with this model a satisfactory explanation of his chromatic adaptation data is obtained: further details will be awaited with interest.

Application of asymmetric matching to the comparison of the adaptive effects of different conditioning stimuli is hampered by uncertainty as to the nature of the change of state produced and the difficulty of specifying

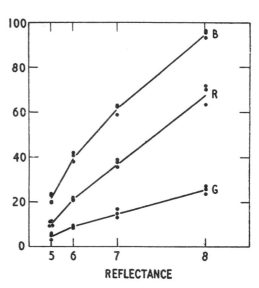

C$_5$/D M5 (R.W.G.H.) 1°FIELD

Figure 12.

Example of non-linear relation between the intensities of comparison primaries at asymmetric match (plotted as ordinate) and the intensity of a test colour of fixed chromaticity (plotted as abscissa). Surround of test colour equal to about one-third the intensity of surround of comparison primaries (the numbers marked on the abscissa are arbitrary identification numbers of the samples used to provide test stimuli of the same chromaticity but different intensity). (Unpublished data of R. G. W. Hunt obtained in investigation described in Hunt, 1953).

it quantitatively. Direct comparisons of matches can be made however and some further observations by Hunt (1950) bring out an important point. He determined the effect on the apparent colour and brightness of test stimuli when the surround used to control the adaptation of the test area was temporarily extinguished for the brief period while the binocular match was being made. His object was to resolve the total adapting effect into a contribution ascribable to simultaneous contrast between test stimulus and surround, and a contribution of a more persistent kind which did not depend on the actual presence of the surround. He found that when the effect of simultaneous contrast was eliminated, the adaptive colour shifts were certainly smaller but generally of the same kind i. e. in the same direction in the chromaticity diagram. Hunt also measured the time taken by surround to produce the full adaptive colour shifts in a test eye originally dark-adapted, and the time for the eye to recover fully after the removal of the sorround. He obtained values of the order of 100 sec. The smaller but quite measurable effects of simultaneous contrast on the other hand were very rapid, taking less than a second to operate after the abrupt removal of the surround. The fact that a very rapid and a much slower process — probably both neural — enter into photopic adaptation is an important one and has been particularly elaborated by Schouten (1939) in his work on apparent brightness. In this lecture I have treated adaptation as including both processes and in fact there is little quantitative work on apparent colour which enables them to be sharply separated. In observational conditions when the eyes move continually from point to point over complex patterns of brightness and colour, the operation of adaptational effects of widely different time period is likely to play a vital role. We can in fact understand that some kind of time integral of all the stimuli in a complex scene, viewed normally, would determine in the course of a fairly short time of a minute or two (depending on the condition of the eye at the start), the contribution to adaptation of the slow component, and that this would be little changed as the eye moved around. The contribution of the rapid component to the adaptation of a particular retinal area, however, would be determined by the immediate stimuli falling on and around the area and would follow fairly faithfully the inter-fixational eye movements. The small involuntary eye movements during fixation are not of course in question here.

The approach on these lines to an explanation of the colours perceived in an ordinary scene under naturalistic, unrestriced conditions of observation, ignores any factor associated with meaning. But the work of psychologists seems to indicate that information sent by our eyes to the brain about the nature of the scene we are viewing feeds back so as to modify the visual, including the colour, perceptions by wich it was conveyed. The terminology of these phenomena is not well defined but where apparent colours are modified we may speak of colour transformation. The operation of colour transformation has been brought to the fore recently by the beautiful demonstrations of two-colour pictures by Edwin Land (1958). The pictures — mainly elaborate still lifes — are produced by projecting in exact register two black and white positives — obtained originally by using in turn red and green filters over the camera lens. The two projectors emit lights of different colour, — white and red for example — and Land showed, among other things, that pictures of complex scenes could be produced in this way showing a remarkable variety and richness of colour, comparable in some cases with three colour projections. This could be done even if monochromatic projector sources were used provided their wavelengths were not too close : in the yellow region the separation need be no more than about 20 mμ. Land rejects explanations of the colours seen in terms of the accepted concepts of trichromatic theory and chromatic adaptation (but he appears to have in mind only the slow component), and elaborates a set of principles of colour perception in complex scenes summarising his observations. Detailed rejoinders have been made by several specialists on colour, notably by Dr. D. B. Judd (1960) who gave successful explanations of many of Land's observations based on his own fairly elaborate formulae for apparant brightness and colour developed in 1940. The main element in these explanations is contained in a simpler discussion by Woolfson (1959). Woolfson used aprroximate methods to determine, in effect, the possible range (three-dimensional) of the tristimulus vectors corresponding to small areas in the Land proyection of a complex picture produced by a particular pair of monochromatic projector sources. The tristimulus values were determined in a fundamental system close to those to which most colour research leads—the choice is not very critical. He then applied a simple von Kries type transformation, by dividing the respective components of the tristimulus vectors by three constants. The transformed vector, treat-ed as stimuli viewed in isolation or in a standard white surround, correspond to apparent colours which Woolfson accepts as sufficiently well-defined by the positions of their chromaticities in the standard chromaticity chart. The apparent colours in the actual Land projection are supposed to coincide with those derived in this way.

The upshot of Woolfson's extensive calculations is that the ranges of colours observable in Land's proyections with the various possible choices of the two projection wavelengths are predicted fairly well by the method used, provided the constants in the von Kries transformation are suitably chosen. For each pair of proyection wavelengths they must be such as to lead to an apparent chromaticity close to white for an area in the projection that corresponds to a white (neutral) surface in the original of the picture. The small deviation from white of the apparent chromaticity of this area must be in the direction of its true (untransformed) chromaticity in the projection. Woolfson's basic assumption corresponds very nearly to a conception going back to Helmholtz that in judging the colour of objects in a real scenes we make en allowance for the colour of the illuminat. An interpretation in terms of meaning would postulate that the viewer knows certain objects in the picture ought to appear white under «normal» condi-tions of illumination and his eye and brain effect an inevitable and un-conscious colour transformation that makes this true or nearly true. Against this is the fact that when the picture consists of a meaningless assembly of patches in a sufficiently random arrangement, the range of apparent colours seen is at least comparable with that in a meaningful picture the parts of which provide a set of stimulus vectors (untransformed) similar in range to that of the patches. It may be proposed that the element of meaning which fixes the involuntary colour transformation is provided not by the internal content of the picture, but by side clues—for example, light scattered from the projector beams, visible to the observer and informing him of the illuminant colour he must allow for.

The other extreme of interpretation would make no appeal to «meaning» and would attribute the wide range of apparent colours sean in a random arrangement of patches or a complex meaningful picture to simultaneous contrast (short-period chromatic adaptation) generated by the inevitable juxtaposition of areas with markedly different tristimulus vectors. It is certainly true, as shown by Land and others, that in an ordered arrange-ment of patches in which the tristimulus vectors (untransformed) vary in a simple progressive way by small steps on any line across the picture— and especially in a picture where there is a similar continuous variation on any line—the range of apparent colours seen is greatly curtailed. While simultaneuos contrast would be the principal element in the explanation of the wide differences of apparent colour, the long-period component of chromatic adaptation would contribute to determining the average apparent colour of the picture. It is however difficult to maintain the extreme interpretation that «meaning» is not a factor. In some experiments (see 1 for example, Judd, 1940) observes report that they can change the colour they perceive by consciously altering their conception of what it is they are viewing.

In these few concluding remarks on colour transformation, I have of course only scratched the surface of a difficult and controversial problem. It is one in which progress may well depend on the development of quantitative methods of assessing apparent brightness and colour in complex viewing situations.

REFERENCES

AGUILAR, M. and STILES, W. S. 1954 *Optica Acta* 1, 59.
AGUILAR, M. and YUNTA, J. 1953 *Anal. de la Real Sociedad Española de Fis. y Quím.* 49, 281.
ARDEN, G. G. and WEALE, R. A. 1954 *J. Physiol.* 125, 417.
AUERBACH, E. and WALD, G. 1954 *Science* 120, 401.
BAUMGARDT, E. 1950 *Revue d'Optique* 28, 661.
BOUMA, P. J. and KRUITHOFF, A. A. 1947 *Philips Technical Review* 9, 257.
BREWER, W. L. 1954 *J. Opt. Soc. America* 44, 207.
BRINDLEY, G. S. 1953 *J. Physiol.* 122, 332.
BRINDLEY, G. S. 1954 *J. Physiol.* 124, 400.
BURNHAM, R. W., EVANS, R. M. and NEWHALL, S. N. 1957 *J. Opt. Soc. America,* 47, 35.
CRAWFORD, B. H. 1946 *Proc. Roy. Soc.* B 133, 63.
CRAWFORD, B. H. 1947 *Proc. Roy. Soc.* B 184, 283.
HECHT, S., HAIG, C. and CHASE, A. M. 1937 *Journ. Gen. Phys.* 20, 831.
HUNT, R. W. G. 1950 *J. Opt. Soc. America* 40, 362.
HUNT, R. W. G. 1953 *J. Opt. Soc. America* 43, 479.
JUDD, D. B. 1940 *J. Opt. Soc. America* 30, 2.
JUDD, D. B. 1960 *J. Opt. Soc. America* 50, March Issue.
LAND, E. H. 1959 *Proc. Nat. Acad. Sci.* 45, 115 and 636.
LAND, E. H. 1959 *Sci. American* 200, 84.
MACADAM, D. L. 1956 *J. Opt. Soc. America* 46, 500.
OTERO, J. M., AGUILAR, M. and YUNTA, J. 1953 *Coloquio Internacional de Optica* (Madrid) 2, 56.
PIRENNE, M. H. 1953 *Brit. Med. Bull.* 9, 61.
RUSHTON, W. A. H., CAMPBELL, F. W., HAGINS, W. A. and BRINDLEY, G. S. 1955 *Optica Acta* 1, 183.
RUSHTON, W. A. H. 1956 a *J. Physiol.* 134, 11.
RUSHTON, W. A. H. 1956 b *J. Physiol.* 134, 30.
RUSHTON, W. A. H. 1958 *Ann. New York Acad. Sci.* 74, 291.
RUSHTON, W. A. H. 1959 *Progress in Biophysics and Biophysical Chemistry* 9, 259.
SCHOUTEN, J. F. and ORNSTEIN, L. S. 1939 *J. Opt. Soc. America* 29, 168.
SJÖSTRAND, F. S. 1959 *Rev. Mod. Physics* 31, 301.
STILES, W. S. 1949 *Documenta Ophthalmologica* 3, 138.
STILES, W. S. 1959 *Proc. Nat. Acad. Sci.* 45, 100.
VAN DEN BRINK, G. and BOUMAN, M. A. 1954 *J. Opt. Soc. America* 44, 8 and 616.
WALD, G. 1954 *Science* 119, 887.
WALTERS, H. V. 1942 *Proc. Roy. Soc.* B 131, 27.
WASSEF, E. G. T. 1958 *Optica Acta* 5, 101.
WASSEF, E. G. T. 1959 *Optica Acta* 6, 378.
WINSOR, C. P. and CLARK, A. B. 1936 *Proc Nat. Acad. Sci.* 22, 400.
WOOLFSON, M. M. 1959 *IBM Journ. Res. Dev.* 3, 313.
WRIGHT, W. D. 1936 *J. Physiol* 87, 23.
WRIGHT, W. D. 1934 *Proc. Roy. Soc.* B 115, 49.

SUMMARY

The problem of formulating quantitative concepts in the study of visual adaptation will be discussed. How far is it possible to specify by means of one or several adaptation variables the state of adaptation of the visual apparatus, or more precisely of that part of it which is concerned with vision in a limited region of the visual field? To what extent can adaptation variables be related to objective properties of the visual apparatus such as the concentrations of visual pigments in the end-organs or the physiological conditions of parts of the nerve system beyond the end-organs? In place of the untenable notion that the adaptation of the scotopic or rod mechanism is determined by a single variable which is related in a simple way to the concentration of rhodopsin in the rods, we have to consider an adaptation system in which both rhodopsin concentration and neural condition play a part, but the answers to the questions proposed are still unclear.

For the scotipic system there is the major simplification that light stimuli of different energy distributions are visually equivalent if their scotopic values based on the scotopic luminous efficiency function are the same. For the photopic, colour-responding, cone system a corresponding if lesser simplification is secured by the trichromatic principle according to which stimuli are equivalent if they have the same tristimulus values. These three values if transformed linearly to a suitable reference system have often been held to represent respectively the stimulations of three visual mechanisms acting concurrently but in some sense independently. The adaptation of the photopic system may then correspond to an internal change of state of each of these mechanisms—in general not the same for the different mechanisms—as a result of which their effective light sensitivities are modified without affecting the way in which the responses they transmit are further elaborated by the retina and brain. The investigators of chromatic adaptation by the two principal techniques—measurements of colour thresholds and measurements of apparent colour and brightness—have generally started with this conception but have found it inadequate in different ways. Some of the implications of this failure will be examined.

The phenomena of simultaneous and successive contrast may be regarded as included in chromatic adaptation. But there remains the question whether in the viewing of complex and meaningful stimulus patterns, other factors may not enter. Of interest here are recent quantitative interpretations of Land's work on two-primary colour projections.

Erratum

Page 151. 15 lines up: replace suitable by suitably.

Paper XIII: Reprinted from Journal of the Colour Group, No. 11, 1967.

Mechanism Concepts
in Colour Theory

W. S. STILES, O.B.E., D.Sc., F.R.S.

Recently I had occasion to look again at various simple concepts used to extend colour theory beyond the basic idea of trichromatic matching, and I thought some discussion of these might be of interest. The concepts I shall speak of are, in fact, psychophysical and in referring to them as "mechanism concepts" I am using the term mechanism in a special sense. In the complex neural systems extending from the end-organs through the retina and beyond, it is not yet possible to identify certain subsystems as the mechanisms that carry colour information to the brain. Clearly, psychophysical measurements can contribute nothing directly to our knowledge of the objective properties of colour mechanisms. In most studies the experimenter ends up with a collection of values specifying physical light stimuli all of which correspond to some fairly elementary visual judgement, such as "complete match" or "just detectable" which the subject is instructed to make. In analysing his results the experimenter will try to arrange them—to organise them—in a particularly significant or striking form which may suggest some rather simple model of what may be happening in the unknown processes between stimulus and response. Such models are often constructed of parts which are dignified with the title of mechanisms. Compared with the actual mechanisms in retina and brain, the psychophysicist's mechanisms have a rather ethereal existence; initially, at least, they may be merely elements in a mathematical analysis of a set of data. Having made this slightly abstract point, I hasten to add that in constructing models based mainly on psychophysical material, all the presently available objective evidence on the early stages of the visual process is pressed into service, and we expect that as more is learnt of the later stages actual counterparts of our models and their mode of action may be identified.

I shall confine myself to two lines of work that lead to ideas of colour mechanisms: asymmetric matching, as used in much work on colour adaptation, and colour discrimination including increment threshold sensitivity.

Ordinary trichromatic matching can be summed up in the equations for a complete match between two stimuli of spectral distributions $\{E_\lambda d\lambda\}$ and $\{E^1_\lambda d\lambda\}$ (in quantum units), viewed side-by-side in a bipartite field:

$$U \equiv \int E_\lambda \bar{u}_\lambda d\lambda = \int E^1_\lambda \bar{u}_\lambda d\lambda \equiv U^1,$$

plus two similar equations with $\bar{u}_\lambda$, U, U^1 replaced respectively by $\bar{v}_\lambda$, V, V^1 and $\bar{w}_\lambda$, W, W^1. The colour-matching functions $\bar{u}_\lambda$, $\bar{v}_\lambda$, $\bar{w}_\lambda$ are derived from actual matches, and will be supposed referred to three given fixed wavelengths as primaries. This determines them completely, and the corresponding empirical tristimulus values U, V, W, of any stimulus are uniquely determined. These equations express the strong form of the trichromatic principle, valid for foveal vision for not too high stimulus intensities. They are exactly those that would hold if the visual effect of a stimulus was produced by the light absorption of three photosensitive pigments contained in the retinal end-organs, and if, for all the end-organs containing a particular pigment, the *relative* spectral absorption factor of that pigment was the same, and remained unchanged whatever stimuli were applied. Here by absorption factor of a particular pigment in an end-organ, containing possibly other pigments, I mean the fraction of the radiation incident on the end-organ which is absorbed by the pigment in question. This definition leaves open whether the pigment in the end-organ is to be regarded as a uniform thin or thick layer or as being non-uniformly distributed, and whether because of wave-mode propagation in the end-organ—which I think must occur—there is a non-uniform distribution of the stimulating radiation. The condition for the spectral absorption coefficient may well not be satisfied when matching or adapting intensities become very high, but, if it fails, it is almost certain that the trichromatic matching equations will also cease to hold; they would survive only if some other factor counterbalanced exactly the deviations in relative spectral absorption factor. It follows that, within the range of the trichromatic principle, there will be a linear relation between the empirical colour-matching functions and the relative spectral absorption factors (ρ_λ, γ_λ, β_λ) of the three pigments in the end-organs, or, more strictly, of these factors multiplied by the transmission (τ_λ) of the pre-receptor light path in the eye; for example:

$$\rho_\lambda^* \equiv \rho_\lambda \tau_\lambda = p_{\rho u}\bar{u}_\lambda + p_{\rho v}\bar{v}_\lambda + p_{\rho w}\bar{w}_\lambda,$$

where $p_{\rho u}$, $p_{\rho v}$, $p_{\rho w}$ are constants.

The objective detection and measurement of cone pigments in recent years has of course strongly consolidated our belief in the pigment absorption explanation of the trichromatic principle. In this explanation, it is immaterial how the three pigments are distributed among the end-organs, or how the end-organs transduce the absorbed radiation into neural activity, or how the latter is elaborated by neural mechanisms in retina or brain.

Conversely, ordinary trichromatic colour-matching gives no information relative to visual processes beyond the pigment absorptions. But asymmetric matching can provide such information within the limitations of psychophysical models. By asymmetric matching we normally mean matches between stimuli imaged on distinct retinal areas that either have different properties because of their different positions on the retina, or that have been brought intentionally into different conditions by different pre-exposed or surround stimuli. The two areas may be on the same retina, as in the studies of extrafoveal colour by Bailey, Moreland and Cruz and Clarke, in which extrafoveal stimuli are matched with three-colour mixtures imaged on the fovea. They may be on the retinae of right and left eyes respectively in the method of binocular matching pioneered by Wright. Also, it is possible, as shown by the work of MacAdam, to maintain in different states of adaptation the retinal areas covered by the two halves of the monocular image of an ordinary bipartite field, the matching stimuli being applied in brief intermissions of the adapting stimuli. Despite considerable differences in technique and objectives, much of this work can be treated in a common framework.

Suppose that within each of two differently conditioned areas A and B the ordinary trichromatic principle is valid and that we know the two sets of empirical colour-matching functions that apply. These will be the same if the two areas have identical colour-matching properties, even though their conditions are different, because ordinary colour matches persist under different adaptations. We will allow, initially, that the colour-matching functions in the two areas may differ, even if only on account of some difference of macular pigmentation. An asymmetric match between two stimuli applied to A and B establishes a correspondence between their tristimulus values.

$$\{E_\lambda\, d\lambda\}\ in\ A. \qquad \begin{pmatrix} U_A \\ V_A \\ W_A \end{pmatrix} \xrightarrow[\leftarrow]{\rightarrow} \begin{pmatrix} U^1{}_B \\ V^1{}_B \\ W^1{}_B \end{pmatrix} \qquad \{E^1{}_\lambda\, d\lambda\}\ in\ B$$
$$U_A = \int E_\lambda \bar{u}_{A\lambda} d\lambda, \qquad\qquad\qquad U^1{}_B = \int E^1{}_\lambda \bar{u}_{B\lambda}\, d\lambda$$
$$V_A,\ W_A \qquad\qquad\qquad\qquad\qquad V^1{}_B,\ W^1{}_B$$

We cannot say that every stimulus applied to A can be matched by some suitable stimulus applied to B, or vice versa. Experiment shows that in general this is not possible, but nevertheless for a considerable domain of tristimulus space the usual kind of three-variable matching can be carried out. If, in this domain, enough experimental matches have been made to establish the characteristics of the correspondence, we have the raw material for testing possible mechanism concepts. As a first step we may suppose that in some sense the responses of three mechanisms in area A are being made equal to the responses of three corresponding mechanisms in area B. Each mechanism is envisaged as a chain of neural processes which is activated by the absorption of light in a selection of the end-organs in the retinal area concerned, and which transmits its response independently of other mechanisms to a higher level where it is brought in relation to a corresponding response from another retinal area. This doesn't get us very far unless we make more specific assumptions. The simplest is

that all the end-organs belonging to a particular mechanism contain the same visual pigment. In that case, the mechanism's response to a stimulus is determined completely by the light absorbed in this pigment, *i.e.* by $J=j\iint\rho_\lambda{}^*E_\lambda\,d\lambda$, where j is the factor that converts relative to absolute absorption factors. This factor may in fact be different when the light absorption changes, if the matching stimuli are able to produce some bleaching. Thus j is some function $\phi(J)$ of the amount absorbed, and this function will in general also contain parameters that represent the effect (constant) of the particular conditioning of the area. We obtain an equation for J: $J=\phi(J)\int\rho_\lambda{}^*E_\lambda\,d\lambda$ whose solution depends only on $\int\rho_\lambda{}^*E_\lambda\,d\lambda$. Thus in an area under fixed conditioning the mechanism's response is a function of J and hence of $\int\rho_\lambda{}^*E_\lambda\,d\lambda$. As the pigment's relative spectral absorption factor is a linear combination of the empirical colour-matching functions, the same linear combination of the empirical tristimulus values of any stimulus will determine the mechanism's response to it.

But there are other possibilities. Each end-organ of the mechanism could contain the same *unvarying* mixture of two or three cone pigments, the absorption of a light quantum by any of the pigments initiating the same effect in the cone. Again the response would be determined by a linear combination of the tristimulus values, but now the coefficients would depend on the composition of the pigment mixture as well as on the spectral absorptions of the pigments. Current objective measurements of the spectral absorptions of individual cones provide little evidence of cones containing more than one pigment, but it is still a possibility. On the other hand, a single response mechanism may be equipped with end-organs, some containing one pigment, some another. Two cases must then be distinguished. The effects of light absorption in cones containing different pigments may combine linearly to produce a common signal before any non-linear step

in the mechanism's response chain is reached. This is the situation envisaged in many zonal theories of colour vision, and, given that the matching
stimuli don't modify appreciably the pigment concentrations, the response
is once more determined by a linear combination of the tristimulus values.
While in ordinary colour-matching we can ignore the actual concentrations
of the pigments in the end-organs and deal only with their relative spectral
absorptions, this is not always so in interpreting the data of asymmetric
matching. When the response of a mechanism depends on the light absorption of more than one pigment in mixtures or in separate end-organs, the
absolute absorption factors, which may be modified by pigment bleaching,

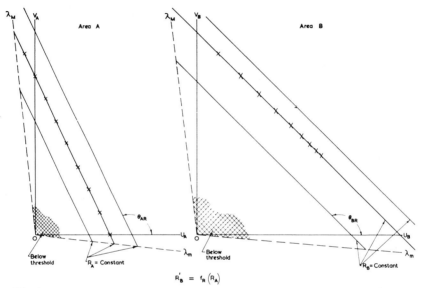

Fig. 1—*Correspondence diagram for dichromatic asymmetric matching. For the case
illustrated, the special directions θ_{AR} and θ_{BR} define families of parallel straight lines
in A and B respectively, all points on one such line in A having their matched counterparts
on a corresponding line of the B family. For parallel straight lines in A not in the direction
θ_{AR} the corresponding lines in B (generally not straight) do not form a parallel family.
(Single pair of special directions.)*

have to be considered. In addition the effects of light absorption in cones
containing different pigments may be subject to some non-linear step before
they combine to produce the mechanism's response. Thus mechanisms
fall into two groups. Firstly, those of single-fundamental type with a
unique relative spectral sensitivity, which may or may not coincide with the
relative spectral absorption factor of a single pigment, but for which the
response to a stimulus is determined by a linear combination of its tristimulus values. Secondly, mechanisms with more than one pigment in
their end-organs, which, because of variations in the pigment concentrations or because a non-linear step intervenes, have no unique spectral

sensitivity. For the second type, the response is still determined by the absorptions in the two or three pigments concerned, and, by an extension of the earlier argument, it can be regarded as a function of the stimulus integrals of the two (or three) relative spectral absorption factors: $\int \rho_\lambda^* E_\lambda \, d\lambda$, $\int \gamma_\lambda^* E_\lambda \, d\lambda$, $\int \beta_\lambda^* E_\lambda \, d\lambda$. These, in turn, equal two (or three) independent linear combinations of the empirical tristimulus values. We may fairly describe the second group as mechanisms of multiple-fundamental type.

To illustrate correspondences graphically it helps to switch from a trichromatic to a dichromatic visual system. (Fig. 1). The points in the two half-diagrams represent stimuli applied to areas A and B, plotted from their empirical distimulus values (U_A, V_A) and (U_B, V_B) respectively. All real stimuli must be represented by points in the sectors defined by limiting lines $O\lambda_M$ and $O\lambda_m$ which will normally correspond to monochromatic stimuli at the two ends of the spectrum. If in area A there is a mechanism dependent on a single fundamental, its response to a stimulus will be fixed by a linear combination of the empirical distimulus values, which will be defined as the fundamental distimulus value of the stimulus, R_A say. All stimuli giving some fixed response will have their representative points on a straight line $R_A = const.$ and for different fixed responses the straight lines will be parallel. If in an asymmetric match the response of the mechanism is being made equal to the response of a corresponding mechanism in area B which is also dependent on a single fundamental, the match points in diagram B of all points on any line $R_A = const.$ in diagram A will lie on a straight line $R_B = const.$, and these latter lines will also be parallel. Of course the spacing of corresponding points and lines will not generally be the same in the two diagrams. But if we can find a pair of directions, one in A and the other in B, defining two families of parallel lines with the property just described, we can conclude that in the asymmetric match we are equalising the responses of mechanisms in A and B respectively, each of single-fundamental type. There may be no such pair of special directions, or there may be just one pair or just two pairs, indicating a corresponding number of pairs of mechanisms of this type. The only other alternative is that there are indefinitely many pairs of special directions, and that to every direction in the A diagram there is a corresponding direction in the B diagram. This will be so if, at match, the distimulus values of the two stimuli are related by a fixed linear transformation, which is the necessary condition for the von Kries law of coefficients to be applicable. For the moment, however, suppose we have found in our experimental correspondence just two pairs of special directions. We can at once determine all four fundamental, spectral sensitivities, two for the mechanisms in A, from the slopes θ_{AR} and θ_{AG} of the special directions in A and the A colour-matching functions, and similarly two for the mechanisms in B. Also, from the positions of corresponding lines in the two diagrams, the functions (one of which is necessarily non-linear in this case) relating the responses of corresponding mechanisms at match are readily derivable: $R_B{}^1 = f_A(R_A)$ and $G_B{}^1 = f_B(G_A)$. Should any special direction drawn through the origin cut into the sector of real stimuli, it would mean that some real stimuli produced a positive, some a negative response from the mechanism, whose spectral sensitivity would then necessarily change sign in the spectrum and could not arise from a single visual pigment. This is the result to be expected if an opponent colour mechanism played a part in the asymmetric match.

If the colour-matching properties, and hence the colour-matching functions, are the same in the two areas, we should expect the fundamentals to be the same and the directions in each special pair to be parallel. If this was found not to be so, some change in the spectral sensitivity of the mechanism with change in its adaptation would be indicated. This couldn't happen if the end-organs of the mechanism contained just one pigment, but it might arise for other variants of the single-fundamental type. Non-parallelism of the directions in a special pair would be produced by a difference merely in the pre-receptor (e.g. macular) pigment in the two areas, but the colour-matching functions would not then be the same.

The notions developed for dichromatic vision are readily extended to the more practical case of trichromatic vision. Special pairs of directions are replaced by special pairs of planes and there are at most three such pairs, unless the number is unlimited, when the von Kries law of coefficients is valid. Much earlier and some recent experimental work is tied to this law and accepts that the tristimulus values in the two areas are related by a fixed linear transformation. Given this, and making the further assumptions that there are three mechanisms depending on single fundamentals, the same in the two areas, whose sensitivities are changed only by constant factors under different conditioning, a standard calculation leads to the fundamentals and von Kries factors. While this procedure sometimes yields fundamentals in general accord with pigment absorptions, applied to other data it gives complex solutions which are physiologically meaningless. The results of most later studies, notably those of Hunt and MacAdam, indicate that under their conditions the tristimulus values in the differently conditioned areas are not linearly related at match. From an intensive analysis of his own and other data, MacAdam has shown that the results can be well fitted by a non-linear scheme which is equivalent to adopting the following matching conditions:

$$a_{1A}+a_{2A}(R_A)^{a_{3A}}=a_{1B}+a_{2B}(R^1{}_B)^{a_{3B}}$$

$$b_{1A}+b_{2A}(G_A)^{b_{3A}}=b_{1B}+b_{2B}(G^1{}_B)^{c_{3B}}$$

$$c_{1A}+c_{2A}(B_A)^{c_{3A}}=c_{1B}+c_{2B}(B^1{}_B)^{b_{3B}}$$

The fundamental tristimulus values are computed from spectral sensitivities carefully chosen as most satisfactory in preliminary calculations on the data. Then for each pair of differently conditioned areas, the constants a_{1A}, a_{2A} . . a_{1B}, a_{2B}, etc., were derived to give the best fit with the observations. MacAdam refrains from any physiological interpretation of his data fitting, but we may nevertheless look at his equations from the standpoint

113

of mechanism concepts. Clearly they imply, for each area, three mechanisms of single-fundamental type with identical fundamentals in the two areas. Also if we assume that all the parameters with the A suffix depend only on the conditioning stimuli applied to the area A, all with suffix B on the conditioning of B, the equations give expression to an important principle of transitivity in asymmetric matching. This says that if we match a stimulus E_1 in area A under conditioning C_A with a stimulus E_2 in area B under conditioning C_B, and then, in another experiment, E_2 under C_B with a third stimulus E_3 in an area C under conditioning C_C, then, E_3 under C_C will match E_1 under C_A. If transitivity does not apply, our notions of mechanisms are much weakened. If it does, we have the valuable rule that the matching conditions must be capable of being written in the form

Fig. 2—*Chromaticities of matched stimuli exposed in areas A and B, conditioned respectively to high and low levels of white light. Low level: selected chromaticities (Circle points). High level: corresponding chromaticities of the asymmetrically matched stimuli, (1) assuming single-fundamental mechanisms and the power law, $R_B=(k\ R_A)^2$, $G_B=(k\ G_A)^2$, $B_B=(k\ B_A)^2$ (Cross points), (2) assuming multiple-fundamental mechanisms and the law, 0.7 log k R_B+0.3 (log k G_B+ log k B_B)=log R_A plus two similar equations with the roles of the tristimulus values interchanged (Triangle points).*

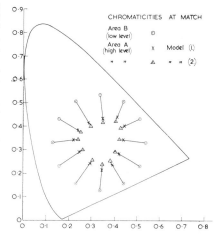

of equations with all quantities relating respectively to the two matching areas on opposite sides of the equality sign. MacAdam's own colour adaptation data were obtained under conditions that seem rather favourable to a breakdown in transitivity, as the adapting stimuli were applied to juxtaposed areas of the same retina. In binocular matching, a breakdown could occur only at higher levels and is less likely.

The most significant parameters in the MacAdam expressions are the power indices, and, using all his material, he succeeds in showing how they depend systematically on the chromaticity of the conditioning stimulus. I shall not try to discuss this interesting dependence, except to note that it is the variation of the power indices with the conditioning chromaticity that is emphasised. In fact, for most of the data fitted, the asymmetric matches were between areas conditioned to stimuli of different chromaticity but not

279

very different in luminance. Another situation arises when the conditioning is by white light stimuli of widely different luminance, as studied by Hunt. I will pick out one salient feature of his work, namely the quantitative picture it gives of the qualitative observation that, when we are adapted to higher brightness levels, colours appear more vivid, more varied. Hunt's data by the binocular matching method show that the chromaticities of stimuli exposed in the area adapted to the higher level are all displaced inwards in the chromaticity diagram towards a point somewhere near the white point, and that for stimuli in the higher level with chromaticities in an outer zone (the most saturated colours) no matches can be made, because all stimuli exposed in the lower level are too desaturated. As stressed by Hunt, the von Kries scheme is quite incapable of explaining this behaviour. Can mechanisms of single-fundamental type with power law response functions do so? Yes, if the power indices are allowed to depend on the luminance as well as the chromaticity of the conditioning stimulus. To illustrate this, take a very simple power law with indices 2 and 1 for the high and low levels respectively, the same for all three fundamental tristimulus values as we are dealing with white conditioning. As Fig. 2 shows, the matching chromaticities at high and low levels yield the right kind of effect on saturation. But of course it would take a searching analysis of all Hunt's data—not yet done, I think—to establish that a suitable power law would be fully adequate.

Moreover there are other models, more sophisticated because they do not assume mechanisms of single-fundamental type, but not unattractive on physiological grounds. A model of this kind put forward by Hunt assumes three mechanisms each of which receives signals mainly from end-organs containing one of the cone pigments, but subject to crosstalk, to some transfer of signals carried by the other mechanisms. Thus the final response in each mechanism depends on the absorption in all three pigments, and as the transfer of signals occurs in the neural stages after the almost certainly non-linear transducer process of the end-organs the final response is not determined by any linear combination of the empirical tristimulus values of the stimulus. Qualitatively this certainly can give the right kind of effect of brightness level on colour saturation. To go a little further, suppose that the non-linear step is equivalent to taking the logarithm of the light absorption in the end-organs containing a particular pigment. Put the final response in say the red-sensitive mechanism equal to a major contribution from the erythrolabe pigment, plus a smaller contribution from the other two pigments, i.e.:

final "red" response $= (1-\alpha) \log R + \alpha (\log G + \log B)$

where α depends on the white conditioning level, and assume similar expressions for the response of the other mechanisms with the roles of R, G, B interchanged.

Again, as shown in Fig. 2, the right kind of effect on saturation is reproduced when we put $\alpha = 0.3$ at the lower level, and $\alpha = 0$ at the upper. But when we consider the full specifications of the matched stimuli in terms of tristimulus values and not only in terms of chromaticities, the two simple models give radically different asymmetric correspondences. For an analogous dichromatic case, Fig. 3 shows the correspondence when the matching mechanisms are of single-fundamental type with power law response functions (diagrams (a) and (b)), and when they are of multiple-fundamental type with a response expressible as a mixture of the log signals (diagrams (a) and (c)). The axes used here are fundamental distimulus values, but transformations, in particular to the empirical distimulus values, show a no less striking difference in the patterns. The many matches

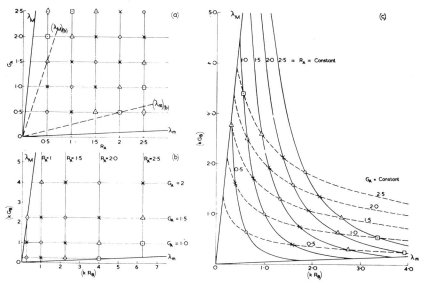

Fig. 3—*Asymmetric correspondence diagram (dichromatic) for areas A and B adapted respectively to high and low levels of white light.* (a) and (b) *Single-fundamental mechanisms with power law,* $R_B = (k\ R_A)^2$, $G_B = (k\ G_A)^2$. (a) and (c) *Multiple-fundamental mechanisms with the law* $\log k\ R_B + 0.5 \log k\ G_B = \log R_A$, $\log k\ G_B + 0.5 \log k\ R_B = \log G_A$. *Constant hue lines:* $G_A / R_A = constant = H_A$, $G_B / R_B = constant = H_B = H^2_A$. *All real stimuli exposed at the low level ((b) or (c)) are matched at the high level (a) by points in the sector* $(O\lambda_{M(b)}\ \lambda_{m(b)})$; *the constriction from the sector* $(O\lambda_M\lambda_m)$ *corresponds, in the trichromatic case, to the loss of saturation at low levels.*

required, especially in the trichromatic case, to determine adequately the correspondence diagrams, makes it less easy than might appear to distinguish the two types of mechanism, but in principle this can always be done. Potentially therefore there is much we can learn about colour mechanisms from asymmetric matching, provided we make enough matches, and an examination of the mechanism concepts themselves can be of value in the most economical planning of the matching experiments.

The ideas of mechanisms with single and multiple fundamentals are equally important in the analysis of the data of chromatic discrimination.

We have then the simplification that the mechanisms involved are all in one retinal area and subject to the same conditioning. The simplest conditioning situation is that used in the two-colour threshold method in which a comparatively large area of the retina is adapted to a uniform coloured field, and discrimination is studied by determining the increment threshold for a small coloured test stimulus applied at the centre, usually as a flash. The analysis of results by this method has been dominated by the notion of mechanisms each dependent on a single fundamental. Imagine such a mechanism acting alone. If, for fixed chromaticities of test and field

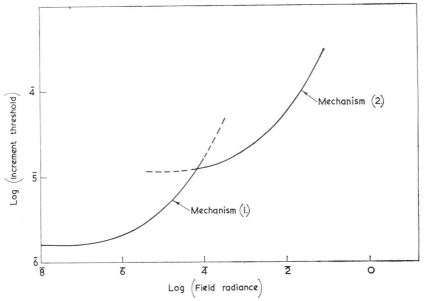

Fig. 4—*Log (increment threshold) versus log (field intensity) for two single-fundamental mechanisms. (Based on the actual curves obtained for the green-sensitive (π_4) and the blue-sensitive (π_1) mechanisms in measurements using a blue test stimulus and a green field.)*

stimuli, the variation of the increment threshold with the field intensity could be determined, the variation for any other test and field colours would be derivable from the mechanism's unique relative spectral sensitivity.

In a logarithmic plot (Fig. 4) this means that a curve of fixed shape is displaced parallel to the axes of log (threshold) and log (field intensity) respectively, as test and field colours are changed. A second similar mechanism, acting alone, would give another fixed curve but subject to different displacements when the colours were changed because of its different spectral sensitivity. If, when both act, the resultant threshold is equal to the smaller of the individual thresholds, except perhaps for a small summation effect when the two are equal, it is possible to get characteristic two-branch threshold versus field-intensity curves. The observation of such curves for foveal vision of a 1° test stimulus—so that there was no question of their representing a rod-cone transition—provided the starting point for the scheme of threshold mechanisms known as the Π mechanisms. Without going into details of these and their applications, I would say they have served to organise to a first approximation a mass of threshold data for colour fields extending in some cases to intensities well beyond the limits of validity of the strict trichromatic principle. But later work has shown, in a direct way, at least one of their inadequacies. The earliest measurements on this point I made in 1959 while a guest worker at the National Research Council, Ottawa, and I would like to mention my indebtedness to Dr. Howlett and Dr. Wyszecki of National Research Council for the facilities given me and to my assistant G. H. Fielder. In Fig. 5 the plotted curves show the log reciprocals of the increment thresholds of the individual Π mechanisms for monochromatic test stimuli through the spectrum when the uniform adapting field is a high or low intensity green. (The shapes and positions on the ordinate scale of these curves derive from earlier work.) The log reciprocal of the resultant threshold should follow the upper envelope of these curves and for the subjects used this checked within expected individual differences. The main experiment was to measure the threshold for various mixtures of two monochromatic test stimuli to see how far the results were consistent with a scheme of mechanisms of this kind.

For a mixture of two wavelengths both on a section of the envelope provided by one mechanism, Π_5' say, the mechanism integrates completely and at the threshold of the mixture the quantities of the constituent wavelengths are fractions adding up to unity if these quantities are expressed in units equal respectively to the thresholds for the separate wavelengths. For an equal mixture these fractions are equal, and minus the logarithm of their values is defined as the summation index, equal in this case to 0.301. On the other hand, for two wavelengths in sections belonging to different mechanisms, the summation index will be smaller, as the mechanisms are assumed independent and can only collaborate in determining a resultant threshold by what is known as probability summation. This arises because the threshold corresponds to a fifty per cent chance of seeing the test stimulus, and, if two completely independent mechanisms each give a fifty per cent chance, the resultant chance is seventy-five per cent, corresponding to a lower threshold. From the steepness of experimental frequency-of-seeing curves it is found that because of probability summation the summation index cannot be less than 0.1 log units or a little more. In Fig. 6 are plotted measurements at the high field intensity of the summation index for pairs of wavelengths of which one is kept fixed at 640nm on the Π_5' section while the other is varied through the spectrum. Despite inevitable scatter, the points are in tolerable accord with expectation when the second wavelength is also on the Π_5' section, or when it is on the

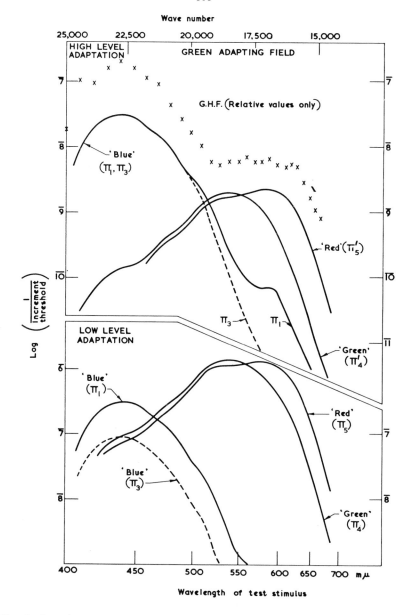

Fig. 5—*Log (reciprocal increment threshold) versus test wavelength for the* II *mechanisms, adapted to uniform green fields (filter band 510 to 630 nm. peaking at 555 nm.) of approximate intensity 30,000 trolands (high). 200 trolands (low).*

Π_1 section. The striking discrepancy occurs for intermediate positions around 530*nm* where the summation index drops to zero. This is inexplicable if the discrimination mechanisms are independent and each has a single, always positive, fundamental. The conclusion holds whether or not the properties ascribed to the Π mechanisms are accurate; no set of independent mechanisms with always positive spectral sensitivities can lead to a summation index less than 0.1 log units. Comparable anomalies occur in other similar data which include measurements by Boynton, Ikeda and Stiles in which the summation index for mixtures of a positive increment of one wavelength with a negative increment of another was studied. Some modification of the scheme of Π mechanisms must be made but the form this should take is not yet clear. In fact, these summation anomalies present

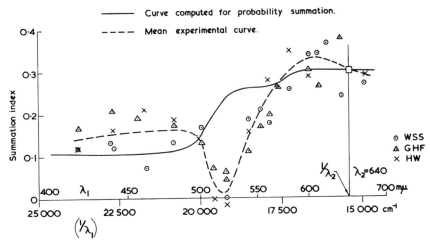

Fig. 6—*Summation index for high intensity green field, and for test wavelengths $\lambda_1 = 640$ nm. (fixed) and λ_2 variable through the spectrum. Test stimulus: 1°, 0.2 sec.*

a complicated picture. For example, on reducing the intensity of the green adapting field to a much lower value, the anomaly disappears, and Ikeda has found that it is also absent if very brief increment flashes of about one hundredth of a second are used. It seems likely that two complicating extensions may have to be made. Firstly, differences in the signals transmitted by two main mechanisms may make an independent contribution to discrimination. This corresponds to introducing a supplementary colour-differencing mechanism. Secondly—and this applies particularly to the red-sensitive mechanism—the effective spectral sensitivity to the test stimulus may differ from the spectral sensitivity to the adapting field. Clearly any acceptable modifications must continue to provide explanations of the data to which the scheme of Π mechanisms has been successfully applied.

The notion of colour-differencing mechanisms is already firmly entrenched in various formulae used to define equal steps in lightness-colour space, or in tristimulus space. These formulae, based on data such as the Brown-MacAdam discrimination ellipsoids, and on much earlier work by a variety of methods, refer to observational conditions which differ a good deal from those of the two-colour threshold method, and which allow a possible conditioning effect of a surround on a comparatively small discrimination area. Each of the formulae has its special interest and I shall touch only on one or two general points in their interpretation in terms of mechanisms. According to most formulae the condition for two neighbouring colours to differ by a fixed or threshold step is that the sum of the squares of three terms should be a constant, each term being dependent on the tristimulus values $(R, G, B; R+\Delta R, G+\Delta G, B+\Delta B)$ of the two colours (or on some of these values) evaluated for a special set of fundamentals which in some cases can be identified with the spectral absorption factors of the pigments. The terms correspond in effect to the contributions to discrimination of three independent mechanisms, which assist each other by probability summation to the extent represented by the sums of squares form. This form for just two mechanisms would correspond to a summation index of 0.15 log units which is a reasonable value. The way a term depends on the tristimulus values R, G, B, and the differentials $\Delta R, \Delta G, \Delta B$ (which normally enter only as first powers) implies certain characteristics of the corresponding mechanism. A term containing only one differential ΔR and the related tristimulus value R indicates a mechanism of single-fundamental type. Its response function will be some function of R—$F(R)$ say—and neighbouring colours will generate a difference ΔF that will be seen if ΔF exceeds a threshold T. If the threshold is constant we obtain a term

$$\frac{\Delta F(R)}{T} = \frac{1}{T} \cdot \frac{dF}{dR} \cdot \Delta R = f(R). \ \Delta R, \text{ where } \frac{F(R)}{T} = \int^{R} f(R). \ dR.$$

Thus given $f(R)$ we can always find a response function $F(R)$ associated with a constant threshold. If a term while still involving only one differential ΔR depends also on more than one tristimulus value, the response of the mechanism must still be a function of R only. But the threshold cannot be a constant nor dependent only on the mechanism's own response. A term with two differentials, ΔR and ΔG, and the corresponding tristimulus values R and G will be of the form: $f_R(R, G). \ \Delta R + f_G(R, G). \ \Delta G$. Its response function must be dependent on both R and $G - F (R, G)$ say —but for the threshold there are two alternatives. Firstly, $f_R(...)$ and $f_G(...)$ may depend on R and G in such a way that with a suitably chosen response function $F(R, G)$, the associated threshold is a constant or is dependent only on the mechanism's own response: $T = T\{F(R, G)\}$. Alternatively f_R and f_G may be such that this is impossible and, however the response function is chosen, the associated threshold depends on R and G in a way that cannot be expressed in the form $T = T\{F\}$. This means, in effect, that the responses of the other mechanisms will contribute to

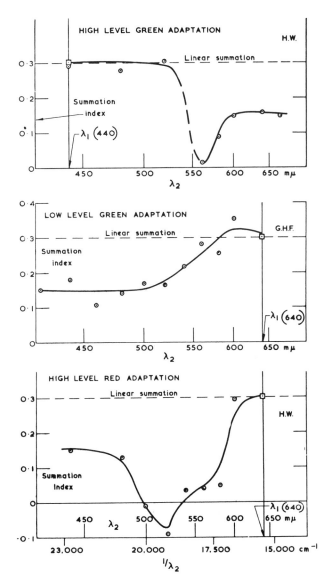

Fig 7—*Other summation index measurements for 1°, 0.2 sec. test stimulus.*

determining the threshold. Finally, for terms involving all three differentials, the response must be a function of all three tristimulus values, and for the threshold there are similar alternatives to those of the previous case. If we cannot find a response function with which is associated a threshold whose value depends only on the mechanism's own response, the mechanism cannot be regarded as independent in the fullest sense. While independence corresponding to probability summation of the contributions to discrimination of several mechanisms may be retained, the fact that other mechanisms help to determine the threshold implies a degree of interdependence at some

$$\Delta L = \frac{1}{=0.030}\left(\frac{\Delta R}{R} + \frac{\Delta G}{G}\right)$$

$$F_1(R, G) = \ln R + \ln G; \ T_1 = \text{constant} = 0.030$$

$$\Delta C_{r\text{-}g} = \frac{1}{\beta}\left(\frac{\Delta R}{R} - \frac{\Delta G}{G}\right); \ \beta = \frac{0.015 \, R^2}{R^2 + G^2} \quad \text{for } R > G$$

$$= \frac{0.015G^2}{R^2 + G^2} \quad \text{for } R < G$$

$$F^1{}_2(R, G) = \ln R - \ln G + Z; \ T^1{}_2 = \text{constant} = 0.015$$

$$\text{where } Z = \frac{1}{2} - \frac{G^2}{2R^2} \quad \text{for } R > G$$

$$= \frac{R^2}{2G^2} - \frac{1}{2} \quad \text{for } R < G$$

$$F_2(R, G) = \ln R - \ln G; \ T_2(F_2) = 0.015 \, (1 + e^{-2|F_2|})^{-1}$$

$$\Delta C_{y\text{-}b} = \frac{1}{\gamma}\left(\frac{\Delta R}{2R} + \frac{\Delta G}{2G} - \frac{\Delta B}{5.3B}\right); \ \gamma = 0.015 \quad \text{for } G < 2.5B$$

$$= \frac{0.015G}{2.5B} \quad \text{for } G > 2.5B$$

$$F_3(R, G, B) = \frac{\ln R}{2} + \frac{\ln G}{2} - \frac{\ln B}{5.3}$$

$$T_3(F_1, F_2, F_3) = 0.015 \quad \text{for } x < \ln 2.5$$

$$= \frac{0.015e^x}{2.5} \quad \text{for } x > \ln 2.5$$

$$\text{where } x = 5.3F_3 - \frac{F_2}{2} - \frac{4.3F_1}{2}$$

Table I. *Terms of Friele's formula resolved into response functions and thresholds.*

level. Physiologically this might mean in some cases no more than a spread of "neural noise" from the signals in different mechanisms.

Helmholtz's early formula for chromatic discrimination and my later modification both use three terms of the single-fundamental type. Another early expression due to Schrodinger has terms all of which imply mechanisms whose thresholds depend on the response of other mechanisms. Dr. Friele's first formula (see Table I), designed to represent the data of the Brown-MacAdam discrimination ellipsoids, has a lightness term ΔL, and a first colour-differencing term $\Delta C_{r\text{-}g}$, for both of which the response functions—F_1 and F_2^1—can be chosen so that the associated threshold is constant, although for the colour-differencing term a simpler response function—F_2—still with a threshold—$T_2(F_2)$—dependent only on the mechanism's own response, may be physiologically preferable. Friele's third

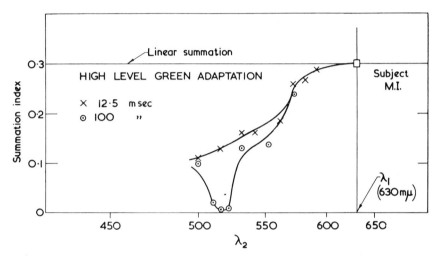

Fig. 8—*Summation index for high intensity green field, $\lambda_1=630$ nm., λ_2 variable. Test stimulus: 10 min. diam., 0.012 or 0.1 sec. flash period. (M. Ikeda.)*

term, a second colour-differencing term, $\Delta C_{y\text{-}b}$, implies a mechanism whose threshold $T_3(F_1, F_2, F_3)$ depends on the response of all three mechanisms. Friele's formula has been used merely to illustrate a general point; an adequate interpretation of it and of Dr. Friele's later formulae would of course demand a much fuller discussion.

I have devoted this talk to simple mechanism concepts, and I think that to recall them from time to time is of value. But my concluding remark must be that the over-riding need in colour theory is more experimental data, determined under carefully controlled, and perhaps to some extent standardised conditions.

Errata

Page 107. Line 10: insert, for stimuli expressed in quantum units, . . . after colour-matching functions . . .

Pages 117 to 119. Wherever the symbols Π, Π_1, Π_5' etc. occur, replace the capital Greek pi by the small Greek pi, suffixes and priming being retained as now.

Bibliography

1. F. Rinne's *Crystals and the Fine Structure of Matter*, translation from the German (Methuen and Co. Ltd., London, 1924).
2. "Recent measurements of the effect of glare on the brightness difference threshold" Proc. Comm. Intern. de l'Eclairage 7, 220-238 (1928).
3. "On the intensity of the scattered light from an unpolarized beam", Phil. Mag. 7, 204 (1929).
4. "Glare and visibility in artificially lighted streets", Illum. Engr. (London) 21, 195-199, 233-241 (1929).
5. "Talbot's Law, fatigue and non-linearity in photoelectric cells", Phil. Mag. 7, 812-820 (1929).
6. "The effect of glare on the brightness difference threshold", Proc. Roy. Soc. (London) B104, 322-351 (1929).
7. "The effect of glare on the brightness difference threshold", Illum. Res. Tech. Paper No. 8 (H.M. Stationery Office, London, 1929).
8. "The scattering theory of the effect of glare on the brightness difference threshold", Proc. Roy. Soc. (London) B105, 131-146 (1929).
9. "Talbot's Law in photoelectric cells" (with T. H. Harrison), Phil. Mag. 8, 64 (1929).
10. "The nature and effects of glare", Illum. Engr. (London) 21, 304-309 (1929).
11. "A brightness difference threshold meter", Illum. Engr. (London) 22, 279-280 (1930).
12. "The international aviation lighting meeting in Berlin", The Aeroplane, 882-886 (1930).
13. "The street lighting requirements of different types of street" (with J. F. Colquhoun), Proc. Intern. Congr. Illum. (Cambridge University Press, Cambridge, England, 1931), pp. 584-591.
14. "Mass experiments in streetlighting", Proc. Intern. Congr. Illum. (Cambridge University Press, Cambridge, England, 1931), pp. 576-583.
15. "Thermionic Emission", Radio Research Special Report No. 11 (H.M. Stationery Office, London, 1931).
16. "Appraisal of streetlighting installations" (with C. Dunbar), Illum. Res. Tech. Paper No. 13 (H.M. Stationery Office, London, 1931).
17. "The evaluation of glare in streetlighting installations", Illum. Engr. (London) 23, 162-166, 187-189 (1931).
18. "Equivalent adaptation levels in localised retinal areas" (with B. H. Crawford), Rept. Discussion Vision (The Physical Society, London, 1932), pp. 194-211.
19. "Comment on visual phenomena and quantum theory", Rept. Discussion Vision (The Physical Society, London, 1932), pp. 326-327.
20. G. Castelfranchi's *Recent Advances in Atomic Physics* (with J. W. T. Walsh), translation from the Italian (J. and A. Churchill, London, 1932).
21. "The luminous efficiency of rays entering the eye pupil at different points" (with B. H. Crawford), Proc. Roy. Soc. (London) B112, 428-450 (1933).
22. "The evaluation of glare from motor car headlights" (with C. Dunbar), Illum. Res. Tech. Paper No 16 (H.M. Stationery Office, London, 1934).
23. "Yellow-blue ratio and personal errors in heterochromatic photometry", Phil. Mag. 17, 660-668 (1934).

24. "The liminal brightness increment as a function of wavelength for different conditions of the foveal and parafoveal retina" (with B. H. Crawford), Proc. Roy. Soc. (London) **B113**, 496-530 (1933).
25. "The liminal brightness increment for white light for different conditions of the foveal and parafoveal retina" (with B. H. Crawford), Proc. Roy. Soc. (London) **B116**, 55-102 (1934).
26. "Comparison of the revealing powers of white and coloured headlight beams in fog", Illum. Engr. (London) **27**, 313-319 (1935).
27. "Bewertung von Autoscheinwerfern hinsichtlich der Blendungsfreiheit", Die Licht-technik **12**, 17-22 (1935).
28. "A brightness difference threshold meter" (with B. H. Crawford), J. Sci. Instr. **12**, 177-185 (1935).
29. "Problems of headlight illumination: dazzle and fog", Engineering, 50-52 (1937).
30. "Visibility of light signals with special reference to aviation lights" (with M. G. Bennett and H. N. Green), Aeronautical Res. Com., Rept. and Mem. No. 1793 (H.M. Stationery Office, London, 1937), p. 68.
31. "Glare", Rept. Progr. Phys. **3**, 310-317 (1937).
32. "The luminous efficiency of monochromatic rays entering the eye pupil at different points and a new colour effect", Proc. Roy. Soc. (London) **B123**, 90-118 (1937).
33. "Luminous efficiency of rays entering the eye pupil at different points" (with B. H. Crawford), Nature **139**, 246 (1937).
34. "Visibility in fog", Elec. Rev. 782-783 (1937).
35. "The effect of a glaring light source on extrafoveal vision" (with B. H. Crawford), Proc. Roy. Soc. (London) **B122**, 255-280 (1937).
36. "The use of coloured light for motor car headlights", Illum. Res. Tech. Paper No. 20 (H.M. Stationery Office, London, 1937).
37. "The directional sensitivity of the retina and the spectral sensitivities of the rods and cones", Proc. Roy. Soc. (London) **B127**, 64-105 (1939).
38. "Variation with temperature of the electrical resistance of carbon and graphite between $0°$ and $900°C$" (with L. J. Collier and W. G. Taylor), Proc. Phys. Soc. (London) **51**, 147-152 (1939).
39. "The directional sensitivity of the retina", Sci. Progr. **33**, 670-689 (1939).
40. "The effectiveness of lighting: its numerical assessment" (with W. D. Wright, K. J. W Craik and S. J. MacPherson), Trans. Illum. Engr. Soc. (London) **8**, 43-53 (1943).
41. "A mean scotopic visibility curve" (with T. Smith), Proc. Phys. Soc. (London) **56**, 251-255 (1944).
42. "Current problems of visual research", Proc. Phys. Soc. (London) **56**, 329-356 (1944); Nature **154**, 290-293 (1944).
43. "Photometer for measuring the scotopic candlepowers of self-luminous ophthalmic test objects", Brit. J. Ophthalmol., 629-637 (1944).
44. "Colour vision of the fovea centralis", Nature **155**, 177 (1944).
45. "A modified Helmholtz line element in brightness-colour space", Proc. Phys. Soc. (London) **58**, 41-65 (1946).
46. "The basic sensation curves of the three-color theory", J. Opt. Soc. Am. **36**, 491-492 (1946).
47. "Separation of the 'blue' and 'green' mechanisms of foveal vision by measurements of increment thresholds", Proc. Roy. Soc. (London) **B133**, 418-434 (1946).
48. "Wartime problems of glare and dazzle", Brit. Med. Bull. **5**, 50-52 (1947).
49. "Mechanism of colour vision", Nature **160**, 664-665 (1947).
50. "Binocular colour matching: an essay review of W. D. Wright's 'Researches on Normal and Defective Colour Vision' ", Sci. Progr. **35**, 342-346 (1947).

51. "The physical interpretation of the spectral sensitivity curve of the eye", Trans. Optical Convention of the Worshipful Company of Spectacle Makers (Spectacle Makers' Company, London, 1948), 97-107.

52. "The directional and spectral sensitivities of the retinal rods to adapting fields of different wavelengths" (with F. Flamant), J. Physiol. **107**, 187-202 (1948).

53. "The visibility of targets in a naval searchlight beam" (with W. D. Chesterman), Symposium on Searchlights (Illum. Engr. Soc., London, 1948), 75-102.

54. "Apparent shape and size of the pupil viewed obliquely" (with K. H. Spring), Brit. J. Ophthalmol., 347-354 (1948).

55. "Variation of pupil size with change in the angle at which the light stimulus strikes the retina" (with K. H. Spring), Brit. J. Ophthalmol., 340-346 (1948).

56. "The determination of the spectral sensitivities of the retinal mechanisms by sensory methods", Ned. Tijdschr. Natuurk. **15**, 125-145 (1949).

57. "Increment thresholds and the mechanisms of colour vision", Doc. Ophthalmol. 3, 135-136, 138-163 (1949).

58. "Investigation of the scotopic and trichromatic mechanisms of vision by the two-colour threshold technique", Rev. Opt. **28**, 215-237 (1949).

59. "Sensibilidad de bastones y conos en la parafovea" (with J. Cabello), Anales Real soc. Espan. Fis. Quim. **A46**, 251-282 (1950).

60. "Spectral reflexion factor of the cat's tapetum" (with R. Gunter and H. G. W. Harding), Nature **168**, 293 (1951).

61. "The eye, brightness and illuminating engineering", Trans. Illum. Engr. (London) **17**, 241-282 (1952).

62. "Colour vision: a retrospect", Endeavour **11**, 33-40 (1952).

63. "Visual properties studied by subjective measurements on the colour-adapted eye", Brit. Med. Bull. **9**, 41-49 (1953).

64. "Further studies of visual mechanisms by the two-colour threshold technique", Coloq. Probl. Opt. Vis. (U.I.P.A.P., Madrid, 1953) **1**, 65-103 (1953).

65. "Visual factors in lighting", Illum. Engr. (New York) **49**, 77-91 (1954).

66. "Saturation of the rod mechanism of the retina at high levels of stimulation" (with M. Aguilar), Opt. Acta **1**, 59-65 (1954).

67. "The basic data of colour-matching: 18th Thomas Young Oration", Phys. Soc. Year Book, 44-65 (1955).

68. "Colour specification: possible revision of the C.I.E. system", Nature **176**, 95-97 (1955).

69. "N.P.L.'s investigation of colour-matching: interim report" (with J. M. Burch), Opt. Acta **4**, 168-181 (1955).

70. "Remarks on the line-element", Farbe **4**, 275-279 (1955).

71. "The average colour-matching functions for a large matching field", N.P.L. Symp. No. 8 (Visual problems of colour) **1**, 201-247 (1958).

72. "Colour vision", Nature **180**, 1395-1397 (1957).

73. "The trichromatic scheme" in *Mechanisms of Colour Discrimination* (Pergamon Press, London, 1960), pp. 187-195.

74. "Colour vision: the approach through increment threshold sensitivity", Proc. Natl. Acad. Sci. **45**, 100-114 (1959).

75. "N.P.L. colour-matching investigation: final report (1958)" (with J. M. Burch), Opt. Acta **6**, 1-26 (1959).

76. "Lighting and research", Trans. Illum. Engr. Soc. (London) **26**, 53-65 (1961).

77. "The colour change of monochromatic light with retinal angle of incidence" (with J. M. Enoch), Opt. Acta **8**, 329-358 (1961).

78. "Adaptation, chromatic adaptation, colour transformation", Anales Real Soc. Espan Fis. Quim. **A57**, 147-175 (1961).

79. "Field trials of color-mixture functions" (with G. Wyszecki), J. Opt. Soc. Am. **52**, 58-75 (1962).

80. "Counting metameric object colours" (with G. Wyszecki), J. Opt. Soc. Am. **52**, 313-328 (1962).

81. "The directional sensitivity of the retina", Ann. Roy. Coll. Surg. England **30**, 73-101 (1962).

82. "N.P.L. colour-matching investigation: addendum on additivity", Opt. Acta **10**, 229-232 (1963).

83. "Interactions among chromatic mechanisms as inferred from positive and negative increment thresholds" (with R. M. Boynton and M. Ikeda), Vision Res. **4**, 87-117 (1964).

84. "Foveal threshold sensitivity on fields of different colors", Science **145**, 1016-1017 (1964).

85. *Color Science* (with G. Wyszecki) (J. Wiley and Sons, Inc., New York, 1967).

86. "Mechanism Concepts in Colour Theory" (Newton Lecture), Journ. of the Colour Group No. **11**, 106-123 (1967).

87. "Intersections of the spectral reflectance curves of metameric object colours" (with G. Wyszecki), J. Opt. Soc. Am. **58**, 32-40 (1968).

88. "Interrelations among Stiles' π-mechanisms" (with M. Ikeda and T. Uetsuki), J. Opt. Soc. Am. **60**, 406-415 (1970).

89. "The line element in colour theory: a historical review", Proc. Helmholtz Memorial Symposium on Colour Metrics, Driebergen, Netherlands, Sept. 1971 (AIC Holland, c/o Institute for Perception TNO, Soesterberg, 1972), 1-25.

90. "Rod intrusion in large-field colour-matching" (with G. Wyszecki), Acta Chromatica (Japan) **2**, 155-163 (1973).

91. "Colour-matching data and the spectral absorption curves of visual pigments" (with G. Wyszecki), Vision Res. **14**, 195-207 (1974).

92. "Counting metameric object color stimuli using frequency limited spectral reflectance functions" (with G. Wyszecki and N. Ohta), J. Opt. Soc. Am. **67**, 779-784.

93. "Early threshold observations of transient tritanopia", Appendix to "An anomaly in the response to light of short wavelengths" by J. D. Mollon and P. G. Polden, Phil. Trans. Roy. Soc. (London) *278B*, 207-240 (1977).

Subject Index

Page numbers refer to the overall numbering system and not to page numbers
of the original papers